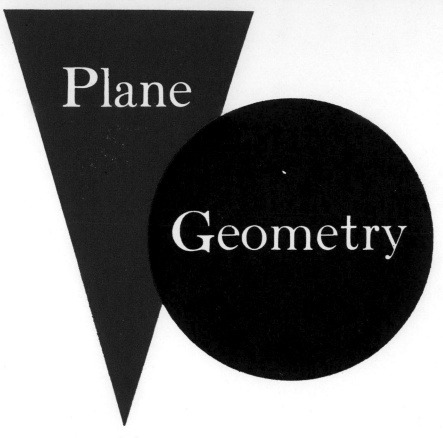

Plane Geometry

BY **ROLLAND R. SMITH**

Co-ordinator of Mathematics, Public Schools
Springfield, Massachusetts

AND **JAMES F. ULRICH**

Mathematics Department, Township High School
Arlington Heights, Illinois

With the co-operation of **John R. Clark**

World Book Company

YONKERS-ON-HUDSON, NEW YORK

Preface

Two fundamental aims in the teaching of demonstrative geometry are suggested by the words *demonstrative* and *geometry*. The first aim, and the one given the greater emphasis in *Plane Geometry*, is to show what is meant by a logical demonstration. The second aim is to develop the concepts of geometry; that is, to provide the statements of geometric relationship and to illustrate the fundamental facts of geometry that are needed in everyday life, in many vocations, and in further courses in mathematics and science.

The following paragraphs indicate the most important considerations of the authors in preparing and writing *Plane Geometry*.

I. Review. The early part of the book deals with subject matter that is familiar to most students — the study of lines, angles, triangles, and constructions. But these subjects are treated on a higher plane of maturity with the definite aim of using them for furthering ideas about demonstration. There is a gradual change from *conclusions based on measurement* to *conclusions without measurement*.

II. If-Then Relationship. The logical significance of the if-then relationship, which experience and experiment have shown to be a stumbling block to the beginner in demonstrative geometry, has been developed concretely by means of constructions. Figures are constructed according to what is given and conclusions are checked by measurement. Students can actually *see* the difference in significance between hypothesis and conclusion. They are aided visually by the use of two colors in many of the diagrams.

III. Demonstration. The meaning of proof has been given careful attention. The students have experience with very simple deductions with both geometric and non-geometric material before they are expected to think through and write formal proofs. The role of undefined terms, defined terms, postulates, and axioms is discussed. What are acceptable reasons in a proof is made clear. The students learn in a variety of simple ways that a conclusion cannot be drawn unless all the conditions of an accepted general statement are fulfilled. Furthermore, they are given practice in understanding what the conditions are and when they have been fulfilled.

They are taught the concept of holding to the data — to pay careful attention to the hypothesis and not to be misled by the appearance of a figure. All this is done to prevent memorization without understanding and to develop the ability to make and analyze a demonstration.

IV. Algebra in Proofs. The authors believe in using algebra in proofs. In the chapter on arcs and angles in circles, all the theorems are proved by means of algebra. But for the teacher who prefers to omit the algebra, there are proofs of these theorems by means of numerical examples and analysis.

V. Formality. The book is so written that the teacher may be as formal or as informal as he pleases. In the earlier written proofs it is wise to be formal to make sure the students understand what is being done. When the teacher is sure that his students understand what a proof is, he may wish to cover more ground quickly by being informal. For example, in the chapter on *Areas of Polygons*, several of the formulas may be accepted after numerical examples are given or they may be proved deductively. Once understanding of demonstration is firmly established, it may be better to concentrate on the numerical rather than the logical aspects of area.

VI. Individual Differences. Attention is given to individual differences in students. First of all, there is careful development for everyone. The superior students are provided with EXTRA exercises as well as a page of *Problems for Pacemakers* in most chapters. There are many *optional* pages which may well encourage the better students to further study. For the slower students, many of the geometric relationships have been postulated to lessen the number of theorems required and to give more time for other work. For a minimum course the teacher may well postulate the relationships so indicated, omit as much of the optional material as he sees fit, and give his attention to the easier exercises.

VII. Analytic Geometry. In an optional chapter, students are shown what powerful tools algebra and the co-ordinate system can be in geometry. This chapter deals with such topics as *Distance between Two Points, Midpoint of a Line Segment, Slope of a Straight Line, The Equation of a Mathematical Graph,* and *Proving Theorems by Analytic Geometry.*

VIII. Reasoning in Non-Geometric Fields. Special attention is paid to the nature of reasoning in general at the end of Chapter 7 and in Chapter 19. An analysis of induction and deduction is made in non-mathematical situations. Common fallacies in reasoning are discussed and exercises are provided to give practice in identifying these fallacies. The use of non-mathematical examples bridges the gap which often exists between mathematical and everyday reasoning.

IX. Color. Color is used in various ways both to enhance the appearance of the book and to serve as a teaching aid. For example, in the development of the if-then relationship and the logical significance of what is given and what is to be proved, color makes a visual distinction between hypothesis and conclusion. Elsewhere color helps the student visualize the component parts of some of the more complicated diagrams.

R. R. S.
J. F. U.

Contents

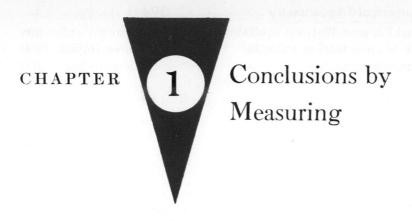

CHAPTER ① Conclusions by Measuring

You will study geometry for a twofold purpose. From its study you will learn many facts about such figures as triangles, parallelograms, and circles. An understanding of the principles of geometry is essential to navigators, pilots, astronomers, engineers, architects, scientists, designers, and many others.

You will also have careful training and practice in logical thinking. As far back as the time of Plato, the value of the study of geometry was appreciated. A sign over the gateway of his olive-grove school read, "Let those ignorant of geometry not enter here." This meant that he did not care to be bothered with students who could not reason closely or follow through a careful argument. Especially if you are going on to higher mathematics will the logical side of geometry be of value to you.

■ Triangles and Circles

The figure at the right is a **triangle**. Every triangle has three **sides** which are straight lines. In the figure the sides of the triangle are AB, BC, and CA. The symbol for triangle is △. Thus △ABC means triangle ABC.

A triangle also has three **vertices**. In this figure they are points A, B, and C, the points where the sides meet. *Vertices* is a plural word. The singular is *vertex*. A is one vertex; A, B, and C are the three vertices of the triangle.

Triangles may have many different shapes. If the three sides are equal, it is called an **equilateral triangle**. If two sides are equal, it is an **isosceles triangle**. If no two sides are equal, it is a **scalene triangle**.

The marks on the triangles below indicate which sides of the triangle are equal. For example in $\triangle ABC$, $AB = BC = CA$ and in $\triangle DEF$, $DF = EF$.

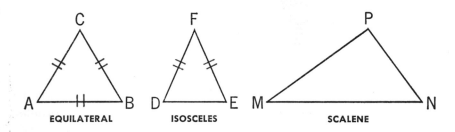

EQUILATERAL   ISOSCELES   SCALENE

The equal sides of an isosceles triangle are called its **arms,** DF and EF in the above figure. Any one of the three sides of a triangle may be chosen as its **base**. In an isosceles triangle, however, base usually refers to the side which is not one of the arms. In $\triangle DEF$ above, DE is the base.

The **perimeter** of a triangle is the sum of its sides.

The figure at the right is a **circle**. The symbol for circle is $\odot$. A circle can be drawn by means of an instrument called a **compass** (sometimes called **compasses**), with which you are already familiar. The point O, where the metal point of the compass is placed to draw the circle, is the **center**. Every point on the circle, such as A, B, C, or D, is the same distance from the center as every other point. If the distance from O to A is 1 inch, the distances from O to B, from O to C, and from O to D are also 1 inch.

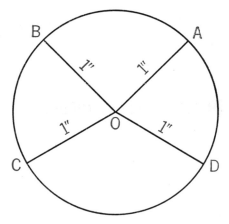

$\triangle$ *A circle is a closed curve all points of which are in the same plane* (flat surface) *and are equally distant from a point within called the center.*

△ *A straight line from the center of a circle to any point on the circle is called a* **radius** *(plural,* **radii**). In the figure, OA, OB, and OE are radii.

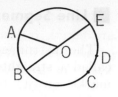

△ *A straight line through the center of a circle with its ends on the circle is a* **diameter**. BE is a diameter.

From the definitions we get the following statements:

All radii of the same circle are equal; a diameter is equal in length to two radii; all diameters of the same circle are equal.

△ *Any part of the line forming the circle is called an* **arc**. BA, AE, and CD are examples of arcs.

△ *A* **semicircle** *is half a circle.* Is a semicircle an arc?

△ *Two or more circles having the same center but different radii are called* **concentric circles**.

In common usage the surface bounded by the closed curve is sometimes referred to as a circle. For example, we say, "Compute the area of a circle."

EXERCISES

1. Name the vertices of triangle ABC, shown at the right.

2. Name the sides of this triangle.

3. What side is *opposite B*?

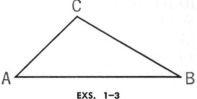

EXS. 1–3

4. a What is an equilateral triangle?
b an isosceles triangle?   **c** a scalene triangle?

5. Draw a circle with a compass. Indicate the center, a radius, a diameter, and an arc.

6. Place a point O on a piece of paper. Put the point of your compass on O and draw a circle with a radius of 2 inches. Now draw five radii of this circle and mark them OA, OB, OC, OD, and OE. How long is each one of these radii?

7. Draw another circle with a radius of 2 inches. In it draw five diameters. How long is each of these diameters?

8. Place two points A and B 3 inches apart on a piece of paper. With A as center draw a circle with a radius of $1\frac{1}{2}$ inches. With B as center draw a circle with a radius of 2 inches. The two circles will intersect (cross each other) at two points. Mark these points C and D. How far is it from A to C and from A to D? from B to C and from B to D?

■ Line Segments

The instrument used in geometry for drawing straight lines is called a **straightedge.** You will use your ruler, disregarding the marks on it, for your straightedge.

A line through points A and B can be extended indefinitely in either direction.

△ *A definite part of a line of indefinite length is called a* **line segment.**

AB, BC, and CA, in triangle ABC, Fig. 1, are line segments because they are definite parts of lines that can be extended indefinitely, as shown by the colored arrows in Fig. 2.

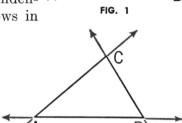

FIG. 1

When there is no confusion, a line segment is called simply a line. The word *line* alone means *straight line.*

In geometry there is a difference in meaning between *draw* and *construct.* When you are asked to **construct** a figure, you will use only the two instruments, the compass and the straightedge. To **draw** a figure you may use any convenient instruments.

FIG. 2

Construction A Making equal line segments using compass and straightedge only.

Suppose you wish to make a line segment equal to AB.

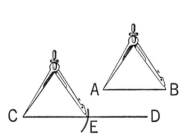

1. Use your straightedge to draw a line CD of indefinite length.

2. Place the metal point of the compass on A and the pencil point on B.

3. Tighten your compass to keep the correct distance between the points.

4. Place the metal point of the compass on C and with the pencil point draw a short arc across CD meeting CD at E. $CE = AB$.

This figure shows how to make a line equal to $a + b$ when segments a and b are given.

$$CE = a + b.$$

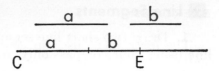

Construction B Making an equilateral triangle with a given base using compass and straightedge only.

Suppose you wish to make an equilateral triangle that will have the base AB.

1. With A as center for your compass and AB as radius draw an arc. The arc may be on either side of line AB.

2. With B as center and the same radius draw an arc intersecting the first arc at C.

3. Draw AC and BC. $\triangle ABC$ is the required equilateral triangle.

STEPS 1 AND 2

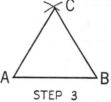
STEP 3

△ *To* **bisect** *means to divide into two equal parts.* AB is bisected at the point C if $AC = CB$.

△ *A point that bisects a line is called the* **midpoint** *of the line.*

Construction C Bisecting a line segment with compass and straightedge only.

You start with AB. (In the language of geometry we say, "**Given** AB.")

1. With A as center and AB as radius draw an arc on each side of AB. (If you wish you may use any radius greater than one half AB.)

2. With B as center and the same radius draw arcs intersecting the first arcs at C and D.

3. Draw CD which will intersect AB at E. E is the required point of bisection. $AE = EB$.

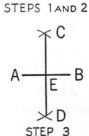
STEPS 1 AND 2

STEP 3

CONSTRUCTIONS

1. Draw two short line segments a and b. Then, on a working line using your compass only, make a line equal to $2a + 3b$.

2. Draw two line segments a and b (a longer than b). On a working line, using your compass only, make a line segment equal to $a - b$.

3. With any point A as center (you will mark a point A on a piece of paper) draw concentric circles with radii 2 inches, $2\frac{1}{2}$ inches, and 3 inches.

4. Using a compass and straightedge, make an equilateral triangle with a 2-inch base.

5. Using a method similar to the one you used in Ex. 4, make an isosceles triangle whose base is $1\frac{1}{2}$ inches and whose arms are 2 inches each.

6. Make a scalene triangle whose base is 2 inches and whose other two sides are $1\frac{1}{2}$ inches and $2\frac{1}{2}$ inches.

7. With your compass and straight-edge, make a line segment equal to AB and then bisect it.

A ├──────────────────┤ B

8. Draw three line segments at random on paper — horizontal, vertical, and slanting. Bisect each of these lines.

9. Draw a triangle ABC with side AB in a horizontal position. Bisect BC. (When you bisect this line, try to ignore the other two sides. Concentrate on this line alone. Use first one end of the line and then the other end as a center for your compass.)

10. Draw another triangle ABC with side AB horizontal. Bisect BC and then bisect CA.

11. Draw a triangle and bisect all three sides.

12. If the base of an isosceles triangle is 4 in. and each of the arms is 6 in., what is the perimeter?

13. Find the perimeter of triangles whose sides are as follows:

a 248 ft., 364 ft., 489 ft.   b $62\frac{1}{2}$ in., $49\frac{3}{4}$ in., $88\frac{5}{8}$ in.
c 3.64 ft., 9.87 ft., 8.75 ft.   d $5\frac{1}{3}$ yd., $6\frac{1}{2}$ yd., $4\frac{3}{4}$ yd.

14. What is the perimeter of an equilateral triangle each of whose sides is as follows?

a 4 ft.   b 67 in.   c $16\frac{3}{4}$ yd.   d 6.23 ft.

15. What is the perimeter of an isosceles triangle whose base and arms are respectively as follows?

a $2\frac{1}{2}$ in., $3\frac{3}{4}$ in.　　　b $4\frac{1}{2}$ ft., $3\frac{2}{3}$ ft.　　　c 9.8 in., 5.7 in.

EXTRA

16. With your straightedge, draw a scalene tri-angle. Bisect the three sides to find the middle point of each side. Connect the three middle points by straight lines.

17. Make AB 2 in. Using your compass, bisect AB by the line CD. (See figure.) Make $EF = AE = EG = EB$. With A, B, F, and G as centers and a radius of 1 inch draw circles.

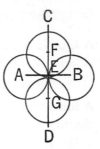

EX. 17

18. Draw AB $1\frac{1}{2}$ in. and then make the equi-lateral triangle ABC. With your compass, bisect AB, BC, and CA to find the middle points D, F, and E. Draw circles as shown.

19. Make an equilateral triangle ABC, each side of which is $2\frac{3}{8}$ in. Bisect AB, using your compass. Draw a straight line from the mid-point of AB to the vertex C of the triangle.

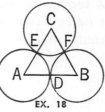

EX. 18

20. The perimeter of an isosceles triangle is 24 inches and the length of the base is 6 inches. How long is each one of the two equal sides?

21. The first number in exercises a, b, c, and d below is the perimeter of a triangle. The next two numbers are the lengths of each of two sides of that triangle. How long is the third side in each case?

a 1000 ft., 275 ft., 492 ft.　　b $192\frac{7}{8}$ in., $53\frac{3}{4}$ in., $46\frac{1}{2}$ in.
c 24.06 ft., 6.34 ft., 9.87 ft.　　d $20\frac{7}{12}$ yd., $8\frac{1}{3}$ yd., $4\frac{3}{4}$ yd.

22. If the perimeters of equilateral triangles are as follows, how long is each side of the triangle?

a 21 ft.　　　b 63 in.　　　c $16\frac{3}{4}$ yd.　　　d 15.36 ft.

23. If you know the perimeter and the length of the base of an isosceles triangle, how do you find the length of one of the equal sides?

24. If you know the perimeter of an equilateral triangle, how do you find the length of one side?

■ Geometry in Simple Arches — *Optional*

In the following five drawings of arches some of the geometry used by the draftsman in constructing the designs is shown. Study the designs and copy each one.

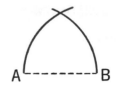

A Gothic arch — The arcs are drawn with A and B as centers and with AB as radius.

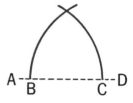

A lancet arch — A line AD is drawn and AB marked off equal to CD. The arcs are drawn with A and D as centers and with AC as radius.

A segmental arch — Construction **C** is used to bisect AB by line CED. The arc is drawn from any point F on CD below AB as center and with AF as radius.

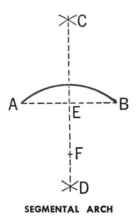

SEGMENTAL ARCH

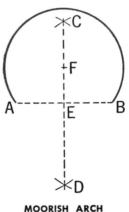

MOORISH ARCH

A Moorish arch — Construction **C** is used to bisect AB by line CED. The arc is drawn from any point F on CD above AB and with AF as radius.

A Persian arch — Triangle ABC is equilateral. AB, BC, and CA are bisected at D, E, and F, respectively. With AD as radius, arcs are drawn with D, E, F, and C as centers and also from M and N as centers.

The curve in color is the arch.

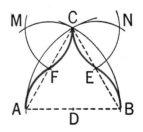

CONCLUSIONS BY MEASURING

◼ Angles

△ An **angle** is a figure formed by two straight lines that meet at a point. The point is called the **vertex** and the lines are called the **sides** of the angle. The symbol for angle is ∠. In this figure, B is the vertex and the sides are BA and BC.

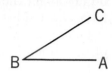

Rotation and size of an angle. If, as shown in Figures 1–6 below, a line is rotated about a point, from the position of OA to the position of OB, angle AOB is formed. The size of ∠AOB depends upon the amount of rotation. The amount of rotation is indicated by a curved arrow.

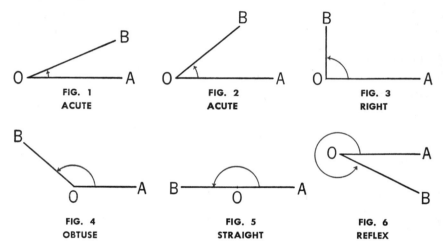

In Figure 1, OA would have to rotate very little to take the position of OB. ∠AOB is a small angle. The angle in Figure 2 is larger because the amount of rotation is greater. In Figure 3, OA has made one quarter of a complete rotation to position OB.

△ An angle formed by one quarter of a rotation is called a **right angle**. An angle less than a right angle is called an **acute angle**.

The angle in Figure 4 is larger than a right angle. In Figure 5, OA has made one half of a complete rotation; OA and OB lie in a straight line.

△ An angle formed by one half of a rotation is called a **straight angle**. An angle greater than a right angle but less than a straight angle is called an **obtuse angle**. An angle greater than a straight angle but less than a complete rotation (as shown in Figure 6) is called a **reflex angle**.

The amount of rotation does not in any way depend upon the lengths of the sides of the angle and so the lengths of the sides do not affect the *size* of an angle. For example, a right angle might have short sides, long sides, or sides of unequal length.

Draw two angles of about the same size but having the sides of one much longer than the sides of the other.

Every triangle, of course, has three angles. Triangles may be classified according to the kinds of angles they contain.

△ A **right triangle** *is a triangle one of whose angles is a right angle.*

△ An **obtuse triangle** *is a triangle one of whose angles is an obtuse angle.*

△ An **acute triangle** *is a triangle all of whose angles are acute.*

△ An **equiangular triangle** *is a triangle all of whose angles are equal.*

Draw a triangle in which one angle is obtuse. Draw a curved arrow in each angle to indicate the amount of rotation.

Reading angles. When there is only one angle at a vertex, the angle may be named by the letter at its vertex, as ∠*A*, ∠*G*.

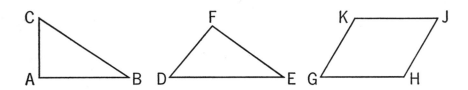

1. Make figures like these and draw curved arrows in ∠*A*, ∠*F*, and ∠*K* to indicate the amount of rotation.

2. Does ∠*F* in the second figure above appear to you to be a right angle, an acute angle, or an obtuse angle? Write your answer, then test the angle with the square corner of a piece of paper.

Since, in the figure at the right, there is more than one angle with vertex at *O* (Do you see six angles?), you would not know which angle is meant by ∠*O*. In cases like this, an angle may be named by using three letters. Thus, the angle with sides *AO* and *OB* is ∠*AOB*; the angle with 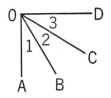 sides *AO* and *OC* is ∠*AOC*. The letter denoting the vertex is placed between the other two letters.

$\angle AOB$ may be designated as $\angle 1$, $\angle BOC$ as $\angle 2$, and $\angle COD$ as $\angle 3$; but $\angle BOD$, because of the line OC, cannot conveniently be designated by a number. Small letters as a, b, and c may be used in place of the numbers 1, 2, and 3.

3. In your copy of the figure $GHJK$ on page 10, draw a dotted line KM inside the figure, so that $\angle GKM$ appears to be a right angle.

△ *The angle opposite the base of an isosceles triangle is called the **vertex angle**.*

4. Construct an isosceles triangle and name the vertex angle using one letter only.

EXERCISES

1. Name these three angles in the following two ways: 1. Use one letter in naming them. 2. Use three letters in naming them.

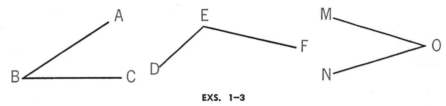

EXS. 1–3

2. What is the vertex of $\angle ABC$ above? What are the sides of this angle?

3. Name the vertex and the sides of $\angle DEF$ and of $\angle MON$ above.

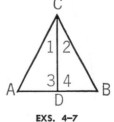

4. $\angle 1$ can be read as $\angle ACD$. Similarly $\angle 2$, $\angle 3$, and $\angle 4$ can be read as _?_, _?_, and $\angle$_?_.

5. Is $\angle CAD$ equal to or smaller than $\angle CAB$?

6. Is $\angle CBA$ larger than or equal to $\angle CBD$?

EXS. 4–7

7. Name the total angle at C using three letters.

8. You can tell whether an angle is equal to, greater than, or less than a right angle by placing on it a square corner of a card as shown. Is $\angle ABC$ greater or less than a right angle?

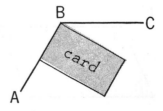

9. In this figure name all the angles, except the reflex angles, by one letter, by a number, or by three letters — whichever method is the simplest and clearly identifies the angle.

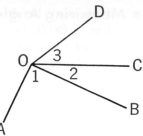

10. What single angle is the same as ∠1 + ∠2?

11. What single angle is the same as ∠2 + ∠3?

12. What single angle is the same as ∠1 + ∠2 + ∠3?

13. Write the letters *a* through *y* in a column and after each letter write the word *right, obtuse,* or *acute* to identify correctly each lettered angle in the following figures. If you cannot decide what kind of angle it is by looking at it, test it with the square corner of a card.

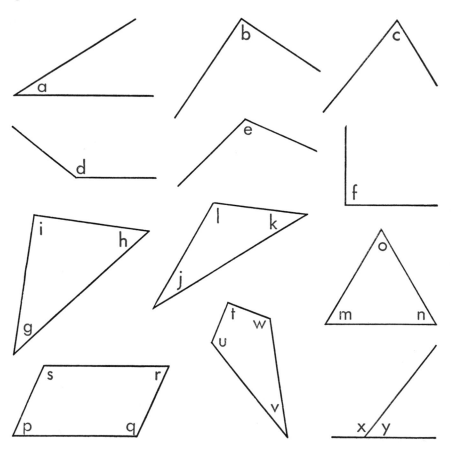

CONCLUSIONS BY MEASURING

■ Measuring Angles

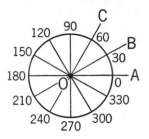

△ *The unit of measurement of angles is called a* **degree.** *It is $\frac{1}{360}$ of a complete rotation.* The symbol for degree is °.

This unit of measure has come down to us from the Babylonians. They thought that a year consisted of 360 days. They divided a circle into 360 equal parts, one for each day. The resulting figure proved to be a convenient instrument for measuring angles. In the figure above, ∠AOB might be said to have size 30, while ∠AOC has size 60. That is, the first angle is 30 degrees (30°) and the second is 60 degrees (60°).

A right angle contains 90°. An acute angle is an angle between 0° and 90°. A straight angle is 180°. An obtuse angle is an angle between 90° and 180°. A reflex angle is an angle between 180° and 360°.

All right angles are equal.

All straight angles are equal.

The instrument illustrated below is a combination ruler and **protractor.** The protractor consists of a curved scale marked off in degrees in two directions from 0° to 180° and a straight line **base** with its center at O.

The picture shows how an angle such as ∠AOB is measured. How many degrees would you say is in ∠AOB?

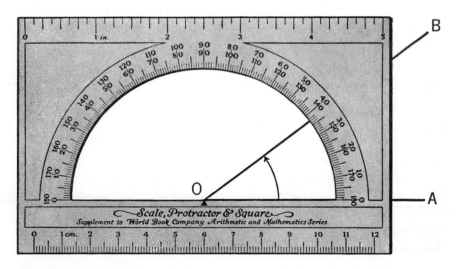

To measure an angle with a protractor:

a Place the center of the protractor on the vertex of the angle.

b Place its base along one side of the angle. (See *AO* on preceding page.)

c Be sure that the protractor lies across the opening of the angle. (See figure on preceding page.)

d There are two scales on the protractor. Read the scale that begins at 0° (not 180°) on one side of the angle.

e If the sides of the angle are not long enough to reach to the scale, extend the sides.

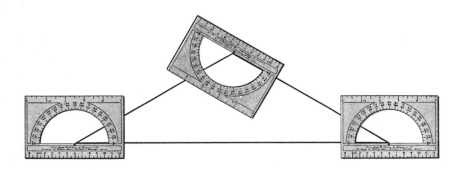

The figure above will help you to see how to place your protractor in measuring the angles of a triangle.

1. Practice measuring the angles of triangles until you can do it expertly. As you know from your previous studies, the sum of the three angles of each triangle should be 180°.

2. Practice measuring the angles of *quadrilaterals* (four-sided figures) until you can do it expertly. The sum of the angles should be 360°.

To make an angle of any number of degrees, say 50°, with a given line *OA* as a side and *O* as vertex, proceed as follows: Place the center of the protractor at *O* and the base along *OA*. Place a point at the 50° mark on the scale. Remove the protractor and draw a line from *O* through this point. The resulting angle (*AOB* in the figure) will be 50°.

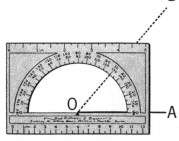

1. With a protractor measure to the nearest degree each of the following angles. How many degrees are there in each angle?

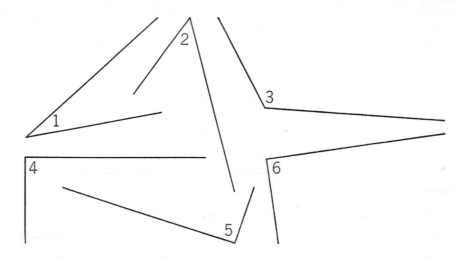

2. Measure each of the angles in the following figures to the nearest degree. (Show your answers like this: $\angle 1 = \_?\_°$.)

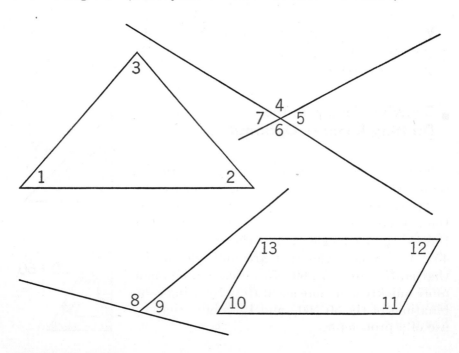

3. Make AB $1\frac{1}{2}$ inches. Then at each end of the line make angles of 42°. Measure $\angle ACB$. How many degrees are there in $\angle ACB$?

4. Make $AB = 2$ inches, $\angle B = 51°$, $BC = 1$ inch, $\angle C = 51°$, and $CD = 2$ inches.

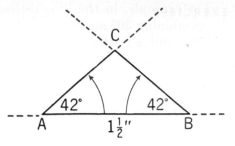

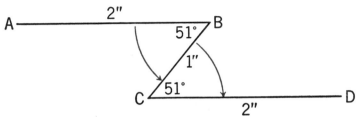

EXTRA

Do Exercises 5–7 without measuring:

5. $\angle 1 = 30°$, $\angle 2 = 40°$, and $\angle 3 = 50°$. $\angle AOC = \underline{\ ?\ }°$; $\angle BOD = \underline{\ ?\ }°$; and $\angle AOD = \underline{\ ?\ }°$.

6. In the same figure, $\angle 1 + \angle 2 = \angle AOC$; $\angle 2 + \angle 3 = \angle \underline{\ ?\ }$; and $\angle 1 + \angle 2 + \angle 3 = \angle \underline{\ ?\ }$.

7. In the same figure $\angle AOD - \angle BOD = \angle 1$; $\angle AOC - \angle 2 = \angle \underline{\ ?\ }$; $\angle AOD - \angle 3 = \angle \underline{\ ?\ }$.

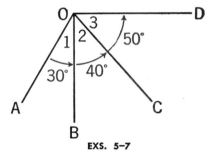

EXS. 5–7

■ Drawing Angles in the Drafting Room — *Optional*

Two very common instruments in the drafting room are the 30°-60° right triangle and the 45° right triangle. In the 30°-60° right triangle one of the acute angles is 30° and the other is 60°. In the 45° right triangle each of the acute angles is 45°. Common angles that are multiples of 15; that is, 15°, 30°, 45°, 60°, 75°, etc., can be made more quickly and more accurately by using combinations of the 30°, 60°, and 45° angles than by use of a protractor.

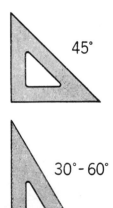

45°

30°- 60°

For example, in the illustration below an angle of 75° is made by combining 30° and 45°; and an angle of 105° is made by using the remaining part of the straight angle as shown.

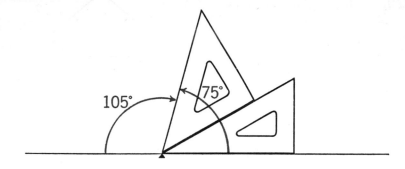

These diagrams show how angles of various sizes are made.

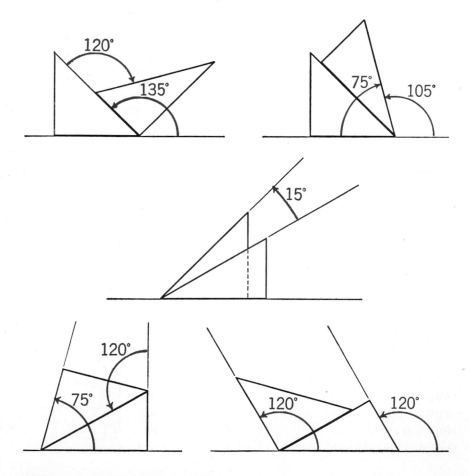

■ Constructing Equal Angles

In the figure, BD bisects $\angle ABC$ if $\angle 1$ $= \angle 2$.

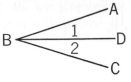

△ An **angle bisector** *is a line that divides an angle into two equal parts.*

By means of a protractor you can draw a line that divides an angle into two equal parts. Suppose you wish to divide the angle at the right into two equal parts.

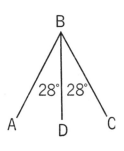

1. Measure the angle. In this case you will find it to be 56°.

2. Divide the measurement by 2. $56° \div 2$ $= 28°$.

3. Using your protractor draw a line through the vertex B so that $\angle ABD$ equals 28°, which is one half the given angle.

4. $\angle CBD$ is also one half of the given angle ($56° - 28° = 28°$), so BD bisects $\angle ABC$.

In geometry, it is customary to bisect an angle with straight-edge and compass rather than to draw the bisector with the aid of a protractor.

Construction D   Bisecting an angle.

You start with $\angle ABC$; that is, you are given $\angle ABC$.

1. With B as center and any convenient radius draw an arc intersecting BA at E and BC at D.

2. With the same radius and D and E as centers draw two arcs intersecting at F.

3. Draw BG through B and F. BG bisects $\angle ABC$.

To make easier the bisecting of an angle in a somewhat complex figure, you should generalize the above method; that is, you should describe the method without the use of letters.

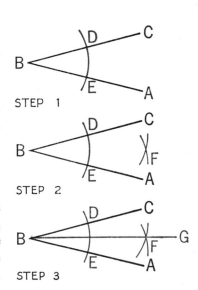

STEP 1

STEP 2

STEP 3

Then the method will refer not only to $\angle ABC$, as on the preceding page, but to *any* angle in *any* figure. The first center is the vertex of the angle you wish to bisect. The radius is any convenient radius. The arc is drawn across the sides of the angle. (Complete the generalization.)

Construction E   Making an angle equal to a given angle.

You are *given* $\angle ABC$ and you *are required* to construct an angle equal to it.

1. Draw a line ED corresponding to side BA of $\angle ABC$. E is the vertex of the desired angle.   (In many cases this line is already drawn.)

2. With B as center and any convenient radius draw an arc intersecting BA at H and BC at G.

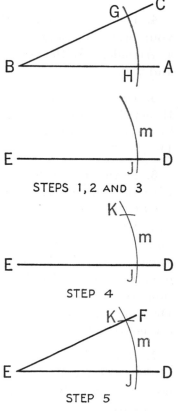

STEPS 1, 2 AND 3

STEP 4

STEP 5

3. With E as center and the same radius draw an arc m intersecting ED at J.

4. Take the distance from H to G on the given angle as a radius.   With this radius and J as center draw an arc intersecting arc m at K.

5. Draw EF through E and K.
$\angle DEF$ is equal to $\angle ABC$.

You should generalize the above method not using the letters of these figures.   You must draw three arcs. The center of the first arc is the vertex of the given angle.   The radius is any convenient radius.   Draw the arc across the given angle.

The center of the second arc is the vertex of the desired angle.   The radius is the same radius you used before.   Draw the arc.

The center of the third arc is the point where the second arc crosses the given side of the desired angle.   The radius is the distance across the given angle where the first arc crosses it.   Draw this third arc so that it will intersect the second arc.

1. Draw an acute angle, a right angle, and an obtuse angle. Without measuring, draw a line through the vertex of each angle so that the angle is approximately bisected. Measure to see how accurate you have been. How many degrees were you in error in each case?

2. Draw $\triangle ABC$ with obtuse angle at B. Then draw by estimate the bisectors of the three angles. Measure to test your accuracy.

3. With your protractor draw an angle of 76°. Then, using only straightedge and compass, bisect the angle. Check your accuracy by measurement.

4. Draw a base line AB 2 inches long. At each end make with your protractor angles of 55° so that the resulting figure will be a triangle. With your compass and straightedge bisect $\angle A$ and $\angle B$.

5. Draw a scalene triangle with one angle an obtuse angle. Bisect the three angles with straightedge and compass. The three bisectors should intersect at one point. Do they?

6. Draw an $\angle ABC$ and a line DE with point F on it. Then construct $\angle DFG = \angle ABC$. (Note that one side, DF, of the angle is already drawn and that F is the vertex of the desired angle. The dotted line is drawn here merely to show you the general position of the second side of the angle. Drawing GF will be the last step in the construction.)

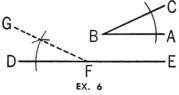

EX. 6

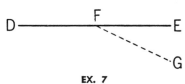

EX. 7

7. Repeat Ex. 6 with this difference. Make $\angle EFG$ equal to $\angle ABC$ in the position shown by the dotted line in the figure.

8. Draw an $\angle ABC$. Construct $\angle BAD$ equal to $\angle ABC$ in the position shown by the dotted line in the figure.

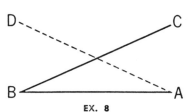

EX. 8

■ Angles in Air Flight

A pilot of a large airplane must take a machine weighing as much as 50 tons off the ground into the air, take the plane to its destination, and bring it down carefully to the ground. He is assisted in his operation of the plane by instruments that show him the angle of his position in relation to the horizon, to his course, and, if necessary, to the stars.

When an airplane takes off from the runway it climbs at an angle to gain altitude. This angle is the angle of *climb*. In the top figure the angle of climb is 13°.

A sort of automatic pilot, called a *bank-and-climb gyro*, is connected to the instrument panel which shows the angle at which the plane is flying in relation to the horizon.

When a plane is in flight, the nose of the plane is held so that the wing makes a small angle with the direction of the air flowing past the plane. This angle is called the angle of *attack*.

When climbing, turning, gliding, or in level flight, the pilot holds the plane at the most efficient angle of attack. The size of this angle depends on the type of plane.

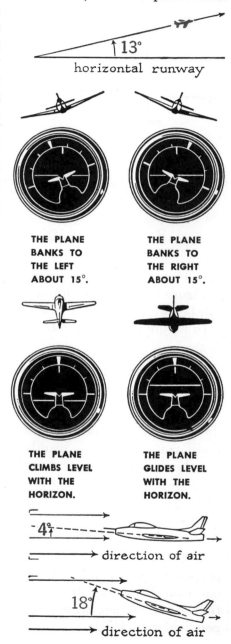

13°

horizontal runway

THE PLANE BANKS TO THE LEFT ABOUT 15°.

THE PLANE BANKS TO THE RIGHT ABOUT 15°.

THE PLANE CLIMBS LEVEL WITH THE HORIZON.

THE PLANE GLIDES LEVEL WITH THE HORIZON.

4°

direction of air

18°

direction of air

■ Perpendicular Lines

In Figures 1–3, CD is *perpendicular* to AB (written in symbols $CD \perp AB$) if $\angle 1$ and $\angle 2$ are right angles.

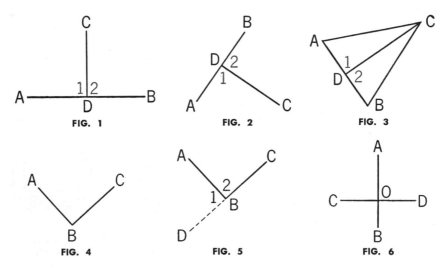

FIG. 1   FIG. 2   FIG. 3

FIG. 4   FIG. 5   FIG. 6

In Figure 4, $AB \perp BC$ or $BC \perp AB$ if $\angle B$ is a right angle. If CB of Figure 4 is extended through B to D as shown in Figure 5, there will be two right angles as in Figures 1–3.

In Figure 6, if $AB \perp CD$, all four of the angles shown are right angles.

△ *Perpendicular lines are lines that make right angles (or a right angle) with each other.*

It is important for you to be able to visualize the position of perpendiculars in various figures. Until you can do this readily you may need to use the square corner of a card as a help.

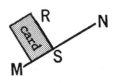

1. Draw a line AB and place a point C on it. Then draw a line perpendicular to AB at C. To do this place a card as shown with one side along AB and the corner at C. Then draw the line CD.

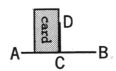

2. Draw a line through R so that it will be perpendicular to MN. Place the card so that one edge lies along MN and another edge just touches R. Then draw RS, which will be perpendicular to MN.

3. In a figure like this one it is necessary to extend BA before you can draw a line through C perpendicular to AB. There is no other way to draw a line through C so that it will make right angles with AB.

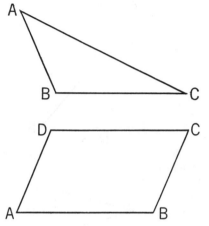

Draw a line AB and place a point C as shown. Then extend BA and draw CD perpendicular to BA. Use the square corner of a card for the perpendicular to BA if necessary.

4. Draw a large triangle shaped like the one at the right with an obtuse angle at B. Through B draw a line perpendicular to AC and ending in AC at D. This line is an *altitude*. (Use a card if necessary.)

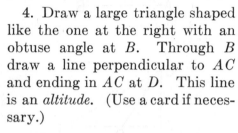

△ An **altitude of a triangle** *is a line from any one vertex of the triangle, perpendicular to the opposite side, and terminated (ended) by that side.*

5. Draw a large four-sided figure shaped like this one. Then draw a line through C perpendicular to AB. It will be necessary to extend AB to the right.

6. Do these exercises over again without using the card to help you draw the perpendiculars.

EXERCISES

Draw figures shaped like those on page 24, only larger. Then follow the directions under each figure. In each case you are to draw a perpendicular which must pass through (or to) the point indicated and make right angles with the line indicated. For instance, if you are asked to draw a line through P perpendicular to XY, you know even without a figure that the line must go through P and it must make right angles with XY. Use a corner of a square card at first if you need to. However, you should continue to practice until you can draw fairly accurate perpendiculars from a point on a line or from a point to a line without the card.

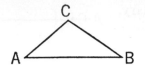

1. Draw a line from C perpendicular to AB.

2. Draw lines perpendicular to AB at A and at B.

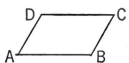

3. Draw a line from D perpendicular to AB and from C perpendicular to AB.

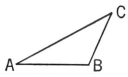

4. From B draw a line perpendicular to AC.

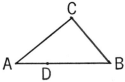

5. From D draw a line perpendicular to BC.

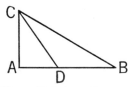

6. From D draw a line perpendicular to BC.

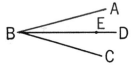

7. From E draw a line perpendicular to AB.

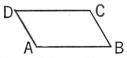

8. From C draw a line perpendicular to DA.

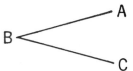

9. $\angle B$ is acute. At B draw a line perpendicular to AB and another perpendicular to BC.

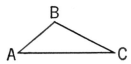

10. $\angle B$ is obtuse. From C draw a line perpendicular to AB.

■ Constructing Perpendiculars

Construction F **Constructing a line perpendicular to a given line at a given point on the line.**

Given line AB with point C on it.

Required to construct a line perpendicular to AB at C.

1. With C as center and any convenient radius draw arcs intersecting AB at D and E.

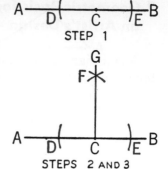
STEP 1

2. With D and E as centers and the same radius for both, draw arcs intersecting at F.

3. Draw CG through C and F.
$CG \perp AB$ at C.

Do you see a similarity between *Constructions D* and *F*?

STEPS 2 AND 3

Construction G

Constructing a line perpendicular to a given line from a given point not on the line.

Given line AB with point C not on it.
Required to construct a line perpendicular to AB from C.

1. With C as center and any convenient radius draw arcs intersecting AB at D and E.

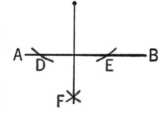

2. With D and E as centers and the same radius for both, draw arcs intersecting at F.

3. Draw CF, which is the required perpendicular.

Note that in each of these constructions the metal point of the compass is first placed on the given point. Then two arcs are drawn on the line indicated. The two points thus determined (located) are then used as centers to draw intersecting arcs.

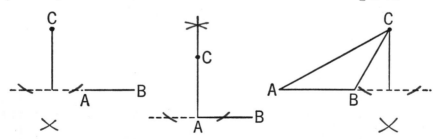

If the point and line are so situated that you cannot make two arcs on the given line, extend the line until you can, as shown in the above figures.

■ Geometric Basis for an Artist's Design — *Optional*

The design below shows the use of geometry in creating a design for a decorated ceiling.

In the design the eight concentric circles are drawn with radii $\frac{5}{8}''$, $\frac{11}{16}''$, $1''$, $1\frac{1}{8}''$, $1\frac{7}{8}''$, $2\frac{1}{16}''$, $2\frac{1}{4}''$, and $3''$.

AB and CD are perpendicular diameters. Each right angle is divided into four equal angles by bisecting the right angles and then bisecting the halves.

The arcs in the corners of the square have their centers on the 3-inch circle. The eight arcs that curve toward the center have their centers on the $2\frac{1}{4}$-inch circle.

The upper right-hand fourth of the diagram shows the details of the finished design with the construction lines removed.

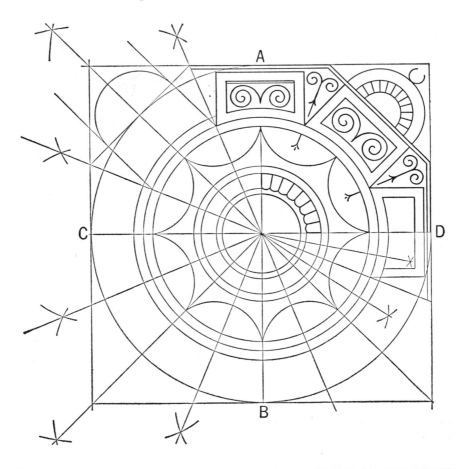

1. Refer to the ten exercises on page 24. Draw each of the figures as you did before, but this time *construct* the required perpendiculars.

2. Draw an acute triangle and construct a line from each vertex perpendicular to the opposite side and terminating on that side (*an altitude*). Note that these three altitudes meet at a point within the triangle.

3. Draw figures like those below and in each case construct a line perpendicular to AD from B.

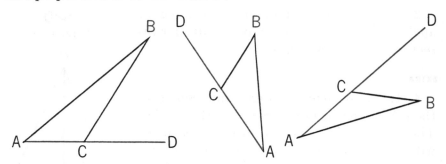

4. Draw an obtuse triangle and construct its three altitudes. To do this you will have to extend some of the lines. Note that these altitudes, if extended, meet at a point outside the triangle.

■ Perpendicular Bisector

CD is the *perpendicular bisector* of AB if $AD = DB$ and $\angle 1$ and $\angle 2$ are right angles.

Δ The **perpendicular bisector** *of a line segment is a line perpendicular to the segment at its midpoint.*

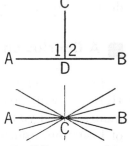

If C is the midpoint of AB, any line drawn through C bisects AB. A line may have an unlimited number of bisectors all passing through its midpoint. A line may have an unlimited number of lines perpendicular to it at different points on the line, but only one perpendicular bisector.

The method of bisecting a line shown on page 5 is also the method of constructing the perpendicular bisector.

EXERCISES

1. Draw *AB* of any convenient length and construct *CD* the perpendicular bisector of *AB*. (The method is shown at the right.)

2. Draw *AB* 2 inches long. Construct *CD* the perpendicular bisector of *AB* and make it 2 inches long. Draw *CA* and *CB*. Measure *CA* and *CB* and note that △*ABC* is isosceles. (The figure below at the right is to help you with the position of the lines.)

3. Draw two lines *AB* and *BC* forming an angle *ABC*. Construct the perpendicular bisectors of these two lines.

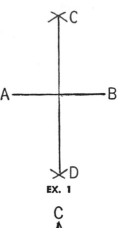

EX. 1

EXTRA

4. Draw an acute triangle and construct the perpendicular bisectors of the three sides. These three lines should meet at a point within the triangle. Using this point as center and the distance from the point to one of the vertices as radius, draw a circle. The circle should pass through the three vertices.

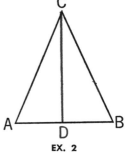

EX. 2

5. Draw a line *DE* and place a point *C* outside of it. From *C* construct a line perpendicular to *DE* meeting it at *A*. Extend *CA* to *F* so that *AF* = *CA*. Take a point *G* on *DE* and draw *CG* and *GF*.

6. Construct a right triangle *ABC* with right angle at *A*. Where do the three altitudes meet?

■ A Conclusion from Measurement

There are experiments in geometry just as there are in science. Here you will start with a triangle whose base has a given measurement. Then you will bisect the other two sides, connect the points of bisection, and by means of measurement come to a conclusion about the length of the connecting line in comparison to the length of the base.

1. Draw a line *AB* 8 centimeters long (follow the figure).

2. Complete △*ABC* with any dimensions you choose.

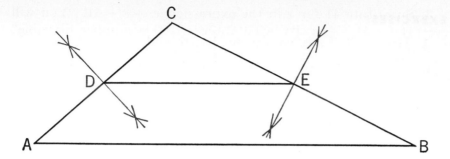

3. Bisect AC and call the midpoint D.

4. Bisect BC and call the midpoint E.

5. Draw a straight line from D to E and measure DE.

6. Line DE should be 4 centimeters on everyone's triangle even though the lengths of the sides AC and BC of the various triangles are different.

In this case the line DE is just half the length of AB. It is the same for all your classmates. Is this enough to convince you that the line DE will always be one half of AB?

Try this experiment again with other values for AB, such as 6 cm., 9 cm., and 10 cm. The more cases you try the more probable it becomes that the relationship is true in general.

You may suspect that there is something about the make-up of this figure that causes the relationship to be always true. You are correct. You will learn later a method of proof.

This kind of reasoning is called **inductive reasoning** — reasoning from the particular to the general. It assumes that the results found in many specific cases will be true in general. The greater the number of specific cases tried, the more likely is the conclusion general. (See page 503.)

EXERCISES

1. Show by inductive reasoning that the sum of the angles of a triangle is 180°. (Draw several triangles, measure the angles, and record the sum of the angles of each triangle.)

2. Substitute the numbers 1, 2, 3, 4, 5, 6, and 7 for x in the expression $x^2 + x + 41$. Note that all your answers are prime numbers. Have you tried enough cases to make you believe that the substitution of any integer will give you a prime number?

3. Substitute 41 for x in the expression $x^2 + x + 41$. You will get $(41)^2 + 41 + 41$. By what integer is this number divisible? Is it prime?

4. Show by inductive reasoning that if a closed figure has n sides and all possible lines are drawn from one vertex to every other vertex, the number of triangles formed is $n - 2$. Draw figures of 4, 5, 6, and 7 sides and find the number of triangles as compared to the number of sides. Have you tried enough cases to make you believe that the rule is always true?

5. Show by inductive reasoning that the number of diagonals in a figure of n sides is $\dfrac{n(n-3)}{2}$.

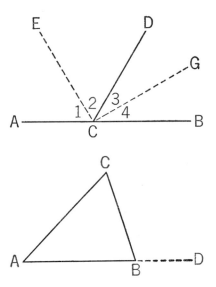

6. ACB is a straight line and CD is any line meeting it. Show inductively that no matter what the size of $\angle ACD$ (except that it must be less than 180°), if CG bisects $\angle DCB$ and CE bisects $\angle ACD$, then $\angle ECG = 90°$.

7. The figure ABC is a triangle and AB is extended in a straight line to D. Show inductively that no matter what the shape or size of $\triangle ABC$, $\angle CBD = \angle A + \angle C$.

■ A Construction Using only a Compass — *Optional*

The restriction of tools to straightedge and compass goes back to Plato, about 400 B.C. Some mathematicians have gone further than this and restricted constructions to the compass alone. Mascheroni, who lived in the latter part of the nineteenth century, showed how all standard constructions usually done with straightedge and compass can be done without the straightedge using only the compass.

The following construction using a compass only is given as a matter of interest.

Dividing a circle into four equal parts, using only compass.

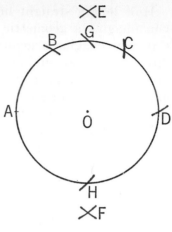

1. Start at any point A on a circle and with radius AO lay off on the circle three equal arcs AB, BC, CD.

2. With A and D as centers and with radius AC draw arcs intersecting outside the circle at E and F.

3. With A as center and radius OE (or OF) draw arcs intersecting circle at G and H.

Then arc AG = arc GD = arc DH = arc HA.

Dividing a circle into four equal parts using a straightedge and a compass.

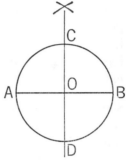

Draw any diameter AOB and at O construct a perpendicular to AB. This perpendicular will intersect the circle at C and D.

The points A, D, B, and C then divide the circle into four equal parts.

▉ Geometric Concepts

Geometric line. So far you have been considering triangles and other figures as actually printed or drawn with a pencil or pen. The lines in such figures, of course, have some width and even a slight thickness.

Think of lines drawn with finer and finer pen points and then imagine a line that has no width or thickness whatsoever. Such a line we call a *geometric line* as distinguished from an actual line drawn on paper.

Do you think it is possible for any actual line to be absolutely straight? Suppose that you drew a line as straight as you possibly could with a sharp pencil and straightedge. If you could magnify it to a thousand times its size, it would look as jagged as the edge of a saw. It is easy, however, to *imagine* a geometric line to be absolutely straight. *Think* what we mean by "straight" and you are thinking of a geometric straight line.

How long a straight line could you draw with a pencil? Can you imagine a geometric straight line that is longer than that? Can you imagine a geometric straight line that extends in both directions for an unlimited distance — even to the farthest star, or farther? A geometric straight line, unless specified as beginning and ending at certain points, is considered as extending without limit in both directions.

We shall continue to speak of "drawing a line" when we mean drawing an actual line to represent a geometric line.

Curved line or curve. A *curved line,* or *curve,* is a line no part of which is straight.

Geometric point. We say that two straight lines intersect at a point (if they are not parallel). If we are speaking of actual pencil lines, does the point of intersection have width? Does it have some thickness? The intersection of two geometric lines has no dimensions whatever — just position. Such a point we call a *geometric point.*

Surface. You may think of a geometric line as the path made by a moving geometric point. Similarly, a *geometric surface* may be thought of as the path of a moving geometric line. For example, a vertical line moving along a horizontal line would form a plane surface, as the surface of a wall. A vertical straight line moving around a horizontal circle would generate a cylindrical surface. A straight line passing through a point above a circle and moving around the circle would generate a conical surface. A circle rotating about a diameter would generate a spherical surface. Since the line that generates a surface has no thickness, a surface has no thickness.

Solid. A portion of space enclosed by a geometric surface or by geometric surfaces is called a *geometric solid.* Various solids are the sphere, cube, pyramid, prism, etc.

Geometric figures. In the discussions of the lines that form geometric figures, such as triangles, squares, circles, etc., the lines are to be considered as geometric lines.

Meaning of the word any. The word *any* is often found in mathematics and in mathematics it has a special meaning. You may be asked to take *any* point on a line, or to draw *any* triangle, or to consider *any* quadrilateral (four-sided figure). What is meant is to take *one* point or *one* triangle or *one* quadrilateral that will represent all such points or triangles or quadrilaterals. Suppose you were asked to draw *any* four-sided figure using your straightedge only. You might draw a square □, a rectangle ▭, or a parallelogram ▱. This would be wrong. Although these are all quadrilaterals, they cannot represent all quadrilaterals, because they are special kinds of quadrilateral. You should have drawn a quadrilateral that has no special characteristics (no equal sides, and no equal angles). Whenever you are asked to draw *any* figure, be sure to draw the most general one that satisfies the given conditions.

Note: Read these pages on geometric concepts carefully for understanding. Do not attempt to memorize them.

SUPPLEMENTARY EXERCISES

1. Use three letters to fill in the blanks. ∠1 is the same as ∠ADF, ∠2 = ∠_?_, ∠3 = ∠_?_.

2. Is ∠ADF equal to or greater than ∠ADE?

3. If ADC is a straight line, what is the sum of ∠1 and ∠4?

4. Is the sum of ∠ABC and ∠CBF as much as 180°? Explain.

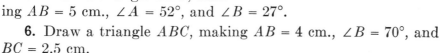

EXS. 1–4

5. Draw a triangle ABC, making AB = 5 cm., ∠A = 52°, and ∠B = 27°.

6. Draw a triangle ABC, making AB = 4 cm., ∠B = 70°, and BC = 2.5 cm.

7. Draw a scalene triangle. Bisect its three angles and continue the bisectors until they meet.

8. Draw an acute angle ABC. Extend line CB through B to a point D. Bisect ∠ABC by a line BE and ∠ABD by a line BF. Measure ∠FBE. It is _?_°.

9. Do Ex. 8 over again, starting with a different-sized angle. Can you explain why ∠FBE is the same size as before?

10. Triangle ABC is equilateral. Measure one side to the nearest tenth of a centimeter and compute the perimeter.

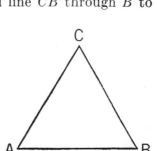

EX. 10

GEOMETRIC CONCEPTS

11. If the perimeter of a triangle is 496 in. and two of the sides are 176 in. and 219 in., how long is the third side?

12. If the base of an isosceles triangle is $2\frac{1}{2}$ in. and one of the arms is $1\frac{3}{4}$ in., what is the perimeter?

13. Construct a scalene triangle whose sides are 1, 2, and $1\frac{1}{2}$ in.

14. Can you construct a triangle whose sides are 8, 4, and 2 cm.? Explain.

15. Draw a scalene triangle. Using your compass, find the midpoints of the three sides. Connect the three middle points by straight lines.

16. Draw any acute angle ABC. Construct $\angle BCD = \angle ABC$ in the position indicated.

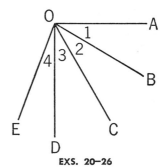

EX. 16

17. Draw a line segment of convenient length (approximately one quarter the width of your work sheet). Call its length a. Then construct a line equal to $\frac{5}{2}a$.

18. Draw a line $4\frac{5}{8}''$ long. Using your compass, bisect it. Check your construction by finding $\frac{1}{2}$ of $4\frac{5}{8}''$ and measuring each half of the line.

19. Draw a hexagon (figure with six sides). Measure the angles with a protractor. What is the sum of the six angles?

20. If, in the figure shown at the right, $\angle 1 = 35°$ and $\angle 2 = 30°$, how many degrees are there in $\angle AOC$?

21. If $\angle 2 = 30°$, $\angle 3 = 20°$, and $\angle 4 = 32°$, how many degrees are there in $\angle BOE$?

22. If $\angle 1 = a°$, $\angle 2 = b°$, and $\angle 3 = c°$, how many degrees are there in $\angle AOD$?

23. If $\angle DOB = 44°$ and $\angle 3 = 20°$, how many degrees are there in $\angle 2$?

24. If $\angle AOD = 90°$ and $\angle BOD = a°$, how many degrees are there in $\angle 1$?

25. If $\angle 1 = \angle 2 = \angle 3$, $\angle 1 = 30°$, and $\angle 4 = 35°$, how many degrees are there in $\angle AOE$?

26. If $\angle 1 = \angle 2$, $\angle 1 = 25°$, and $\angle AOE = 120°$, how many degrees are there in $\angle COE$?

I. Vocabulary.

1. Use each of the following words or terms in a sentence. If a word or a term refers to a geometric figure draw a figure for it.

Triangle	Isosceles triangle	Equilateral triangle
Scalene triangle	Sides of a triangle	Vertices of a triangle
Arms of an isosceles triangle	Base of an isosceles triangle	Vertex angle of an isosceles triangle
Compass	Circle	Perimeter of a triangle
Radius of a circle	Arc of a circle	Diameter of a circle
Semicircle	Concentric circles	Straightedge
Degree of angle	Line segment	Perpendicular lines
Construction	Bisect	Line bisector
Angle bisector	Midpoint	Angle
Sides of an angle	Right angle	Vertex of an angle
Acute angle	Obtuse angle	Straight angle
Reflex angle	Acute triangle	Right triangle
Obtuse triangle	Protractor	Altitude of a triangle
	Perpendicular bisector	

II. Reading angles.

2. In the figure at the right an arc is drawn across ∠1 to indicate rotation. Copy the figure and draw an arc across ∠3 and another arc across ∠*AOC*.

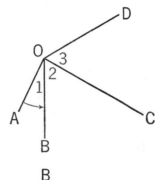

3. Name the angle that is indicated by the arc in the figure at the right.

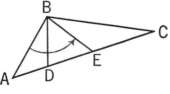

III. Estimating the size of angles and measuring them.

4. Is ∠*ADE* acute or obtuse? Is ∠*BGE* obtuse or acute? Use a square corner of a card if you need to.

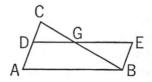

5. How many degrees are there in each angle of the triangle below? What is the sum of the angles?

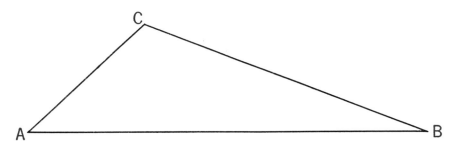

IV. Constructions.

6. Draw two line segments a and b. Construct a line equal to $2a + 3b$.

7. Draw a line 2 inches long. Using this line as a base construct an equilateral triangle.

8. Draw a line segment. Construct its bisector.

9. Draw an acute angle. Construct its bisector.

10. Draw a figure with lines AB and CD as shown below. Take a convenient point F on CD. Then construct $\angle 2$ equal to $\angle 1$ in the position indicated.

11. Draw an obtuse triangle ABC with the obtuse angle at B.

a At C construct a line perpendicular to AC.

b From A construct a line perpendicular to BC.

EX. 10

V. Inductive reasoning.

12. Construct several equilateral triangles. Measure the angles. Do you come to any conclusion?

13. Show that the sum of the first two odd integers (1 and 3) is equal to 2^2, the sum of the first three odd integers (1, 3, and 5) is 3^2, the sum of the first four odd integers is 4^2, and so on up to the sum of the first ten odd integers is 10^2. Does this convince you that the sum of the first n odd integers (n being any whole number) is n^2? Explain.

TEST 1

If a statement is true, write True. *If it is false, write* False.

1. The size of an angle depends upon the lengths of the sides.

2. A line can be bisected by only one line.

3. Two angles with a common vertex and a common side between them must be equal angles.

4. An altitude of a triangle is a line drawn from a vertex, perpendicular to the opposite side, and ending on that side.

5. An angle is the point where two lines meet.

6. A perpendicular to a line always bisects it.

7. The sum of angles 1, 2, 3, and 4 is 360°.

8. $AB \perp BC$. Then $\angle 1 + \angle 2 + \angle 3 = 180°$.

9. An equilateral triangle is always isosceles.

10. An isosceles triangle is always equilateral.

11. If an angle of 162° is bisected, each part must be 81°.

12. A right triangle may also be isosceles.

13. A radius equals one half of a diameter of the same circle.

14. If a line is bisected and then the two halves are bisected, the line is divided into four equal parts.

15. $\angle 1$ and $\angle BCA$ are the same angle.

16. $\angle CDA$ is acute.

17. If $AO \perp OB$, $\angle AOB = 180°$.

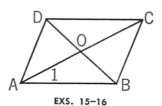

EXS. 15–16

TEST 2

Complete these sentences:

1. The sides of a right angle are _?_ to each other.

2. Two radii are drawn in the same circle. If one radius is 7 inches, the other radius is _?_ inches.

3. An obtuse angle is greater than a _?_ angle but less than a _?_ angle.

4. If you are asked to construct a line from *A* perpendicular to *BC*, you first place the point of the compass at _?_.

5. One fourth of a complete rotation is an angle of _?_°.

6. ∠1, ∠2, ∠3, ∠*BAD*, ∠*BAE*, and ∠*BAC* each has its vertex at _?_.

7. An equilateral triangle has _?_ _?_ sides.

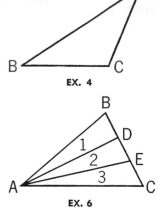

EX. 4

EX. 6

TEST 3

Copy the right answer:

1. The vertex of ∠*ABC* is   a *A*   b *B*   c *C*

2. How many acute angles has an acute triangle?   a one   b two   c three

3. In △*PQR*, *PR* = *QR*. Then the vertex angle of the triangle is   a ∠*P*   b ∠*Q*   c ∠*R*

4. If ∠2 = 90°, then *AB*   a is perpendicular to *CD*   b bisects *CD*   c is equal to *CD*

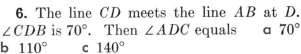

EX. 4

5. If the diameter of a circle is 6 in., the radius is   a 12 in.   b 3 in.   c 9 in.

6. The line *CD* meets the line *AB* at *D*. ∠*CDB* is 70°. Then ∠*ADC* equals   a 70°   b 110°   c 140°
Draw the figure and measure if you need to.

7. If ∠1 = ∠2 = ∠3, ∠1 = *a*°, and ∠4 = *b*°, then ∠*AOE* =   a 3*a*° + *b*°   b 180° − *a*°   c 3*a*° − *b*°

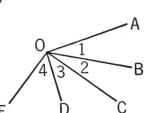

CHAPTER **2** Conclusions without Measurement

IN GEOMETRY you get some of the basic statements by means of measurement but from that point on you reason without measurement.

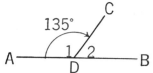

1. You are told that ∠ADC is 135°. You are asked, "Is ∠ADC obtuse or acute?" Your answer is that ∠ADC is obtuse and you know this because any angle between 90° and 180° is obtuse.

You were helped in your thinking by a *definition* you had in mind. You gave the definition of an obtuse angle as a reason for your *conclusion*.

2. You are told that *ADB* is a straight line and that ∠ADC is 135°. You are asked, "How many degrees are there in ∠CDB?"

Your answer is that ∠CDB is 45°. You gave your answer without measuring. You thought this way, "∠ADB is a straight angle because *ADB* is a straight line. ∠CDB = ∠ADB − ∠ADC, so ∠CDB = 180° − 135°, or 45°."

Again you had a definition in mind — the definition of straight angle — and you found the answer, not by measuring, but by reasoning.

EXERCISES

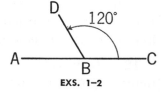

EXS. 1–2

1. *ABC* is a straight line and ∠DBC = 120°. How many degrees are there in ∠ABD? (Do not measure.) Explain your reasoning.

2. If $\angle DBC$, in Ex. 1, were $a°$ instead of $120°$, how many degrees would there be in $\angle ABD$?

3. AB and CD are straight lines. What is the sum of $\angle 1$ and $\angle 2$? How do you know? (Do not measure.) Explain your reasoning.

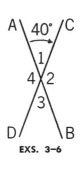

4. AB and CD are straight lines and $\angle 1 = 40°$. How many degrees are there in $\angle 2$? Explain.

5. AB and CD are straight lines and $\angle 1 = 40°$. You have already found the number of degrees in $\angle 2$. How many degrees are there in $\angle 3$?

EXS. 3-6

6. AB and CD are straight lines and $\angle 1 = 40°$. How many degrees are there in $\angle 4$? Explain your reasoning.

7. ADC is a straight line. If $\angle 1 = 130°$, how many degrees are there in $\angle 2$? Explain.

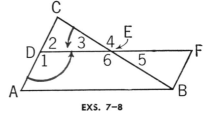

8. DEF and CEB are straight lines. If $\angle 3 = 30°$, how many degrees are there in $\angle 4$, in $\angle 5$, and in $\angle 6$? Do not measure. Explain your reasoning. You must have a good reason for every statement you make.

EXS. 7-8

9. If you are told that $CB \perp AD$, do you know how many degrees there are in $\angle ABC$ and in $\angle ABD$ without measuring? How many degrees are there in each? Explain.

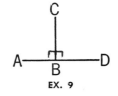

EX. 9

10. If C is the mid-point of AB and AC is 3 in., how long is CB? Explain.

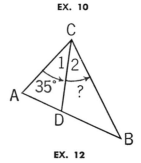

EX. 10

11. Draw a scalene triangle ABC. Locate the mid-points D, E, and F on AB, BC, and CA, respectively. Draw DE, EF, and FD. From what you learned on page 29, tell which line segments are equal.

12. CD bisects $\angle C$ and $\angle 1 = 35°$, how many degrees are there in $\angle 2$? Explain.

EX. 12

Supplementary Angles and Adjacent Angles

In the following pages you will learn some words that have to do with relationships among angles. These relationships will provide further opportunity to draw conclusions without measuring.

△ *Supplementary angles are two angles whose sum is 180°. Each angle is the* **supplement** *of the other.*

For example, angles of 100° and 80° are supplementary. An angle of 70° is the supplement of an angle of 110°.

1. What is the supplement of an angle of 45°?
2. If you were given the number of degrees in any angle, how would you find the number of degrees in its supplement?
3. What is the supplement of an angle of $a°$?
4. Is there any angle that is equal to its supplement?

△ *A degree is subdivided into sixty equal parts called* **minutes** *and a minute into sixty equal parts called* **seconds.**

An angle of $25\frac{1}{2}$ degrees may then be written as 25 degrees, 30 minutes or 25° 30′. An angle of $25\frac{1}{8}$ degrees would be 25 degrees, 7 minutes, 30 seconds or 25° $7\frac{1}{2}$′ or 25° 7′ 30″.

5. Find the supplement of an angle of 35° 40′.

SOLUTION: Write 180° as 179° 60′ just as you might write 5 yd. as 4 yd. 3 ft., and then subtract.

$$\begin{array}{r} 179° \quad 60′ \\ 35° \quad 40′ \\ \hline 144° \quad 20′ \end{array}$$

The supplement is

6. What is the supplement of an angle of 49° 12′?
7. With your protractor draw the supplement of an angle of 35°. (Do not draw the 35° angle.)

△ *Adjacent angles are two angles that have the same vertex and a common side between them.*

Angle 1 and angle 2 in the figure are adjacent, for they have the same vertex D and the common side BD between them. Angle ADB and angle ADC are not adjacent, according to the definition, for, although they have a common vertex D and a common side AD, the common side does not lie *between* them.

Since the angles formed by two perpendicular lines are equal adjacent angles, the definition of perpendicular lines is often stated as follows:

△ **Perpendicular lines** *are two lines that meet so as to form equal adjacent angles.* This definition is often more usable than the one on page 22.

Since a straight angle contains 180°, *two angles whose sum is a straight angle are supplementary.*

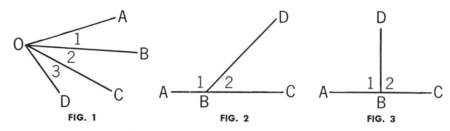

FIG. 1   FIG. 2   FIG. 3

8. Name pairs of adjacent angles in the figures above.

9. If *ABC* in Figure 2 is a straight line, ∠*ABC* is a straight angle. How many degrees are there in the sum of ∠1 and ∠2? Are ∠1 and ∠2 supplementary? Did you have to measure to find if they are supplementary?

Note how Figures 2 and 3 are formed — by one straight line meeting another. Note also that in each, ∠1 and ∠2 are adjacent. From these given (known) statements you can conclude that ∠1 and ∠2 are supplementary. *Note that you have reached this conclusion without measuring.* Your explanation is to quote two definitions — the definition of a straight angle, and the definition of supplementary angles.

If one straight line meets another so as to form adjacent angles, the angles are supplementary.

EXERCISES

1. Find the supplements of angles of the following number of degrees:

a 30°   b 50°   c 70°
d 89° 20′   e 135° 40′   f 90° 00′
g 32° 43′ 12″ h 120° 55′ 3″ i 95° 00′ 40″

2. Is ∠1 adjacent to ∠2? Is ∠*ABC* adjacent to ∠*DBC*? Explain.

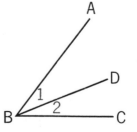

3. *ADB* is a straight line. What is the sum of ∠*CDA* and ∠*CDB*? Explain by quoting the statement just above EXERCISES on the preceding page.

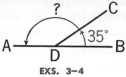

4. *ADB* is a straight line. If ∠*CDB* = 35°, how many degrees are there in ∠*CDA*? Did you have to measure to find out?

EXS. 3–4

5. *AB* and *CD* are two straight lines intersecting at *O*. From this figure you can make four figures showing two adjacent angles formed by one straight line meeting another. One of these figures is shown in color. Sketch the other three.

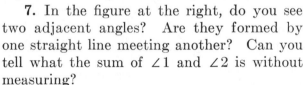

EXS. 5–6

6. *AB* and *CD* are two straight lines intersecting at *O*. What is the sum of ∠1 and ∠2? of ∠2 and ∠4? of ∠3 and ∠4? of ∠3 and ∠1? (Quote the statement about one straight line meeting another as an explanation for your answer.)

7. In the figure at the right, do you see two adjacent angles? Are they formed by one straight line meeting another? Can you tell what the sum of ∠1 and ∠2 is without measuring?

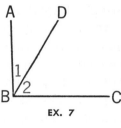

EX. 7

8. *ABC* and *ADC* are two triangles. *ACE* is a straight line. From this figure you can make two figures showing adjacent angles formed by one straight line meeting another. One of them is shown in color. Sketch the other.

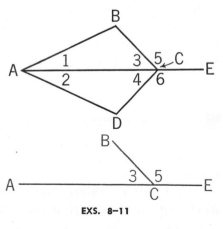

9. In the figure for Ex. 8, if ∠3 is 32°, how many degrees are there in ∠5? Explain your answer.

10. In the upper figure for Ex. 8, what is the sum of ∠4 and ∠6?

EXS. 8–11

11. In the upper figure for Ex. 8, can you tell what the sum of ∠1 and ∠2 is without measuring?

12. *ABC* is a straight line in the figure at the right. There are two pairs of adjacent angles made by a straight line meeting another. Show these two pairs separately by drawing two different figures.

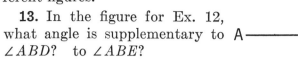

13. In the figure for Ex. 12, what angle is supplementary to ∠*ABD*? to ∠*ABE*?

14. In the figure for Ex. 12, if ∠*ABD* = 65°, which angle is 115°?

EXS. 12–14

15. *ABC* is a triangle and *CD* is drawn from *C* to some point *D* on *AB*. Can you tell what the sum of ∠1 and ∠2 is without measuring? Can you tell what the sum of ∠3 and ∠4 is without measuring? Explain.

16. In the figure for Ex. 15, if you are told that ∠1 = 20°, can you tell how many degrees there are in ∠2 without measuring?

17. In the figure for Ex. 15, if you are told that ∠4 = 75°, can you tell without measuring how many degrees there are in ∠3?

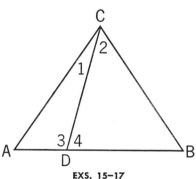

EXS. 15–17

18. a Draw two angles that are adjacent but not supplementary. **b** Draw two angles with your protractor that are supplementary but not adjacent. **c** Draw two angles that are supplementary and adjacent.

■Complementary Angles

Another important relationship among angles is illustrated by *complementary angles*.

△ **Complementary angles** are two *angles whose sum is 90°*. *Each angle is the* **complement** *of the other*.

1. What is the complement of an angle of 40°? of 52° 39′?

2. What is the complement of an angle of *a*°?

Since a right angle contains 90°, it follows from the definition of complementary angles that —

If two adjacent angles form a right angle, the angles are complementary.

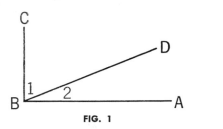

FIG. 1

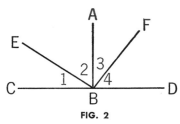

FIG. 2

Thus, if $\angle ABC$ in Figure 1 is a right angle, then $\angle 1$ is complementary to $\angle 2$. In Figure 2 $AB \perp CD$. Name two pairs of complementary angles.

Any one of the following statements may be used when you want to express the relationship of supplementary (or complementary) angles.

$\angle 1$ is supplementary (complementary) to $\angle 2$.

$\angle 1$ and $\angle 2$ are supplementary (complementary).

$\angle 1 + \angle 2 = 180°(90°)$.

Be careful to note the distinction between supplementary and complementary angles.

EXERCISES

1. Find the complement of an angle of 40° and of an angle of 61° 29′.

2. ABC is a triangle. If the angle at C is a right angle, what two adjacent angles form a right angle? What two angles are therefore complementary?

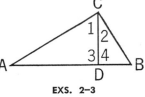

EXS. 2–3

3. In the figure for Ex. 2, $CD \perp AB$. $\angle 3 = \underline{\ ?\ }°$ and $\angle 4 = \underline{\ ?\ }°$; so $\angle 3$ and $\angle 4$ are $\underline{\ ?\ }$ (supplementary, complementary).

4. ABC and DBE are right angles. If $\angle 2 = 30°$, $\angle 1 = \underline{\ ?\ }°$ and $\angle 3 = \underline{\ ?\ }°$. What two angles are equal?

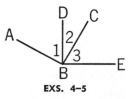

EXS. 4–5

5. In the same figure, if $\angle 2 = 35°$, $\angle 1 = \underline{\ ?\ }°$ and $\angle 3 = \underline{\ ?\ }°$. Angles $\underline{\ ?\ }$ and $\underline{\ ?\ }$ are equal.

■ Supplements of the Same Angle

Suppose you wish to show, without measuring, that —

If two angles are supplementary to the same angle, they are equal.

Probably you would first like to be sure that an angle can have more than one supplement. Consider these angles.

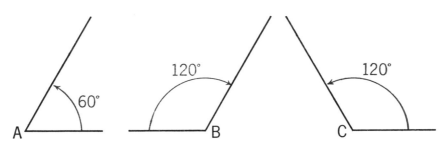

$\angle B$ is supplementary to $\angle A$. Explain. $\angle C$ is supplementary to $\angle A$. Explain. So you have two angles supplementary to the same angle, $\angle A$, and they are equal; they are both 120°. You see that the statement above is true in this case.

Then, in imagination, you can try several other angles, for example, angles of 40°, 70°, 90°, and 135°. Every time you will find that the statement above is true.

This is inductive reasoning. You have not shown that the statement is always true, because you have not tried all possible angles. It would take you forever if you kept on trying this way.

To show that the statement is always true, let the angle be $a°$ ($a°$ represents any number of degrees less than 180°). One supplement of the given angle is 180° − $a°$ and every other supplement of that angle is 180° − $a°$. The supplements have the same number of degrees.

You have now shown that the statement is true for any angle and you have shown it to be true by reasoning, not by measuring.

In the figure at the right you see another example of this statement. AB and CD are straight lines intersecting at O. $\angle 2$ is supplementary to $\angle 1$ and $\angle 4$ is supplementary to $\angle 1$. Explain. So $\angle 2 = \angle 4$ because you know that two angles supplementary to the same angle are equal.

Note: You are not expected to write formal proofs of any of the exercises in this chapter. Explanations are oral.

EXERCISES

The following exercises will give you practice in the use of these two statements:

> When one straight line meets another so as to form adjacent angles, the angles are supplementary.
>
> If two angles are supplementary to the same angle, they are equal.

Whenever you see the question, "Why?" on this page quote one of these two statements as your authority. You are to arrive at the conclusions without measuring.

In the figure AB and CD are two straight lines intersected by straight line EF.

1. Note that there are eight pairs of supplementary angles. Name them.

2. If $\angle 1 = 130°$, then $\angle 3 = \underline{?}°$. Why?

3. If $\angle 8 = 140°$, then $\angle 6 = \underline{?}°$. Why?

4. If $\angle 3 = 35°$, then $\angle 4 = \underline{?}°$. Why?

5. If $\angle 8 = 120°$, then $\angle 7 = \underline{?}°$. Why?

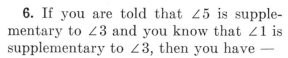

6. If you are told that $\angle 5$ is supplementary to $\angle 3$ and you know that $\angle 1$ is supplementary to $\angle 3$, then you have —

$\angle 5$ is supplementary to $\angle 3$. Given.
$\angle 1$ is supplementary to $\angle 3$. Why?
So $\angle 5 = \angle 1$. Why?

7. If you are told that $\angle 6$ is supplementary to $\angle 4$ and you know that $\angle 2$ is supplementary to $\angle 4$, then you have —

$\angle 6$ is supp. to $\angle 4$. Given.
$\angle 2$ is supp. to $\angle 4$. Why?
So $\angle 6 = \angle 2$. Why?

8. If you are told that $\angle 7$ is supplementary to $\angle 1$, can you show that $\angle 7 = \angle 3$? (Show as in Exs. 6 and 7 that they are both supplementary to the same angle.)

9. Given that $\angle 2$ is supplementary to $\angle 5$. Show that $\angle 2 = \angle 6$.

◪ More about Supplements and Complements

You have already shown that if two angles are supplementary to the same angle they are equal. By similar reasoning you can show that the following relationships are true.

If two angles are supplementary to equal angles, they are equal.

Let $\angle A$ be $a°$, then its supplement, $\angle C$, is $180° - a°$.
According to the statement you have an equal angle. Call it $\angle B$. It, too, will be $a°$, and its supplement, $\angle D$, is $180° - a°$.

You see that the supplements $\angle C$ and $\angle D$ have the same number of degrees and are equal. (Try some numerical cases.)

If two angles are complementary to the same angle, they are equal.

Let $\angle A$ be $a°$, then its complement, $\angle B$, is $90° - a°$. Any other complement, $\angle C$, is also $90° - a°$. $\angle B = \angle C$.

If two angles are complementary to equal angles, they are equal.
(The reasoning is left for you.)

EXERCISES

For the question "Why?" choose one of the three general statements above (in heavy type) or one of the two below.

> When one straight line meets another so as to form adjacent angles, the angles are supplementary.
>
> If two adjacent angles form a right angle, they are complementary.

1. $\angle ABC$ and $\angle DBE$ are right angles. Show as follows that $\angle 1 = \angle 3$.

> $\angle ABC$ and $\angle DBE$ are right angles. Given.
> $\angle 1$ is comp. to $\angle 2$. Why?
> $\angle 3$ is comp. to $\angle 2$. Why?
> So $\angle 1 = \angle 3$. Why?

2. ABC and EDC are straight lines and $\angle 1 = \angle 2$. Show as follows that $\angle 3 = \angle 4$.

> $\angle 1 = \angle 2$. Given.
> $\angle 3$ is supp. to $\angle 1$. Why?
> $\angle 4$ is supp. to $\angle 2$. Why?
> So $\angle 3 = \angle 4$. Why?

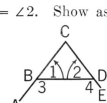

3. $AB \perp CD$ and $\angle 3 = \angle 4$. Show as follows that $\angle 1 = \angle 2$.

$AB \perp CD$. Given.
$\angle ABC$ and $\angle ABD$ are right angles. A perpendicular to a line forms right angles with it.

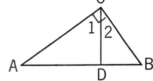

      $\angle 1$ is comp. to $\angle 3$. Why?
      $\angle 2$ is comp. to $\angle 4$. Why?
      $\angle 3 = \angle 4$. Given.
So $\angle 1 = \angle 2$. Why?

4. $\angle C$ is a right angle and $\angle A$ is complementary to $\angle 1$. We wish to show that $\angle A = \angle 2$.

      $\angle A$ is comp. to $\angle 1$. Given.
      $\angle C$ is a right angle. Given.
      $\angle 2$ is comp. to $\angle 1$. Why?
So $\angle A = \angle 2$. Why?

5. If two angles are unequal, would their supplements be equal or unequal? Which of the supplements would be the larger?

To the Student: If you have any difficulty with the relationships in these exercises, assume numerical values for the angles. For example, in Ex. 1 let $\angle 2$ be 30°, then $\angle 1 = 60°$ and $\angle 3 = 60°$.

◼ Vertical Angles

In the illustration, $\angle 1$ and $\angle 3$ are *vertical angles*, and $\angle 2$ and $\angle 4$ are *vertical angles*.
   △ *Vertical angles are the opposite angles, the nonadjacent angles, formed by two intersecting straight lines.*

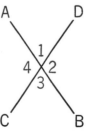

   1. Before reading further, try to show that vertical angles are always equal.
   2. If $\angle 1 = 50°$, how many degrees are there in $\angle 2$ and in $\angle 4$? Note that in this case the vertical angles are equal. Both are supplementary to $\angle 1$.
   3. If $\angle 4 = 100°$, how many degrees are there in $\angle 1$ and in $\angle 3$? Note that in this case also the vertical angles are equal. Both are supplementary to $\angle 4$.
No matter what the size of $\angle 1$ is, $\angle 2$ is supp. to $\angle 1$. Why? $\angle 4$ is supp. to $\angle 1$. Why? So $\angle 2 = \angle 4$. Why? Similarly, $\angle 1$ is always equal to $\angle 3$. Hence —

When two straight lines intersect, the vertical angles are equal.

In some of the following figures you see two straight lines inter-secting. In others you do not see such lines. When there are two straight lines intersecting you will have vertical angles.

Name the numbered vertical angles in each figure below. If there are none, write the word *None*. (All lines are straight.)

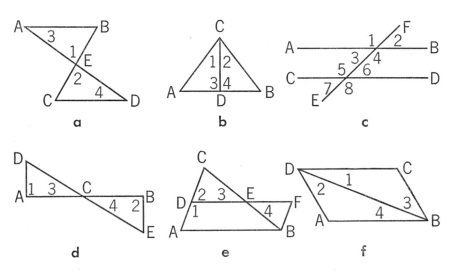

a   b   c

d   e   f

SUPPLEMENTARY EXERCISES

1. If an angle is 52° 30′, how many degrees and minutes are there in half of its supplement?

2. If an angle is less than its supplement, what kind of angle is it?

3. Can two supplementary angles both be obtuse? Explain.

4. How many degrees, minutes, and seconds are there in the complement of an angle of 62° 13′ 25″?

5. If ∠x = 40° and ∠x = ∠y, how many degrees are there in the complement of ∠y?

6. The figure at the right is made of four straight lines. With-out measuring tell the pair, or pairs, of numbered angles you know to be equal. Give a reason for the equality.

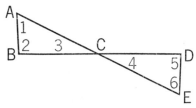

7. *AEB* and *CED* are straight lines. What angle is supplementary to ∠2? Explain how you know that your answer is correct.

8. *AEB* and *CED* are straight lines. Then ∠4 and ∠3 are both supplementary to the same angle. Which angle is that?

9. *CD* is a straight line meeting the straight line *ADB* at *D*. ∠*CDB* = 50°. *DE* bisects ∠*ADC*. *DF* bisects ∠*CDB*. Find the number of degrees in ∠*EDF* without measuring.

10. Can you do this same exercise when ∠*CDB* = *a*°?

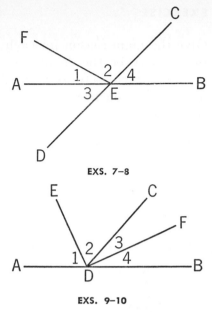

EXS. 7–8

EXS. 9–10

Chapter Summary

1. Read the following general statements and then recall them from memory. Read again the reasoning by which they were proved in this chapter.

  a If one straight line meets another so as to form adjacent angles, the angles are supplementary.

  b If two adjacent angles form a right angle, they are complementary.

  c If two angles are supplementary to the same angle, they are equal.

  d If two angles are supplementary to equal angles, they are equal.

  e If two angles are complementary to the same angle, they are equal.

  f If two angles are complementary to equal angles, they are equal.

  g When two straight lines intersect, the vertical angles are equal.

2. In this figure *ACE* is a straight line and ∠3 = ∠4.

Fill in the blanks and choose the correct statements from Ex. 1 to give as reasons for the "Why?"

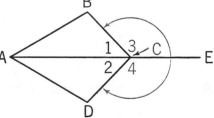

  ACE is a straight line. Given.
    ∠1 is supp. to ∠_?_. Why?
    ∠2 is supp. to ∠_?_. Why?
    ∠3 = ∠4. Given.
So ∠1 = ∠2. Why?

Give the main reason for each of the following statements. The reason may be the definition of perpendicular lines, the bisector of a line, the bisector of an angle, or one of the general statements under Ex. 1 on page 51. You must be able to quote these general statements as reasons. (The first exercise is done for you.)

1. If CD bisects AB, then $AE = EB$.

A bisector divides a line into two equal parts.

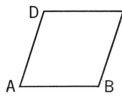

EX. 1

2. If $AB \perp CD$, then $\angle 1$ and $\angle 2$ are right angles. (See figure below.)

3. If AB bisects $\angle A$, then $\angle 3 = \angle 4$.

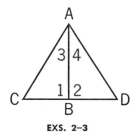

EXS. 2–3

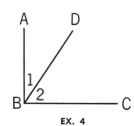

EX. 4

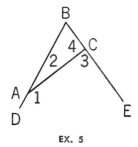

EX. 5

4. If $\angle ABC$ is a right angle, then $\angle 1$ is complementary to $\angle 2$.

5. DAB and ECB are straight lines, so $\angle 1$ is supplementary to $\angle 2$ and $\angle 3$ is supplementary to $\angle 4$.

6. If $\angle A$ is complementary to $\angle 1$ and $\angle 2$ is complementary to $\angle 1$, then $\angle A = \angle 2$.

7. If $\angle B$ is supplementary to $\angle A$ and $\angle D$ is supplementary to $\angle A$, then $\angle B = \angle D$.

8. AC and BD are intersecting straight lines, then $\angle DOA = \angle COB$.

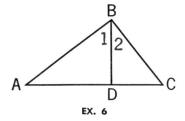

EX. 6

EX. 7

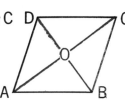

EX. 8

CHAPTER 3   The "If-then" Relationship

You HAVE learned through the process of living normal lives that if you do certain things, then other things result — things over which you have no control. If you throw a ball into the air, then it will come down. If you drop salt in water, then it will dissolve. If a lighted match comes in contact with gasoline vapor, then there will be an explosion. "If-then" is the law of the world in which we live. What you need to learn in this chapter is the logical significance of "if-then" in geometry.

Just as a matter of interest, before you study further, tell what you think is the difference between the following two statements.

If two sides of a triangle are equal, then the angles opposite those sides are equal.

If two angles of a triangle are equal, then the sides opposite those angles are equal.

If-then Sentences

Consider these five sentences, repeated from above.

1. If you throw a ball into the air, then it will come down.
2. If you drop salt in water, then it will dissolve.
3. If a lighted match comes in contact with gasoline vapor, then there will be an explosion.
4. If two sides of a triangle are equal, then the angles opposite those sides are equal.
5. If two angles of a triangle are equal, then the sides opposite those angles are equal.

The first three sentences describe situations that are very familiar to you. They have two things in common. What is stated in the **if**-part of each sentence comes in point of time before what is stated in the **then**-part. And furthermore, what is stated in the **then**-part comes inevitably (it is bound to happen) once the **if**-part has taken place. You throw the ball into the air first, then it comes down without any effort on your part. You put the salt in the water first. The dissolving is inevitable. The lighted match and the gasoline vapor come together. Then an explosion occurs.

You should see the same kind of thing in the last two of the if-then sentences. If you *make* a triangle in which two sides are equal, then you will *find* that the angles opposite those sides are equal. If first the sides are equal, then the angles are inevitably equal.

If you *make* a triangle in which two angles are equal, then you will *find* that the sides opposite those angles are equal. If first the angles are equal, then the sides are inevitably equal.

It is important for you to understand this relationship and the way it is stated for you will soon be working abstractly with relationships of this sort.

■ Conditions — Conclusion

1. Construct △ABC so that $AC = BC$. Then measure ∠A and ∠B. They should be equal.

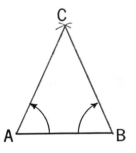

You have *made* a triangle with two sides equal. You *found*, as a result, that the angles opposite those sides are equal.

Two sides equal is the **given condition** (shown in color). *Two angles equal* is the **conclusion** (shown in black).

This exercise illustrates the meaning of the statement:

If two sides of a triangle are equal, the angles opposite those sides are equal.

Note that the *then* has been omitted. It is usually omitted when the omission does not affect the clarity of the statement.

The given conditions are in the **if**-part of the sentence. The conclusion is in the **then**-part of the sentence.

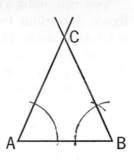

2. Construct $\triangle ABC$ so that $\angle A = \angle B$. Then measure AC and BC. They should be equal.

In Ex. 2 you have reversed the given condition and the conclusion of Ex. 1. The **given condition** is *two angles equal* (shown in color). The **conclusion** is *two sides equal* (shown in black).

Note also that the if-then sentence of Ex. 1 has been reversed. Ex. 2 illustrates the statement:

If two angles of a triangle are equal, the sides opposite those angles are equal.

■ More Illustrations of If-then

Consider these three statements:

1. If $AC = BC$ and $\angle 1 = \angle 2$, then $\angle A = \angle B$ and $AD = DB$.

2. If $AC = BC$ and $AD = DB$, then $\angle A = \angle B$ and $\angle 1 = \angle 2$.

3. If $\angle A = \angle B$ and $AD = DB$, then $AC = BC$ and $\angle 1 = \angle 2$.

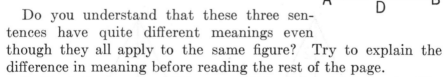

Do you understand that these three sentences have quite different meanings even though they all apply to the same figure? Try to explain the difference in meaning before reading the rest of the page.

In Ex. 1 the given conditions are $AC = BC$ and $\angle 1 = \angle 2$. The conclusions are $\angle A = \angle B$ and $AD = DB$. Where are the given conditions and the conclusions found in this first statement? This sentence means that if you know that $AC = BC$ and $\angle 1 = \angle 2$, then you can be sure that the conclusions, $\angle A = \angle B$ and $AD = DB$, are true.

What are the given conditions and the conclusions in Exs. 2 and 3?

You can show your understanding of Ex. 1 by constructing a figure according to the given conditions. To do this construct a triangle with $AC = BC$. Then bisect $\angle C$ so that $\angle 1 = \angle 2$. Note that you are following the given conditions (shown in color). The figure has now been constructed. Measure to see if the conclusions are correct. $\angle A$ should equal $\angle B$ and AD should equal DB.

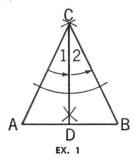

EX. 1

The study of the "if-then" relationship is important to you for your future work in geometry when you will be reasoning from given conditions to conclusions. By means of these constructions you can learn to distinguish between the two and see how it is that the conclusion is the inevitable outcome of the conditions. When you construct a figure according to the given conditions you learn to restrict yourself to these conditions alone. Even though the figures for two different exercises look alike, the construction will be different if the given conditions are different.

Now construct a figure according to the conditions of Ex. 2. That is, make $AC = BC$ and $AD = BD$ (bisect AB). Measure to see if the conclusions are correct.

Finally construct the same figure again, this time according to the conditions of Ex. 3. (Here, as in Ex. 2, AB has been bisected.)

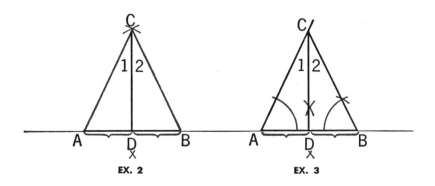

EX. 2   EX. 3

The figures should help you to see if your constructions are correct.

EXERCISES

1. In this figure, if ∠1 = ∠2 and $BE = BF$, then EG = FG and ∠3 = ∠4.

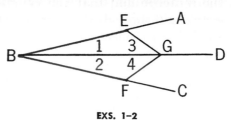

What are the given conditions? Tell what you would do to construct this figure according to the conditions. (*Answer: I would make* ∠1 = ∠2 *and* $BE = BF$.)

What are the conclusions? Tell what you would do to test the conclusions. (*After the figure was constructed, I would measure EG and FG,* ∠3 *and* ∠4 *to see if the conclusions are correct.*)

2. In order to construct the figure for Ex. 1 according to the conditions follow these directions:

Draw any angle ABC and bisect it by a line BD to make ∠1 = ∠2. Take point G on BD and point E on AB. Draw EG. Construct $BF = BE$ and draw FG. (The figure is drawn here to show you the positions of the points and the lines. It is only a guide. The particular lengths of lines and size of angle you choose to begin with are unimportant.)

3. Now construct this same figure according to different conditions following these directions:

Draw another angle ABC and bisect it by a line BD. Take any point G on BD and any point E on AB. Draw EG. Construct ∠4 = ∠3. Measure EG and FG, BE and BF. Note that you made ∠1 = ∠2 and ∠4 = ∠3. Then you found that $EG = FG$ and $BE = BF$.

4. Describe Ex. 3 by stating an "*if-then*" sentence. Follow the pattern of Ex. 1 but make the necessary changes.

5. If, in this figure, $AC = AD$ and $BC = BD$, then ∠1 = ∠2 and ∠3 = ∠4.

What are the given conditions?
What are the conclusions?
Construct the figure according to the given conditions, then measure to see if the conclusions are correct.

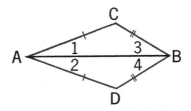

Remember that the given conditions are in the "*if*"-part of the sentence and that the conclusion is in the "*then*"-part. In exercises 6 through 13 construct the figures according to the given conditions, then measure with a ruler or a protractor to test the conclusions. Each figure on the page serves as a guide for more than one exercise. However, since no two sets of conditions are identical, you must make a different construction for each figure.

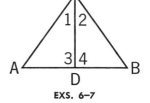
EXS. 6-7

6. If $AC = BC$ and CD bisects $\angle C$, then CD bisects AB and $CD \perp AB$.

7. If CD is the perpendicular bisector of AB, then $AC = CB$ and CD bisects $\angle C$.

8. If $AC = AD$ and $\angle 1 = \angle 2$, then $CB = BD$ and $\angle 3 = \angle 4$.

9. If $\angle 1 = \angle 2$ and $\angle 3 = \angle 4$, then $AC = AD$ and $BC = BD$.

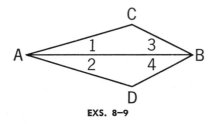
EXS. 8-9

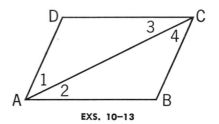
EXS. 10-13

10. If $AB = DC$ and $\angle 2 = \angle 3$, then $AD = BC$ and $\angle 1 = \angle 4$.

11. If $\angle 1 = \angle 4$ and $\angle 2 = \angle 3$, then $AB = DC$ and $AD = BC$.

12. If $BC = AD$ and $AB = DC$, then $\angle 1 = \angle 4$ and $\angle 2 = \angle 3$.

13. If $BC = AD$ and $\angle 1 = \angle 4$, then $AB = DC$ and $\angle 2 = \angle 3$.

14. If E is the middle point of BC, $AB \perp BC$, $CD \perp BC$, and AED is a straight line, then $AB = DC$ and $AE = ED$.

15. If $AB \perp BC$, $DC \perp BC$, $AB = CD$, and AED is a straight line, then $BE = EC$ and $AE = ED$.

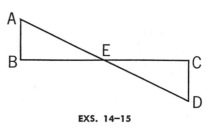
EXS. 14-15

■ Results from Conditions — *Optional*

1. The carpenter bisects an angle using his square. If he fulfills the conditions, the result is certain.

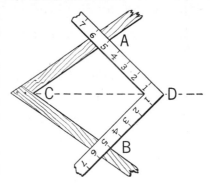

C is an angle made of two pieces of wood. If A and B are marked off so that $AC = BC$ and the square is held so that $DA = DB$, then the line CD bisects $\angle C$.

What must the carpenter do to fulfill the conditions? What is the result?

2. A surveyor fulfills certain conditions to find the measurement of an inaccessible distance.

The distance AB can be found as follows:

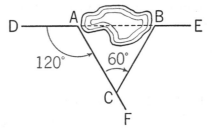

The surveyor sets out stakes at D, A, and F so that $\angle DAF = 120°$. He also sets a stake at B so that DAB forms a straight line. He walks along the line AF until he comes to a point C where $\angle ACB$ = 60°. Then he can measure AC, which is equal to AB.

3. The machinist uses a center square (pictured below) to find the center of a circular piece of metal.

He places the instrument in one position and draws the line CD. (See detail at right.) He then places it in a different position and draws the line AB. These lines are diameters. The point O where these two lines intersect is the center.

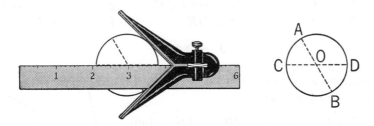

Complete this sentence:
If the diameters AB and CD intersect at O, then ___?___.

SUPPLEMENTARY EXERCISES

Construct figures according to the given conditions of the following statements.

1. If two sides of a triangle are equal, the angles opposite those sides are equal.

2. If two angles of a triangle are equal, the sides opposite those angles are equal.

3. If a line bisects the vertex angle of an isosceles triangle, it bisects the base and is perpendicular to it.

4. If a line connects the middle point of the base of an isosceles triangle with the vertex of the triangle, it bisects the vertex angle.

5. If lines are drawn from any point on the perpendicular bisector of a line to the ends of the line, they are equal.

Chapter Summary

I. Given Conditions — Conclusions.

1. Draw the right triangle ABC with right angle at A. Make $\angle C = 60°$ with your protractor. Bisect $\angle C$. From D construct $DE \perp BC$. (Use the figure as a guide to the position of the letters.)

Which of the following statements are given conditions and which are possible conclusions?

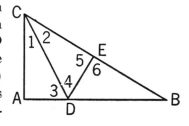

a $\angle 3 = \angle 4$	**b** CD bisects $\angle C$.	**c** $\angle A$ is a right angle.
d $DE \perp BC$	**e** $AD = DE$	**f** $CE = EB$
	g $\angle C = 60°$	

II. Constructing a Figure According to the Given Conditions.

2. If $\angle 4 = \angle 1$ and $DC = AB$, then $DA = BC$ and $\angle 2 = \angle 3$. Construct a figure according to the given conditions.

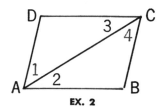

EX. 2

III. If-then Sentences.

3. If a line connects the middle points of two sides of a triangle, it is equal to one half of the third side.

Which of the following statements is the given condition and which is the conclusion?

a $DE = \frac{1}{2}AB$ **b** D and E are the midpoints of AC and BC, respectively.

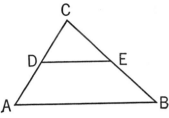

Testing Your Understanding

Construct figures to test the truth of the following statements; that is, construct them according to the given conditions.

1. If $AB \perp CD$ and $\angle 1 = \angle 2$, then $\angle 3 = \angle 4$.

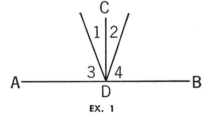

EX. 1

2. If $AB = AD$ and $\angle 1 = \angle 2$, then $BC = DC$.

3. If $\angle 1 = \angle 2$ and $\angle 3 = \angle 4$, then $AB = AD$.

4. If $AB = DC$ and $AD = BC$, then $\angle 1 = \angle 3$ and $\angle 4 = \angle 2$.

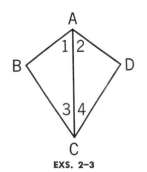

EXS. 2-3

5. If $AB = DC$ and $\angle 2 = \angle 4$, then $AD = BC$ and $\angle 1 = \angle 3$.

6. If $AD = BC$ and $\angle 1 = \angle 3$, then $AB = CD$ and $\angle 2 = \angle 4$.

7. If $\angle 1 = \angle 3$ and $\angle 2 = \angle 4$, then $AB = DC$ and $AD = BC$.

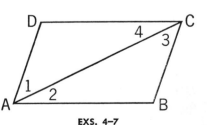

EXS. 4-7

In Exs. 8–9 AEB and DEC are straight lines.

8. If AB and CD bisect each other, then $AD = CB$ and $\angle A = \angle B$.

9. If $AE = EB$ and $\angle A = \angle B$, then $\angle C = \angle D$.

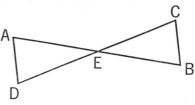

EXS. 8–9

In Exs. 10–11 ACE and BCD are straight lines.

10. If AE bisects BD, $BA \perp BD$, and $DE \perp BD$, then $AB = DE$ and $AC = CE$.

11. If $AB = DE$, $AB \perp BD$, and $DE \perp BD$, then $AC = CE$ and $BC = CD$.

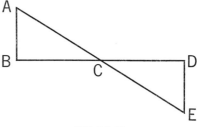

EXS. 10–11

CHAPTER 4 Deductive Reasoning. The Nature of a Geometric Proof

In the last chapter you learned that if certain things are true, certain other things are also inevitably true, whether you will them to be true or not. You constructed certain figures according to given conditions, and then you found what was true as a result of the way you constructed the figures. You became familiar with the meaning of *"if-then"* relationships. This understanding is fundamental to the kind of reasoning you will meet in geometry.

Most of your conclusions in geometry will be reached by reasoning without measurement. You will draw your conclusions by *deduction;* that is, by logical steps on the basis of general statements which you have agreed to use as the foundation of your reasoning. In this chapter you will use relationships in congruent triangles and other relationships both in geometry and outside the field of geometry in a study of the nature of deductive proof.

You see, geometry as you will study it this year, is more than a learning of relationships among geometric figures, important as that is. It is also a study in logical thinking. All your life you have been reasoning informally about things in general. For instance, when you have seen and heard the fire engines passing, you have probably said, "Where's the fire?" You reasoned that the passing engines very likely meant a fire. But you have not done much thinking about the details of reasoning. Here, perhaps for the first time, you will learn about the importance of definitions, assumptions, given conditions, and conclusions. You will see how carefully mathematicians and other scientists reason. You will have a chance to improve your own reasoning by patterning it after the reasoning you will find in *Plane Geometry*.

■ Congruence

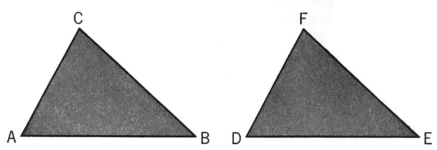

Congruent triangles. They have exactly the same shape and the same size.

The word *congruent* is from the Latin *con*, with, and *gruere*, to agree. It means *in agreement with*.

△ *Congruent figures* are figures all of whose corresponding parts are equal.

The two figures above are congruent. If one were superimposed on the other (laid over it), the corresponding parts would coincide and the outlines of the two figures would exactly agree. The two triangles are truly identical twins.

In demonstrative geometry congruence is a very important subject, for when you prove that two figures are congruent you know many other facts about them. You know that any line or angle in one is equal to the corresponding line or angle in the other. *Anything* that you can show to be true of one figure is true of the other also. The symbol for *is congruent to* is ≅. $\triangle ABC \cong \triangle DEF$ means that $\triangle ABC$ is congruent to $\triangle DEF$.

Applied specifically to triangles, the definition of congruence given above means that *congruent triangles* are triangles that have three sides of one equal to three sides of the other and three angles of one equal to three angles of the other. Such triangles have the same size and the same shape. Then, according to the definition, the above triangles ABC and DEF are congruent, if $AB = DE$, $BC = EF$, $AC = DF$, $\angle A = \angle D$, $\angle B = \angle E$, and $\angle C = \angle F$.

You will learn three ways of constructing one triangle so that it will be congruent to another. You will state by means of *if-then* sentences what you learn about these constructions. Then you will use these statements as a basis for reasoning.

■ Making Triangles Congruent

First method   Draw any triangle ABC.   Construct $DE = AB$, $\angle D = \angle A$, and $DF = AC$ in the order named (see figures below). Draw EF. Measure BC and EF, $\angle C$ and $\angle F$, $\angle B$ and $\angle E$. You see that three sides and three angles of one triangle are equal respectively to three sides and three angles of the other. Triangle DEF is therefore congruent to triangle ABC.

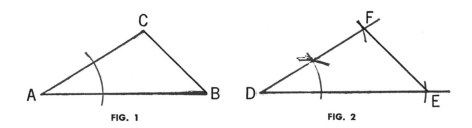

FIG. 1   FIG. 2

1. How many sides of one triangle did you construct equal to sides of the other? How many angles of one did you construct equal to angles of the other?

Note that, although you made only two sides and one angle of one triangle equal to two sides and one angle of the other, the result was two triangles with three sides and three angles of one equal respectively to three sides and three angles of the other.

The angle must be in a definite position with respect to the two sides — it must be the angle formed by the two sides. The angle made by two sides of a triangle is said to be **included** between those two sides.

2. What conditions were fulfilled to make these two triangles congruent? (Two sides and the included angle of one were made equal respectively to . . .) Without reading further try to write as an "if-then" sentence the relationship illustrated here. The statement is given below.

If two triangles have two sides and the included angle of one equal respectively to two sides and the included angle of the other, they are congruent.

The phrase *two sides and the included angle* may be written briefly as *s.a.s.*

Second method   Draw any $\triangle ABC$.   Construct $DE = AB$, $\angle D$ $= \angle A$, and $\angle E = \angle B$ in the order named.   Measure the other corresponding sides and angles.   They should be equal.   Since three sides and three angles of one triangle are equal respectively to three sides and three angles of the other, the triangles are congruent.   (Corresponding sides are found opposite known equal angles and corresponding angles are found opposite known equal sides.)

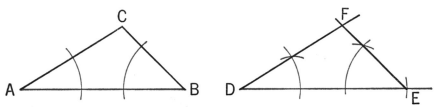

If two triangles have two angles and the included side of one equal respectively to two angles and the included side of the other, they are congruent.

The conditions are $DE = AB$, $\angle D = \angle A$, and $\angle E = \angle B$.   The conclusion is $\triangle DEF \cong \triangle ABC$.

The phrase *two angles and the included side* may be written briefly as *a.s.a.*

Third method   Draw any $\triangle ABC$.   Construct $DE = AB$.   With AC as radius and D as center draw an arc.   With BC as radius and E as center draw an arc intersecting the first arc at F.   Note that you have made three sides of one triangle equal to three sides of the other triangle.   If you measure the corresponding angles, you will find that they also are equal.   Hence the triangles are congruent.

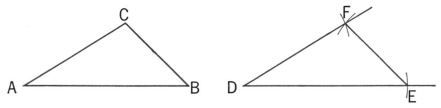

If two triangles have three sides of one equal respectively to three sides of the other, they are congruent.

The conditions are $DE = AB$, $EF = BC$, and $DF = AC$.   The conclusion is $\triangle DEF \cong \triangle ABC$.

The words *three sides* may be written briefly as *s.s.s.*

You will now use these three statements concerning congruent triangles as a basis for reasoning.

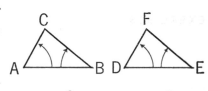

1. If I know that $AB = DE$, $\angle B = \angle E$, and $BC = EF$, then I know that $\triangle ABC \cong \triangle DEF$. Give the correct statement concerning congruent triangles as your authority. (It is *a.s.a.* = *a.s.a.*, *s.a.s.* = *s.a.s.*, or *s.s.s.* = *s.s.s.*)

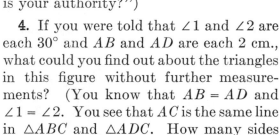

2. If I know that $AB = DE$, $\angle A = \angle D$, and $\angle B = \angle E$, then I know that ?. What is your authority?

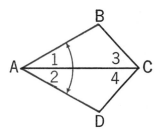

3. If $AB = DE$, $AC = DF$, and $BC = EF$, then ?. Why? (The question "Why?" means "What is your authority?")

4. If you were told that $\angle 1$ and $\angle 2$ are each 30° and AB and AD are each 2 cm., what could you find out about the triangles in this figure without further measurements? (You know that $AB = AD$ and $\angle 1 = \angle 2$. You see that AC is the same line in $\triangle ABC$ and $\triangle ADC$. How many sides of one triangle do you know to be equal to sides of the other? How many angles? Is the angle included between the sides? In these triangles two sides and the included angle of one equal two sides and the included angle of the other. The triangles are therefore congruent. If the triangles are congruent, what other sides and angles do you know to be equal?)

5. If you were given this figure made by four straight lines, and were told that $DE = AE$ and $CE = EB$, would you be able to say that the triangles are congruent without measuring? (Note that $\angle 1$ and $\angle 2$ are vertical angles.) Give your authority. If the triangles are congruent, what sides and angles do you know to be equal in addition to those you knew about at first?

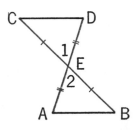

■ Practice with s.a.s. and a.s.a.

On page 70 you will be asked to think informally about some exercises involving congruent triangles. Before you attempt that page there are two things you ought to do. First, you should have practice in choosing *s.a.s.* and *a.s.a.* in various figures. That is the purpose of *this* page.

EXERCISES

Copy the following exercises and fill in the blanks so that the results will correspond to the specifications:

EXAMPLE: *s.a.s.* of △ABD. AB, _?_, BD.

Here you are asked to write the angle that is included between *AB* and *BD*. If you draw the figure and mark *AB* and *BD*, you will see that the included angle is ∠1. Write ∠1 in the blank space.

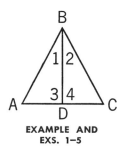

EXAMPLE AND
EXS. 1–5

1. *s.a.s.* of △BDC. BD, _?_, DC.
2. *s.a.s.* of △ABD. BD, ∠3, _?_.
3. *a.s.a.* of △ABD. ∠A, _?_, ∠1.
4. *a.s.a.* of △BDC. ∠2, BC, _?_.
5. *a.s.a.* of △ABD. ∠3, BD, _?_.
6. *s.a.s.* of △ACD. DC, _?_, AC.
7. *s.a.s.* of △ACB. _?_, ∠5, _?_.
8. *a.s.a.* of △ACB. _?_, AC, _?_.
9. *s.a.s.* of △COD. CD, _?_, DO.
10. *a.s.a.* of △AOB. ∠3, AB, _?_.
11. *s.a.s.* of △ACD. _?_, ∠5, _?_.
12. *a.s.a.* of △CEB. _?_, CE, _?_.
13. *a.s.a.* of △ACD. _?_, AC, _?_.
14. *a.s.a.* of △ACE. _?_, AC, _?_.

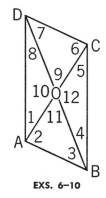

EXS. 6–10

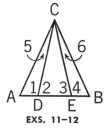

EXS. 11–12

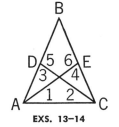

EXS. 13–14

DEDUCTIVE REASONING

■ Drawing Conclusions

The exercises on this page will help you with the second thing you ought to do — learn to draw conclusions only from the given conditions, not from the appearance of a figure.

EXERCISES

1. If the *only* thing you know about this figure is that BD bisects $\angle B$, which of the following equalities can you be sure of without measuring? $AB = BC$, $\angle 1 = \angle 2$, $\angle 3 = \angle 4$, $\angle A = \angle C$, $AD = DC$.

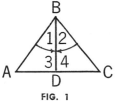

FIG. 1

Although, in Figure 1, it looks as if $AB = BC$, you cannot take such a condition for granted because that condition is not stated. Likewise, you cannot use the statement that $BD \perp AC$ because it is not so stated. The *only* thing you know about the figure is that BD bisects $\angle B$. Hence your *only* conclusion is that 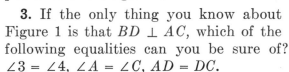.

2. Study Figure 2 at the right in which the only thing you know is that BD bisects $\angle B$. Does AD equal DC in this figure? Does AB equal BC? Does $\angle 3$ equal $\angle 4$? Does $\angle A$ equal $\angle C$? Does $\angle 1$ equal $\angle 2$? This figure will help you to see why you cannot draw conclusions from the appearance of the figure for Ex. 1.

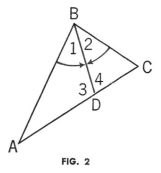

FIG. 2

3. If the only thing you know about Figure 1 is that $BD \perp AC$, which of the following equalities can you be sure of? $AB = BC$, $\angle 1 = \angle 2$, $\angle 3 = \angle 4$, $\angle A = \angle C$, $AD = DC$.

4. If the only thing you know about Figure 1 is that BD must be perpendicular to AC, can you draw the figure so that AB is not equal to BC? If so, draw it. If not, tell why not.

5. If the only thing you know about Figure 1 is that BD bisects AC, which of the following equalities can you be sure of? $AB = BC$, $\angle 1 = \angle 2$, $\angle 3 = \angle 4$, $\angle A = \angle C$, $AD = DC$.

6. If the only thing you know about Figure 1 is that BD must bisect AC, can you draw the figure so that AB is not equal to BC? If so, draw it. If you cannot draw it, tell why not.

■ Using s.a.s. = s.a.s. and a.s.a. = a.s.a.

You have learned three conditions under which triangles are congruent. They are *s.a.s.* = *s.a.s.*, *a.s.a.* = *a.s.a.*, and *s.s.s.* = *s.s.s.* Now see if you can tell when these conditions have been fulfilled in various figures with various given conditions.

EXERCISES

Are the triangles congruent under the conditions as given? If they are congruent, write "Yes" and choose the correct authority. Otherwise write "No." Do not be fooled by appearance.

EXAMPLE: $AC = BC$, $AD = DB$.
Draw the figure and mark it as shown on the right. (Like marks on the lines indicate equal parts.) You know also that CD in one triangle is the same length as CD in the other triangle. $\triangle ACD \cong \triangle BCD$. The answer is "Yes," *s.s.s.* = *s.s.s.*

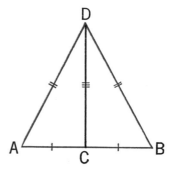

Draw a figure for each exercise and mark the parts you know to be equal before you attempt the exercise.

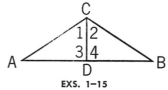

EXS. 1–15

1. $AC = BC$, $\angle 1 = \angle 2$.
2. $\angle 1 = \angle 2$, $\angle 3 = \angle 4$.
3. $AC = BC$, $\angle A = \angle B$.
4. $AD = DB$, $\angle 3 = \angle 4$.
5. CD bisects $\angle C$.
6. $CD \perp AB$.
7. CD bisects AB.   8. $AC = BC$, CD bisects $\angle C$.
9. $CD \perp AB$, $\angle 1 = \angle 2$.   10. CD perpendicular bisector of AB.
11. $\angle 1 = \angle 2$, $\angle A = \angle B$.   12. CD bisects $\angle C$, $\angle A = \angle B$.
13. $CD \perp AB$, $AC = BC$.   14. CD bisects AB, $AC = CB$.
15. $\angle 1 = \angle 2$, $\angle 3 = \angle 4$, $\angle A = \angle B$.
16. $\angle 1 = \angle 2$, $\angle A = \angle C$.
17. $\angle 1 = \angle 2$, $\angle 3 = \angle 4$.
18. $AB = DC$, $AD = BC$.
19. $AD = BC$, $\angle 3 = \angle 4$.
20. $AB = CD$, $\angle 1 = \angle 2$.
21. $AB = CD$, $\angle 3 = \angle 4$.

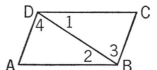

EXS. 16–21

Be sure you understand the work on page 70. If you make errors, explain your thinking orally so that you can discover what causes your mistakes. You can save yourself a good deal of trouble later by making sure right now.

■ Deductive Reasoning

The reasoning so far in this chapter has been informal. You have not thought much about the method or form that lies behind it. For your future work in geometry you need to analyze the reasoning process you use.

The kind of reasoning you have been doing and will continue to do in geometry depends upon the use of a general statement which you accept as true. Suppose, for example, that in your school, Room 100 is the senior home room. This means that if *any student* has Room 100 as a home room, he is a senior. You can use this statement as a basis for reasoning.

Now you meet a new student and in talking to him you find that his home room is Room 100. Immediately, you form the conclusion that he is a senior. This is definitely a thought process. You did not experiment or measure. If anyone should ask you how you know he is a senior, you would give as your reason: *Any student* who has Room 100 as a home room is a senior.

A conclusion reached in this way is a *deduction*. This kind of reasoning is called *deductive reasoning*.

△ *Deductive reasoning means drawing conclusions from accepted general statements.*

Here is another example of deductive reasoning, which makes use of the statement:

When two straight lines intersect, the vertical angles are equal.

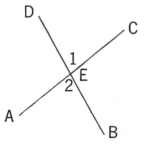

You are told that in this figure the straight lines AC and BD intersect at E. Then you know that $\angle 1 = \angle 2$ because they are vertical angles made by two intersecting straight lines and "When two straight lines intersect the vertical angles are equal."

Again you have reached a conclusion by using an accepted general statement and quoting it as a reason for your conclusion.

■ Fulfilled and Unfulfilled Conditions

No doubt you were able to follow without difficulty the simple illustrations of deductive reasoning on the preceding page. There are pitfalls in the reasoning process, however, for which you must be on your guard. One of the commonest errors is to draw a conclusion from a statement given as a reason when one or more of the conditions of that statement have not been fulfilled.

You cannot draw a conclusion from an accepted general statement unless all of its conditions are fulfilled.

Suppose you know that David Brown has Room 100 as a home room. Then you say that he is a senior because *any student having Room 100 as a home room is a senior* (see page 71). But wait! There are two conditions to be fulfilled by the general statement. David Brown *must be a student* as well as have Room 100 as a home room. From what you know *only one* of the conditions is fulfilled. It may be that David Brown is the teacher. In this case you cannot draw a conclusion.

EXERCISES

Draw a figure and state the relationships necessary to fulfill the conditions of each of the following general statements. (The first is done for you.) Then answer the questions. Remember that the conditions are in the if-*part of the sentence.*

1. If three sides of one triangle are equal to three sides of another triangle, the triangles are congruent.

> The necessary conditions are $AB = DE$, $BC = EF$, and $CA = FD$.

Are there two or three conditions to be fulfilled here? Would the conditions be fulfilled if you know that $AB = DE$ and $BC = EF$?

2. If two sides and the included angle of one triangle are equal to two sides and the included angle of another triangle, the triangles are congruent. Are there three or four conditions to be fulfilled?

3. If a line bisects the vertex angle of an isosceles triangle, it bisects the base also. Would the conditions of this statement be fulfilled in any triangle in which an angle is bisected?

In the following exercises assume that the general statements given as reasons are true. Answer the questions.

4. Given that Frank Green is a student and entered his home room last Monday at 8:35,

I conclude that he was marked tardy, because *if a student arrives in his home room for the first time on any given day after 8:30, he is marked tardy.*

How many conditions are there to be fulfilled in the statement of the reason? What are they? Are they all fulfilled by what is given? Does this illustrate right or wrong reasoning?

5. Given that AB and CD are straight lines intersecting at O,

I conclude that $\angle 1 = \angle 3$ and $\angle 2 = \angle 4$, because *if two straight lines intersect, the vertical angles are equal.*

What are the conditions? Are there two intersecting straight lines? Are the angles mentioned vertical angles? Does this illustrate right or wrong reasoning?

In the following exercises, answer these questions.
1. *Are the conditions of the reason fulfilled?*
2. *Does the exercise illustrate right or wrong reasoning?*

6. I know that $AB = DE$, $\angle B = \angle E$, and $BC = EF$.

I conclude that $\triangle ABC \cong \triangle DEF$, because *s.a.s. = s.a.s.*

7. I know that $AB = DE$, $AC = DF$, and $\angle C = \angle F$.

I conclude that $\triangle ABC \cong \triangle DEF$, because *s.a.s. = s.a.s.*

8. I know that $AB = DE$, $AC = DF$, and $BC = EF$.

So $\angle C = \angle F$, because *s.s.s. = s.s.s.*

9. I know that $\angle 1$ is supplementary to $\angle 2$ and $\angle 3$ is supplementary to $\angle 4$.

So $\angle 1 = \angle 4$, because *if two angles are supplementary to equal angles, they are equal.*

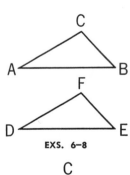

EXS. 6–8

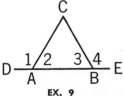

EX. 9

■ Acceptable Reasons

You may not use a statement as a reason in making a deduction unless that statement has already been accepted. Following is a list of geometric relationships discussed previously and accepted.

1 | Two triangles are congruent if *s.a.s.* = *s.a.s.*

2 | Two triangles are congruent if *a.s.a.* = *a.s.a.*

3 | Two triangles are congruent if *s.s.s.* = *s.s.s.*

4 | All right angles are equal.

5 | All straight angles are equal.

6 | All radii of the same circle are equal.

7 | All diameters of the same circle are equal.

8 | If one straight line meets another so as to form adjacent angles, the angles are supplementary.

9 | If two adjacent angles form a right angle, the angles are complementary.

10 | If two angles are supplementary to the same angle or to equal angles, they are equal.

11 | If two angles are complementary to the same angle or to equal angles, they are equal.

12 | If two straight lines intersect, the vertical angles are equal.

The above statements are *geometric propositions.*

△ *A **proposition** is a general statement concerning relationships.*

△ *A **postulate** is a geometric proposition accepted without deductive reasoning. It is an assumption (taken for granted).*

In deductive reasoning there must be a starting point and postulates are the starting point of deductive geometry. Propositions **1** through **5** above are postulates.

△ *A **theorem** is a proposition that is established by means of deductive reasoning.*

Propositions **6** through **12** are theorems. They were established by deductive reasoning even though the thinking was informal.

In checking a proof, look first to see that the propositions you have used as reasons are acceptable.

■ Definitions in Mathematics

A definition of a term in mathematics states the class to which the term belongs and just enough more to distinguish it from other members of the class. (Further discussion on classes and their relationships is given on page 196.) All kinds of triangles belong to the class of triangles. An *isosceles triangle*, therefore, belongs in this class. But it is a particular kind of triangle. It has two equal sides. Hence, an isosceles triangle is defined as a triangle with two equal sides.

To say that an isosceles triangle is a triangle with two equal sides and two equal angles, although correct, would be to say too much. As you will soon learn, if a triangle has two equal sides it *must* have two equal angles. There is no such figure as a triangle with two equal sides without two equal angles.

A definition is always reversible. An isosceles triangle is one with two equal sides. That is the definition. Its reverse is also correct. *A triangle with two equal sides is isosceles.* Since congruent triangles are defined as triangles whose corresponding parts are equal, it is correct to state the reverse: *Corresponding parts of congruent triangles are equal.* (Abbreviated *C.p.c.t.e.*)

Not all statements are reversible as definitions are. For example, all right angles are equal, but all equal angles are *not* right angles.

Any definition, if it applies, may be used as a reason in a deductive proof.

In using a definition as a reason in a proof, you should state it in the form that applies to the particular situation before you. If you know that $AB \perp CD$, then you may say that $\angle 1 = \angle 2$ and the reason is, "A perpendicular to a line forms equal adjacent angles with it." On the other hand, if you know that $\angle 1 = \angle 2$, then $AB \perp CD$ and the reason is the reverse form of the definition; namely, "A line that forms equal adjacent angles with another line is perpendicular to it."

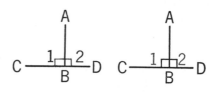

■ Definitions Restated

Following is a list of definitions and their reverses. You have already had these definitions. They are placed here because you will need to use them as reasons in proofs.

1. a *An equilateral triangle is a triangle with three equal sides.*
b *If a triangle has three equal sides, it is equilateral.*

2. a *To bisect a line is to divide it into two equal parts.*
b *If a line is divided into two equal parts, it is bisected.*

3. a *To bisect an angle is to divide it into two equal parts.*
b *If an angle is divided into two equal parts, it is bisected.*

4. a *Perpendicular lines are lines that meet each other and form right angles (or a right angle).*
b *If two lines meet and form right angles (or a right angle), they are perpendicular lines.*

5. a *Perpendicular lines are lines that meet so as to form equal adjacent angles.*
b *If two lines meet so as to form equal adjacent angles, they are perpendicular lines.*

6. a *A perpendicular bisector of a line is a line which not only bisects it but is perpendicular to it.*
b *If a line bisects another and is perpendicular to it, it is the perpendicular bisector of that line.*

7. a *An altitude of a triangle is a line from any one vertex of the triangle, perpendicular to the opposite side, and terminated by it.*
b *If a line is drawn from any vertex of a triangle, perpendicular to the opposite side, and is terminated by it, it is an altitude of the triangle.*

8. a *Supplementary angles are two angles whose sum is 180°.*
b *If the sum of two angles is 180°, they are supplementary.*

9. a *Complementary angles are two angles whose sum is 90°.*
b *If the sum of two angles is 90°, they are complementary.*

10. a *Adjacent angles are two angles that have the same vertex and a common side between them.*
b *If two angles have the same vertex and a common side between them, they are adjacent angles.*

11. a *Vertical angles* are the opposite angles formed by two inter-secting straight lines.

b *If two angles are the opposite angles formed by two inter-secting straight lines,* **they are vertical angles.**

12. a *Congruent triangles are triangles in which the* **corresponding parts are equal.**

b *If two triangles are congruent, the* **corresponding parts are equal.** (*C.p.c.t.e.*)

13. a *A* **right triangle** *is one in which one of the angles is a right angle.*

b *If one angle of a triangle is a right angle, the triangle is a* **right triangle.**

Any of these definitions that are in simple sentence form may be stated as an *if-then* sentence. The wording is different but the meaning is the same. It is the meaning of a definition that is important. For example, the first definition may be written: *If a triangle is equilateral, it has three equal sides.* The second definition may be written: *If a line is bisected, it is divided into two equal parts.*

EXERCISES

State the postulate, theorem, or definition which may be used as authority for each of the following statements. Choose your reasons from the statements on pages 74-77.

1. If $AC = BC$, then $\triangle ABC$ is isosceles.

2. If CD bisects $\angle C$, then $\angle 1 = \angle 2$.

3. If $\angle 1 = \angle 2$, CD bisects $\angle C$.

4. If CD bisects AB, then $AD = DB$.

5. If $AD = DB$, then CD bisects AB.

6. If $CD \perp AB$, then $\angle 3 = \angle 4$.

7. If $\angle 3 = \angle 4$, then $CD \perp AB$.

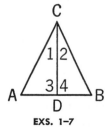

EXS. 1-7

8. If $\angle X$ in $\triangle XYZ$ is a right angle, $\triangle XYZ$ is a right triangle.

9. If $\angle x + \angle y = 180°$, $\angle x$ and $\angle y$ are supplementary.

10. If $\angle ABC$ is a right angle, $\angle 1$ and $\angle 2$ are complementary.

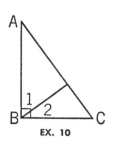

EX. 10

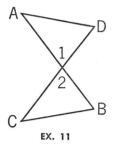

EX. 11

11. If AB and CD are straight lines, $\angle 1 = \angle 2$.

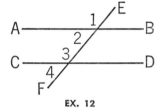

12. If $\angle 1$ is supplementary to $\angle 2$ and $\angle 3$ is supplementary to $\angle 2$, then $\angle 1 = \angle 3$.

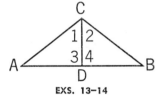

EX. 12

13. If $\angle 1 = \angle 2$, $\angle 3 = \angle 4$, and $CD = CD$, then $\triangle ADC \cong \triangle BDC$.

14. If $\triangle ADC \cong \triangle BDC$ and $\angle A$ corresponds to $\angle B$, then $\angle A = \angle B$.

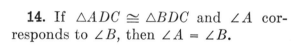

EXS. 13–14

■ A Specimen Proof

Note the steps of the proof below. You have done this before informally; the important thing now is the *form*.

1. The *figure* is drawn.

2. The statement of what is *given*, expressed in terms of the figure, comes next. This is the **hypothesis,** the "If" part of the "If-then" relationship.

3. Next follows the statement of what is to be *proved* — the **conclusion,** the "then" part of the "If-then" relationship.

4. The *plan* of the proof comes next. It is a brief statement of the method of proof. This step need not be written, but it must always be carefully thought through.

5. Finally the *proof* is written out as shown on the next page.

DEDUCTIVE REASONING

Given this figure, in which CD bisects AB and $CD \perp AB$.

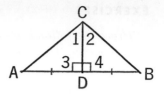

To prove that $AC = BC$.

The *plan* is to prove first that the triangles ADC and BDC are congruent.

Proof.

STATEMENTS	REASONS
1. CD bisects AB.	1. Given.
2. $AD = DB$.	2. If a line is bisected, it is divided into two equal parts.
3. $CD \perp AB$.	3. Given.
4. $\angle 3 = \angle 4$.	4. A perpendicular to a line forms equal adjacent angles with it.
5. $CD = CD$.	5. Identity.
6. $\triangle ADC \cong \triangle BDC$.	6. If two triangles have two sides and included angle, etc.
7. $AC = BC$.	7. Corresponding parts of congruent triangles are equal.

Be sure you know the purpose of each statement and each reason. Are all the reasons *acceptable* ones? Are the conditions of each reason fulfilled?

What is the condition in Reason 2? In what statement is the condition fulfilled?

What is the conclusion in Reason 2? In what statement does this conclusion appear?

Answer similar questions concerning Reason 4.

Reason 5, *Identity*, is an abbreviation of the statement: *Any quantity is equal to itself*, which is taken as a postulate.

A geometric proof is an argument in which each step in the reasoning is built on the statements that have gone before. You should check each proof before you leave it, to make sure it is correct. Use no reasons that have not been previously accepted. Only in this way can a proof be developed. Be sure that the conditions of all your reasons are fulfilled.

Prove the following exercises in good form. The plan in each case is to prove that two triangles are congruent.

1. Given that $AB = AC$, $\angle 1 = \angle 2$.
To prove that $\angle 3 = \angle 4$.

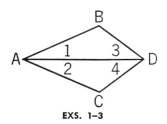

2. Given that $\angle 1 = \angle 2$, $\angle 3 = \angle 4$.
To prove that $AB = AC$.

3. Given that $AB = AC$, $BD = CD$.
To prove that $\angle B = \angle C$.

EXS. 1–3

4. Given that $\angle 1 = \angle 2$, $\angle 3 = \angle 4$.
To prove that $AB = CD$.

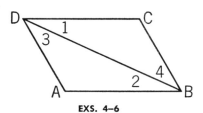

5. Given that $AB = CD$,
$AD = BC$.
To prove that $\angle A = \angle C$.

EXS. 4–6

6. Given that $AD = BC$,
$\angle 3 = \angle 4$.
To prove that $\angle 1 = \angle 2$.

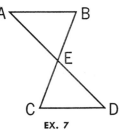

7. Given that AD and BC bisect each
other.
To prove that $AB = CD$.

EX. 7

8. Given that $AC = BC$, CD bisects $\angle C$.
To prove that $AD = DB$.

9. Given that CD bisects $\angle C$, $CD \perp AB$.
To prove that $AC = BC$.

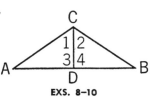

10. Given that $AC = BC$, CD bisects
AB.
To prove that $CD \perp AB$.

EXS. 8–10

Finding Errors in a Geometric Proof

These proofs were taken from pupils' papers. Check them and tell what the errors are.

I. Given this figure, in which BD bisects $\angle B$ and $BD \perp AC$.

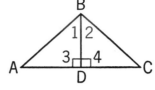

To prove that $AB = BC$.

Attempted proof.

STATEMENTS	REASONS
1. BD bisects $\angle B$.	1. Given.
2. $BD \perp AC$.	2. Given.
3. $\angle 3 = \angle 4$.	3. Angles at the foot of a perpendicular are equal.
4. $AD = DC$.	4. A bisected line is divided into two equal parts.
5. $\triangle ABD \cong \triangle CBD$.	5. $s.a.s. = s.a.s.$
6. $AB = BC$.	6. $C.p.c.t.e.$ (See page 75.)

II. Given that $AB = DC$, $AD = BC$, EF is a straight line passing through O, the middle point of AC.

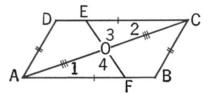

To prove that $FO = OE$.

Attempted proof.

STATEMENTS	REASONS
1. $AB = CD$, $AD = BC$.	1. Given.
2. $AC = AC$.	2. Identity.
3. $\triangle ABC \cong \triangle ADC$.	3. $s.s.s. = s.s.s.$
4. $\angle 1 = \angle 2$.	4. Equal angles formed by a diagonal.
5. $AO = CO$.	5. Given.
6. AC and EF are straight lines.	6. Given.
7. $\angle 3 = \angle 4$.	7. Vertical angles are equal.
8. $\triangle AOF \cong \triangle EOC$.	8. $a.s.a. = a.s.a.$
9. $FO = OE$.	9. $C.p.c.t.e.$

What is the correct reason for Statement 4?

EXERCISES

Prove the following exercises in good form:

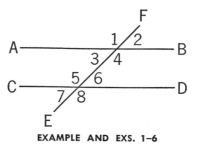

EXAMPLE: **Given** that AB, CD, and EF are straight lines and $\angle 3$ is supplementary to $\angle 5$.

To prove that $\angle 6 = \angle 3$.

The plan is to prove that $\angle 6$ and $\angle 3$ are supplementary to the same angle.

EXAMPLE AND EXS. 1–6

Proof.

STATEMENTS	REASONS
1. $\angle 3$ is supp. to $\angle 5$.	1. Given.
2. EF and CD are straight lines.	2. Given.
3. $\angle 6$ is supp. to $\angle 5$.	3. If one straight line meets another so as to form adjacent angles, the angles are supplementary.
4. $\angle 6 = \angle 3$.	4. If two angles are supplementary to the same angle, they are equal.

In the figure above, AB, CD, and EF are straight lines.

1. Given that $\angle 5$ is supp. to $\angle 3$, prove that $\angle 5 = \angle 1$.

2. Given that $\angle 6$ is supp. to $\angle 4$, prove that $\angle 2 = \angle 6$.

3. Given that $\angle 5$ is supp. to $\angle 3$, prove that $\angle 4 = \angle 5$.

4. Given that $\angle 6$ is supp. to $\angle 4$, prove that $\angle 6 = \angle 3$.

5. Given that $\angle 7$ is supp. to $\angle 1$, prove that $\angle 7 = \angle 3$.

6. Given that $\angle 8$ is supp. to $\angle 3$, prove that $\angle 6 = \angle 3$.

7. The figure at the right is made of three straight lines. If $\angle 1 = \angle 2$, prove that $\angle 3 = \angle 4$.

EX. 7

Plan. Prove them supplementary to equal angles.

8. In the figure at the right ACE is a straight line and $\angle 5 = \angle 6$. Prove that $\angle 3 = \angle 4$.

9. AE bisects $\angle A$, $\angle 5 = \angle 6$. Prove that $\angle B = \angle D$. (What is the plan?)

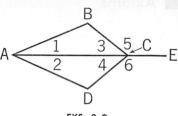

10. If C is the middle point of AB, $\angle 1 = \angle 2$, $EA \perp AB$, and $BD \perp AB$, then $\angle E = \angle D$.

EXS. 8–9

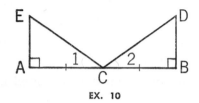

EX. 10

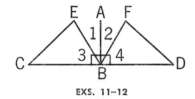

EXS. 11–12

11. If $AB \perp CD$ and $\angle 1 = \angle 2$, then $\angle 3 = \angle 4$.

Plan. Prove $\angle 3$ and $\angle 4$ complements of equal angles.

12. If AB is the perpendicular bisector of CD, $\angle 1 = \angle 2$, and $EB = FB$, then $\angle E = \angle F$.

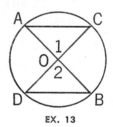

EX. 13

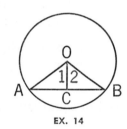

EX. 14

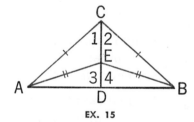

EX. 15

13. AB and CD are diameters. Prove that $DB = AC$.

14. O is the center of the circle and $\angle 1 = \angle 2$. Prove that OC is the perpendicular bisector of AB.

EXTRA

15. If $AC = BC$ and $AE = BE$, then CD is the perpendicular bisector of AB.

Plan. First prove that $\triangle AEC \cong \triangle BEC$; then prove that $\triangle ACD \cong \triangle BCD$.

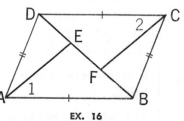

16. If $AB = CD$, $AD = BC$, and $\angle 1 = \angle 2$, then $AE = CF$.

EX. 16

■ Axioms

You have already learned about statements called postulates, theorems, and definitions. You will now learn about other statements, called *axioms*.

△ *An* **axiom** *is a general proposition accepted without deductive reasoning. It is an assumption.*

As we use them here, axioms differ from postulates in that they show relationships between quantities in general while the postulates show geometric relationships. However, the terms *axiom* and *postulate* are often used interchangeably. Below is a list of axioms of equality used in geometric proofs.

Any statement listed as a postulate or an axiom may be used as a reason in a proof.

Do not memorize the list. Read the axioms carefully and see if you understand their meaning. You will learn them through use.

AXIOMS OF EQUALITY

1	A quantity may be substituted for an equal quantity in any expression without changing the value of the expression.
2	If quantities are equal to the same quantity, they are equal to each other. If quantities are equal to equal quantities, they are equal to each other.
3	If equal quantities are added to equal quantities, the sums are equal quantities.
4	If equal quantities are subtracted from equal quantities, the remainders are equal quantities.
5	If equal quantities are multiplied by equal quantities, the products are equal quantities. As a special case of this axiom we have: **Doubles of equals are equal.**
6	If equal quantities are divided by equal quantities, the quotients are equal quantities. As a special case of this axiom we have: **Halves of equals are equal.**
7	Like powers or like roots of equal quantities are equal quantities.
8	The whole is equal to the sum of its parts.

EXERCISES

Using page 84 as reference, state the axiom that can be given as authority for each of the following statements: (Exs. 1–10)

1. If $BC = AD$ and $AC = AD$, then $BC = AC$.

2. If $\angle 1 = \angle 3$ and $\angle 2 = \angle 3$, then $\angle 1 = \angle 2$.

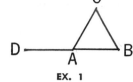

EX. 1

3. If $a + b + c = 180°$ and $d = b$, then $a + d + c = 180°$.

4. If $a = b$ and $c = d$, then $a + c = b + d$.

5. If $a = 2b$, $c = 2d$, and $b = d$, then $a = c$.

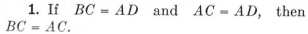

EX. 2

6. If $a = b$ and $c = d$ and also $b = d$, then $a = c$.

7. $AD + DC = AC$. $BE + EC = BC$.

8. If $AD = BE$ and $DC = CE$, then $AC = BC$.

(It will help if you give small numerical values to the lengths of these lines.)

9. If $AD = \frac{1}{2}AC$, $CE = \frac{1}{2}BC$, and $AC = BC$, then $AD = CE$.

10. If $AC = 2AD$, $BC = 2BE$, and $AD = BE$, then $AC = BC$.

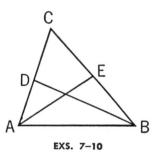

EXS. 7–10

EXTRA

What is wrong with the following statements?

11. If $MN = OP$ and $RS = ST$, then $MN = RS$ because if quantities are equal to the same quantity, they are equal to each other.

12. If $MN = OP$ and $RS = ST$, then $MN = RS$ because if two quantities are equal to equal quantities, they are equal to each other.

13. If $a = b$ and $c = d$, then $a + b = c + d$ because if equal quantities are added to equal quantities, the sums are equal.

USING AXIOMS

■ Overlapping Triangles

Overlapping triangles in geometric figures often cause trouble because they are confusing to the eye. These exercises will help you in working with them. If it will aid you, redraw Figure 1 as many times as is necessary and trace with a colored pencil the triangles with which you are dealing. (See Figure 2, which is the same as Fig. 1 except that $\triangle AOE$ and $\triangle BOF$ are colored.)

1. How many triangles do you see in Figure 1? $\triangle ABC$ is one triangle. $\triangle AOB$ is another. Name the others.

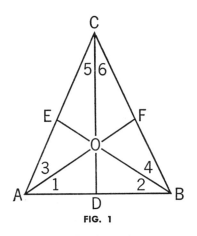

FIG. 1

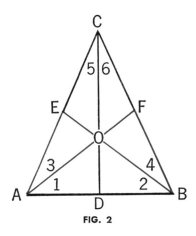

FIG. 2

2. Name the sides and the angles of each of the triangles in Figure 1. Use three letters for the angles when necessary.

For example, look at $\triangle ABF$ in Figure 1. The three sides are AB, BF, and FA. The three angles are $\angle 1$, $\angle ABF$, and $\angle BFA$.

3. List by pairs the triangles which appear to be congruent. For example, see $\triangle ABF$ and $\triangle BAE$, which overlap, or $\triangle AOE$ and $\triangle BOF$.

4. List the apparently corresponding parts of each of the pairs of triangles.

For example, in $\triangle ABF$ and $\triangle BAE$ the apparently corresponding sides and angles are as follows: AB corresponds to AB, BF to AE, and AF to BE; $\angle 1$ corresponds to $\angle 2$, $\angle ABF$ to $\angle BAE$, and $\angle BFA$ to $\angle AEB$.

5. Copy the list at the top of page 87 and fill in the blanks so that the results will correspond to the given specifications.

a s.a.s. of $\triangle ABF$.	AB, _?_, BF.
b s.a.s. of $\triangle ABE$.	AB, _?_, AE.
c s.a.s. of $\triangle ABF$.	_?_, $\angle 1$, _?_.
d s.a.s. of $\triangle ABE$.	_?_, $\angle 2$, _?_.
e a.s.a. of $\triangle AFC$.	_?_, AC, _?_.
f a.s.a. of $\triangle BEC$.	_?_, BC, _?_.
g s.a.s. of $\triangle AFC$.	AC, _?_, CF.
h s.a.s. of $\triangle BEC$.	BC, _?_, CE.

6. ABC and EDC are straight lines. $BC = DC$ and $AB = ED$. Prove that $\angle A = \angle E$.

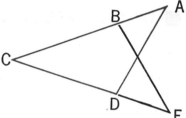

The *plan*. You can prove that $\angle A = \angle E$ if you can prove that $\triangle ACD \cong \triangle EBC$. These are overlapping triangles. Before attempting a proof, write down the corresponding sides and angles by pairs as shown.

$$\triangle ACD — \triangle ECB$$
$$AC — EC \qquad\qquad \angle A — \angle E$$
$$DC — BC \qquad\qquad \angle CDA — \angle CBE$$
$$AD — EB \qquad\qquad \angle C — \angle C$$

From this you can see that $\angle C = \angle C$ because it is the same angle in both triangles. You have given that $DC = BC$. It remains to prove only that $AC = EC$, and you can state that the triangles are congruent. Now prove the exercise in good form.

EXERCISES

1. AE and BD are so drawn that $AD = BE$. Also $\angle CAB = \angle CBA$. Prove that $AE = BD$.

What triangles should you prove congruent?

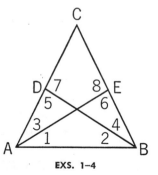

2. $AC = BC$ and $AD = BE$. Prove that $AE = BD$.

3. $AD = BE$ and $AE = BD$. Prove that $\angle 7 = \angle 8$.

4. AE and BD make equal angles with AB, and $\angle CAB = \angle CBA$. Prove that $\angle 5 = \angle 6$ and $\angle 7 = \angle 8$.

EXS. 1–4

What angle does AE make with AB? What angle does BD make with AB? According to the statement of the problem these angles are equal.

OVERLAPPING TRIANGLES

5. ABC and EDC are straight lines. If $AC = CE$ and $AB = DE$, prove that $BE = DA$.

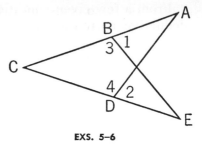

6. If $CB = CD$ and $\angle 1 = \angle 2$, then $AC = EC$.

EXS. 5–6

◼ The Power of Deductive Reasoning

The proof below and the discussion following it are given to emphasize the power and the importance of deductive reasoning.

Given that AE bisects BD, $AB \perp BD$, and $ED \perp BD$.

What can be discovered concerning this figure without measuring?

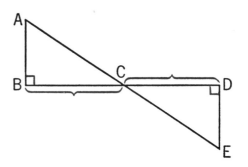

STATEMENTS	REASONS
1. AE bisects BD.	1. Given.
2. $BC = CD$.	2. A bisector divides a line into two equal parts.
3. $\angle ACB = \angle ECD$.	3. If two straight lines intersect, the vertical angles are equal.
4. $AB \perp BD$, $ED \perp BD$.	4. Given.
5. $\angle B$ and $\angle D$ are right angles.	5. Perpendicular lines form right angles.
6. $\angle B = \angle D$.	6. All right angles are equal.
7. $\triangle ABC \cong \triangle EDC$.	7. $a.s.a. = a.s.a.$
8. $AB = DE$, $AC = CE$, $\angle A = \angle E$.	8. $C.p.c.t.e.$

From a few given conditions and general statements as a start, deductive reasoning can often establish an amazing number of new truths. Here we began with a few known facts concerning the figure. Using these facts (Reasons 1 and 4) and making use of three definitions (Reasons 2, 5, and 8), two postulates (Reasons 6 and 7), and a theorem (Reason 3), we have discovered the conclusions in Statements 2, 3, 5, 6, 7, and 8.

■ Additional Postulates

In your work up to this point you have tacitly (without mentioning it) assumed the truth of the propositions listed below.

Note: Some of these postulates, as well as several others given in this book, can be deduced from others, and in that case would be listed as theorems. In a first course in demonstrative geometry, however, it is unwise to start with an irreducible set of postulates.

POSTULATES

1 A straight line can be extended in either direction to any desired length.

2 Two straight lines cannot intersect in more than one point.

3 Through two given points one and only one straight line can be drawn. (Or, two points determine a straight line.)

4 A straight line is the shortest line that can be drawn between two points. (Also, the shortest line that can be drawn between two points is a straight line.)

5 One and only one circle can be drawn with any point as center and any line segment as radius.

6 At a point on a line or from a point outside a line only one perpendicular can be drawn to the line.

7 The shortest distance from a point to a line is the perpendicular from the point to the line.

8 An angle has only one bisector.

9 A line segment has only one midpoint.

In the next chapter you will begin to see how a large number of geometric relationships, which perhaps you have known before through measurement, may be deduced from a few postulates without any measuring whatsoever.

■ Historical Use of Congruent Triangles

A Roman surveyor about 180 A.D. wrote directions for finding the width of a river by using congruent triangles. In modern language the method is as follows:

Take a base line AC along the river. At any point E mark off a line at right angles to AC. Place a stake at the middle point D of AE. From A sight a line making right angles with CA. From D sight the points X and Y so that XDY is a straight line.

Then $\triangle DAY \cong \triangle DEX$ (prove it), and AY may be found by measuring EX.

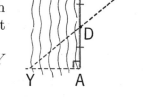

In a book written in Venice in the sixteenth century the following method is given for finding the distance across a river.

AB is a vertical staff with a movable arm CD. The staff is held vertically; that is, it makes right angles with the ground at B. Then the observer sights along CD, tipping the arm until it points at P on the opposite bank of the river.

He holds CD at this angle and rotates the staff until he sights at a point M on the same side of the river. By this method $\triangle ABM \cong \triangle ABP$. The distance BP can be found by measuring MB.

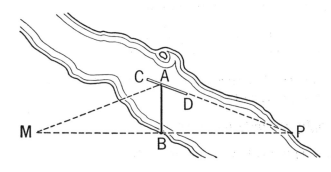

1. Construct two triangles congruent in each of these ways:
1. *s.a.s.* = *s.a.s.*   2. *a.s.a.* = *a.s.a.*   3. *s.s.s.* = *s.s.s.*

2. Find the supplement and the complement of an angle of 42° 35′. What is the difference in degrees between the supplement and the complement? Will this difference always be the same, no matter what the given angle is? Explain.

3. A boy wishes to know the approximate distance across a pond. He places stakes at *A* and *B* and at a convenient point *C*. While he sights from *B* to *C*, a friend puts a stake at *D* in the same straight line with *B* and *C* so that *CD* = *BC*. Similarly he finds point *E*, making *CE* = *AC*. He then measures *DE* to find the length of *AB*. Show that *DE* must equal *AB*.

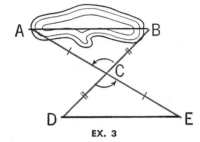

EX. 3

4. Construct an isosceles triangle and bisect the vertex angle. It appears that the base also is bisected. Explain by means of congruent triangles why this has to be true.

5. Construct *CD*, the perpendicular bisector of *AB*. Take any point *E* on *CD* and draw *AE* and *EB*. Explain why *AE* must equal *EB*.

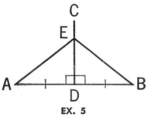

EX. 5

6. Bisect any angle and then from any point on the bisector construct a line perpendicular to each side of the angle. Do you know enough about the two triangles to say without further measurement that they are congruent?

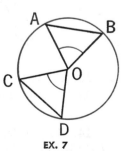

7. Draw a circle with center *O*. Draw two radii *AO* and *BO*. Construct ∠*COD* = ∠*AOB*. Explain why *CD* must equal *AB*.

EX. 7

USING CONGRUENT TRIANGLES

8. AD and BC are two diameters in $\odot O$. Explain why AB and CD must be equal.

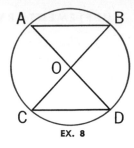

EX. 8

9. If you know only that the figure is made of four straight lines, and that AB and DE are perpendicular to BD, which of the following equalities can you be sure of? $AC = CE,$ $\angle 1 = \angle 2,$ $\angle B = \angle D,$ $BC = CD,$ $AB = DE.$ Explain.

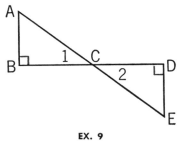

EX. 9

10. This figure shows the construction for bisecting an angle. Explain by means of congruent triangles why $\angle 1 = \angle 2$.

Note: $BE = BD$ and $DF = EF$.

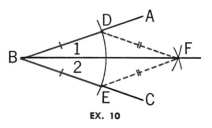

11. Draw an angle and bisect it. At any point on the bisector construct a line perpendicular to the bisector. Explain by means of congruent triangles why the segments cut off on the sides of the angle must be equal.

EX. 10

12. Prove: If $AD = BE$ and $DB = CE$, then $\triangle ABC$ is isosceles.

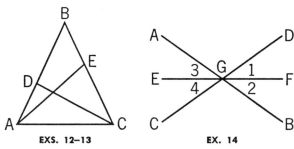

EXS. 12–13   EX. 14

13. Prove: If $AD = BD,$ $CE = EB,$ and $AD = CE,$ then $\triangle ABC$ is isosceles.

14. $AB,$ $CD,$ and EF are straight lines intersecting at G. EF bisects $\angle AGC$. Prove that EF bisects $\angle DGB$.

I. Vocabulary.

1. Use each of the following terms correctly in a sentence.

Congruent triangles

Corresponding parts of congruent
triangles

Two sides and the included angle

Two angles and the included side

Deduction

Deductive reasoning

Fulfilled conditions

Acceptable reasons

Proposition

Postulate

Axiom

Theorem

Mathematical definition

Overlapping triangles

II. Making Triangles Congruent.

2. Construct two triangles so that they will be congruent by each of the following methods: 1. *s.s.s.* = *s.s.s.*, 2. *s.a.s.* = *s.a.s.*, and 3. *a.s.a.* = *a.s.a.*

III. Practice with *s.a.s.* and *a.s.a.*

3. What angle is included between AC and BC?

4. What side is included between $\angle 2$ and $\angle 4$?

5. Are DC, AD, and $\angle 3$ two sides and the included angle of $\triangle ADC$?

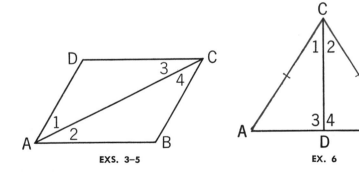

EXS. 3–5   EX. 6

IV. Holding to the Given Relationships.

6. Given this figure in which $AC = BC$. Does $\angle 1 = \angle 2$? Does $\angle 3 = \angle 4$? Explain.

V. Using s.a.s. = s.a.s. and a.s.a. = a.s.a.

7. If parts are equal as indicated, are the triangles congruent? Explain.

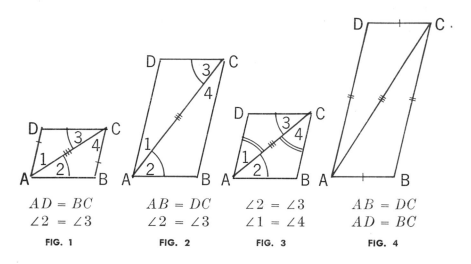

$AD = BC$	$AB = DC$	$\angle 2 = \angle 3$	$AB = DC$
$\angle 2 = \angle 3$	$\angle 2 = \angle 3$	$\angle 1 = \angle 4$	$AD = BC$
FIG. 1	**FIG. 2**	**FIG. 3**	**FIG. 4**

VI. Deductive Reasoning.

Which of the following are examples of correct reasoning and which are incorrect? If an exercise is wrong, tell what is wrong.

8. If $AB \perp CD$, then $CB = BD$ because a perpendicular to a line divides it into two equal parts.

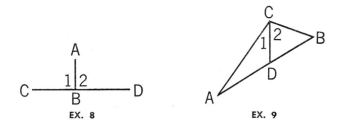

EX. 8   EX. 9

9. If $\angle 1 = \angle 2$, then CD bisects $\angle ACB$ because if an angle is divided into two equal parts it is bisected.

10. If $AB \perp BD$ and $ED \perp BD$, then $\angle B = \angle D$ because a perpendicular to a line forms equal adjacent angles with it.

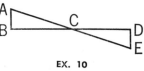

EX. 10

11. If $\triangle ACD \cong \triangle BCD$ and $\angle 1 = \angle 2$, then $AC = BC$ because corresponding parts of congruent triangles are equal.

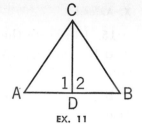

EX. 11

VII. Unfulfilled Conditions.

12. What is wrong with this reasoning?

   If $\angle 2$ is supplementary to $\angle 1$ and $\angle 4$ is supplementary to $\angle 3$, then $\angle 2 = \angle 4$ because supplements of equal angles are equal.

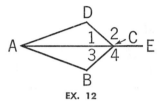

EX. 12

VIII. Acceptable Reasons.

13. Which of the following statements, at the present stage of your study, are acceptable reasons?

a Two triangles are congruent if three sides of one are equal to three sides of the other.

b Two right triangles are congruent if the side opposite the right angle and an acute angle of one triangle are equal to the corresponding parts of the other.

c The sum of the angles of a triangle is 180°.

d The bisector of the vertex angle of an isosceles triangle bisects the base also.

e If two straight lines intersect, the vertical angles so formed are equal.

IX. Definitions.

14. State the reverse of each of the following definitions.

a An equilateral triangle is a triangle with three equal sides.

b Perpendicular lines are lines that meet each other and form right angles.

c Supplementary angles are two angles whose sum is 180°.

d To bisect a line is to divide it into two equal parts.

e An altitude of a triangle is a line from any one vertex of the triangle, perpendicular to the opposite side and terminated by it.

CHAPTER SUMMARY   **95**

X. Axioms.

15. Illustrate the use of each of these axioms.

a If two quantities are equal to the same quantity, they are equal to each other.

b If equal quantities are added to equal quantities, the sums also are equal.

c Halves of equals are equal.

XI. Overlapping Triangles.

16. If $\triangle ACE \cong \triangle BCD$, AC corresponds to BC, and CE corresponds to CD, what are the corresponding angles of the two triangles?

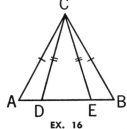

EX. 16

XII. Formal Proofs.

17. Given that AB, CD, and EF are straight lines and that $\angle 4 = \angle 8$, prove that $\angle 1 = \angle 8$.

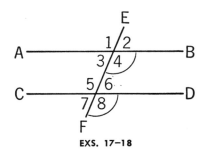

EXS. 17–18

18. Given that AB, CD, and EF are straight lines and that $\angle 4$ is supplementary to $\angle 6$, prove that $\angle 4 = \angle 5$.

19. Given this figure in which straight line ACE bisects $\angle A$ and $\angle 3 = \angle 4$, prove that $\angle D = \angle B$.

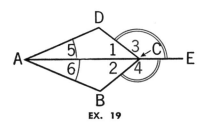

EX. 19

DEDUCTIVE REASONING

TEST 1

Complete these sentences.

1. Congruent figures are figures all of whose ⁻?⁻ are equal.

2. I know three ways of proving triangles congruent: *s.a.s.* = *s.a.s.*; ⁻?⁻ = ⁻?⁻; and ⁻?⁻ = ⁻?⁻.

3. *AB*, ⁻?⁻, and *BD* are *s.a.s.* of △*ABD*.

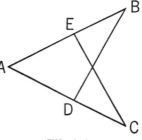

4. Angle ⁻?⁻ is identical to the two triangles *ABD* and *ACE*.

5. ⁻?⁻, *AD*, and ⁻?⁻ are *a.s.a.* of △*ABD*.

6. *AE* is a side of △ ⁻?⁻.

EXS. 3–6

7. A statement should not be used as a reason unless its ⁻?⁻ are fulfilled.

8. If two straight lines intersect, the ⁻?⁻ angles are equal.

9. No statement is allowed as a reason unless it has been previously ⁻?⁻.

10. A postulate is a (an) ⁻?⁻ proposition.

11. You can prove that two lines or two angles are equal if you can show that they are ⁻?⁻ parts of ⁻?⁻ triangles.

12. In an exercise or a theorem, the given facts are referred to as the ⁻?⁻. What you are to prove is the ⁻?⁻.

13. If $a = b$ and $c = d$, then $a + $ ⁻?⁻ $ = $ ⁻?⁻ $ + $ ⁻?⁻.

14. If I have already proved that two sides of one triangle are equal to two sides of another triangle, I can prove that the triangles are congruent by showing either that the ⁻?⁻ angles are equal or that the third ⁻?⁻ are equal.

If a statement is true, give the authority for it. If it is not true, write "No."

1. a $\angle 1 + \angle 2 = \angle DAB$.
  b $\angle 3 + \angle 4 = \angle BCD$.
  c If $\angle 1 + \angle 2 = 70°$ and $\angle 4 = \angle 1$, then $\angle 4 + \angle 2 = 70°$.
  d If $\angle 1 = \angle 4$ and $\angle 2 = \angle 3$, then $\angle DAB = \angle BCD$.
  e If $\angle DAB = \angle BCD$ and $\angle 1 = \angle 4$, then $\angle 2 = \angle 3$.
  f If $\angle 1 = \angle 2$ and $\angle 3 = \angle 4$, then $\angle DAB = \angle BCD$.
  g If $\angle 1 = \angle 2$ and $\angle 3 = \angle 4$ and also $\angle 1 = \angle 3$, then $\angle DAB = \angle BCD$.

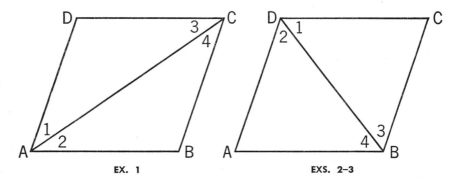

EX. 1   EXS. 2–3

2. If DB bisects $\angle D$, then $\angle 3 = \angle 4$.
3. If DB bisects $\angle B$ and $\angle D$, then $\triangle ABD \cong \triangle DBC$.
4. $EACF$ is a straight line. If $\angle 1 = \angle 2$, then $\angle 3 = \angle 4$.

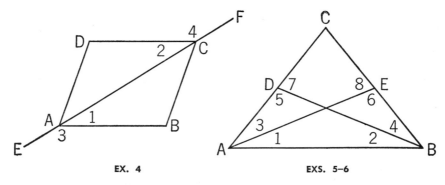

EX. 4   EXS. 5–6

5. If $AE = DB$ and $AD = BE$, then $\triangle ABE \cong \triangle ABD$.
6. If $\angle 1 = \angle 2$ and $\angle A = \angle B$, then $\triangle ABE \cong \triangle ABD$.

                         DEDUCTIVE REASONING

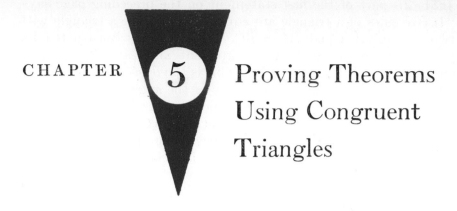

CHAPTER **5** Proving Theorems Using Congruent Triangles

In this chapter you will learn how the definitions, axioms, postulates, and theorems you have already accepted can be used as a basis for demonstrating a new set of theorems. The purpose is not to convince you of the truth of the new statements. You would probably agree to most of them without deductive proof. The purpose is to show you how they are all connected and how they depend upon these previously accepted definitions, axioms, postulates, and theorems. Think of demonstrative geometry as a house. The definition, axioms, and postulates are the foundation blocks. The theorems you will prove are the superstructure.

■ Hypothesis and Conclusion from Verbal Statements

All the theorems will be stated in words. Hence you must be able to choose the hypothesis and conclusion from verbal statements. The *hypothesis* is the *if-* part of a geometric proposition. It states the given conditions. The *conclusion* is the *then-* part. It states what is to be proved.

Consider the next three statements:

1. If two sides of a triangle are equal, the angles opposite those sides are equal.

2. If two angles of a triangle are equal, the sides opposite those angles are equal.

3. If a line bisects the vertex angle of an isosceles triangle, it bisects the base also.

The *if*- part of the first statement on the preceding page says, "If two sides of a triangle are equal." You have a triangle with two sides given equal, $AC = BC$. The figure is constructed for you below at the left. The statement also says, "the angles opposite those sides are equal." This is the *then*- part of the sentence. It tells you that the equality of the angles is beyond your control once you have made the sides equal. You are to prove that $\angle A = \angle B$ starting from the fact that $AC = BC$.

Using your straightedge and compass, reproduce the figure and write under it what is given and what is to be proved.

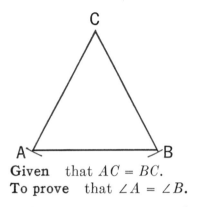

Given that $AC = BC$.
To prove that $\angle A = \angle B$.

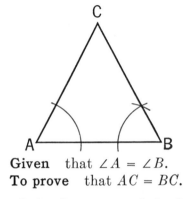

Given that $\angle A = \angle B$.
To prove that $AC = BC$.

In the second statement, the *if*- and the *then*- parts of the first statement have been reversed. Two angles are *given* equal and the figure is so constructed. You are to prove that the two sides opposite the angles are equal. Construct the figure, as shown above at the right, and write the hypothesis and the conclusion.

There are two conditions in the third statement. The triangle must be isosceles and the vertex angle must be bisected. Construct a figure according to the conditions. Write under the figure what is given and what is to be proved; that is, the hypothesis and the conclusion.

A proposition is not necessarily stated in the *if-then* form. For example, the third statement may be written: A line which bisects the vertex angle of an isosceles triangle bisects the base also. Whenever a theorem is stated in this form, the hypothesis is in the subject (and all its modifiers) and the conclusion is in the predicate.

Construct the figure and write the hypothesis and conclusion for this statement: A line which bisects the vertex angle of an isosceles triangle is perpendicular to the base.

EXERCISES

Construct a figure for each of the following exercises and then write the hypothesis and the conclusion in terms of the letters of the figure. Make a careful check to see that you have written all the conditions. Do not prove the exercises.

1. If a line connects the middle points of two sides of a triangle, it is equal to one half of the third side.

2. If lines are drawn from any point on the perpendicular bisector of a line to the extremities (ends) of the line, they are equal.

3. Lines drawn from any point on the perpendicular bisector of a line to the extremities of the line form an angle that is bisected by the perpendicular.

4. If, at any point on the bisector of an angle, a line is drawn perpendicular to the bisector and extended to meet the sides of the angle, the perpendicular is divided into two equal parts at the point.

5. Lines drawn from any point on the bisector of an angle, perpendicular to the sides of the angle and terminated by the sides, are equal.

6. If two sides of a triangle are extended, each its own length, through the common vertex, the line joining the extremities of the extended sides equals the third side of the triangle.

7. If the equal sides of an isosceles triangle are extended beyond the base, equal angles are formed with the base.

8. If the base of an isosceles triangle is extended in both directions, equal angles are formed with the equal sides.

EXTRA

9. The bisectors of the base angles of an isosceles triangle form another isosceles triangle with the same base.

10. The line that connects the vertex of an isosceles triangle with the middle point of the base bisects the vertex angle.

HYPOTHESIS AND CONCLUSION   **101**

■ Geometric Reasoning

Geometric reasoning is deductive reasoning with which you had experience in Chapter 4. You learned that once the given conditions are set up, the conclusions follow logically on the basis of general statements to which you have agreed.

The science of deductive geometry begins with undefined terms and unproved propositions. It is not possible to define the earliest terms used. For example, an equilateral triangle is a triangle. A triangle is a figure formed by three intersecting straight lines. Note that we have gone backward from *triangle* to *line*. When we go backward again, what do we have with which to define *line*? We accept *line* as an undefined term. Can you think of another term that is accepted as undefined?

A very similar thing is true of unproved propositions which are called postulates or axioms. A theorem is proved by citing a previously proved theorem. And that theorem is proved by citing a theorem proved before that one. Eventually, you reach the starting point where there is no previously proved theorem. Then you have to accept some propositions (axioms and postulates) without proof.

Supported by these undefined terms and unproved propositions are, of course, the defined terms and the proved propositions called theorems. Using these four categories, you build up the science of geometry. The figure below suggests the nature of geometric reasoning.

Proof of Exercises

Theorems

Defined Terms

Undefined Terms,
Postulates, and Axioms

On the next page you will begin the formal treatment of proof of theorems.

If two sides of a triangle are equal, the angles opposite those sides are equal.

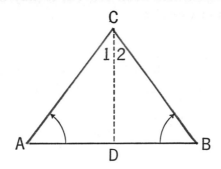

Given   a triangle ABC in which $AC = BC$.
To prove   that $\angle A = \angle B$.
Proof.

First bisect $\angle C$ by line CD.

STATEMENTS	REASONS
1. $AC = BC$.	1. Given.
2. $\angle 1 = \angle 2$.	2. A bisector divides an angle into two equal parts.
3. $CD = CD$.	3. Identity.
4. $\triangle ACD \cong \triangle BCD$.	4. *s.a.s. = s.a.s.*
5. $\angle A = \angle B$.	5. *C.p.c.t.e.*

Even though we have used only one figure here, the proof is general for all triangles having two equal sides.

You should give all reasons in full. We abbreviate, as in Reasons 4 and 5, or we refer to pages, for the sake of brevity.

△ *The equal angles of an isosceles triangle are called **base angles**.*

Auxiliary Lines.   *CD* in the figure above is an *auxiliary line*, an extra line not given in the hypothesis, drawn to help with the proof. Auxiliary lines are usually dotted or dashed to distinguish them from given lines. Remember that lines are determined by two points or by a point and a direction. You may draw any auxiliary lines in a figure to help with the proof just so long as you remember these two conditions.

■ Using Theorems in Proofs

As soon as a theorem has been proved, it may be used to prove other theorems and exercises.

EXAMPLE:

Prove: If the equal sides of an isosceles triangle are extended beyond the base, equal angles are formed with the base.

Given   triangle ABC with the equal sides CA and CB extended to D and E respectively.

To prove   that $\angle 3 = \angle 4$.

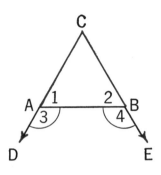

One way to prove this exercise would be to bisect $\angle C$ and prove the triangles congruent. This, however, would be proving Theorem 1 all over again. The better way is to use Theorem 1 to get $\angle 1 = \angle 2$ at once.

Proof.

STATEMENTS	REASONS
1. $CA = CB$.	1. Given.
2. $\angle 1 = \angle 2$.	2. If two sides of a triangle are equal, the angles opposite those sides are equal.
3. $\angle 3$ is supp. to $\angle 1$; $\angle 4$ is supp. to $\angle 2$.	3. Prop. 8, page 74.
4. $\angle 3 = \angle 4$.	4. Supplements of equal angles are equal.

Check this proof. Are all the reasons *acceptable* ones? What are the conditions of Reason 2? of Reason 3? of Reason 4? Are the conditions of each reason fulfilled? Is each conclusion the one called for by the reason? Have you proved the statement you started to prove?

You will note that many of the exercises in this book are theorems. It is agreed, however, not to use exercises as reasons. The statements *labeled* theorems are basic and are the ones to be used as authorities.

EXERCISES

Prove the following exercises in good form. In each exercise look for a triangle with two equal sides and then apply Theorem 1. You should draw a figure for each exercise and mark the sides and angles you know to be equal. As you prove sides or angles equal, mark them also.

1. If the base of an isosceles triangle is extended in both directions, equal angles are formed with the arms.

The figure for Exs. 2–8 consists of five straight lines.

2. If $AB = BC$ and $AD = EC$, then $BD = BE$.

3. If $AB = BC$ and $\angle 1 = \angle 2$, then $\angle 3 = \angle 6$.

4. If $AB = BC$ and $\angle 1 = \angle 2$, then $\triangle BDE$ is isosceles.

5. If $AB = BC$ and $AD = EC$, then $\angle 4 = \angle 5$. (You can prove that $\angle 4 = \angle 5$ if you can prove that $BD = BE$.)

6. If $AB = BC$ and $\angle 1 = \angle 2$, then $\angle 4 = \angle 5$.

7. If $AB = BC$ and $\angle ABE = \angle DBC$, then $\triangle BDE$ is isosceles. (See pages 86 and 87.)

8. If $BD = BE$ and $AD = EC$, then $\angle A = \angle C$.

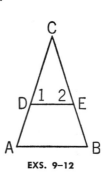

EXS. 2–8

The figure for Exs. 9–12 is made of four straight lines.

9. If $CA = CB$ and $DA = EB$, then $\angle 1 = \angle 2$.

10. If $CD = CE$ and $DA = EB$, then $\angle A = \angle B$.

11. If $CD = DA$, $CE = EB$, and $CA = CB$, then $\angle 1 = \angle 2$.

12. If $CD = DA$, $CE = EB$, and $CD = CE$, then $\angle A = \angle B$.

EXS. 9–12

13. If $DA = DC$ and $BA = BC$, then $\angle DAB = \angle DCB$.

14. If $BA = BC$ and $\angle DAB = \angle DCB$, then $\angle 1 = \angle 2$.

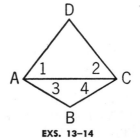

EXS. 13–14

■ Meaning of Corollary

We speak of one statement as being a *corollary* to another, when the first is easily deduced from the second.

△ *A* **corollary** *is a theorem that is easily proved by means of another theorem.* The corollary below is easily proved by using Theorem 1.

Like other theorems, a corollary may be used as a reason in a deductive proof.

△ *An* **equiangular triangle** *is a triangle with three equal angles.*

COROLLARY TO THEOREM 1   **An equilateral triangle is also equiangular.**

Proof. If $CA = CB$, then $\angle A = \angle B$ (Theorem 1). If $AC = AB$, then $\angle C = \angle B$ (Theorem 1). Hence $\angle A = \angle B = \angle C$ (Axiom 2, page 84).

Before you study Theorem 2   The proof for the next theorem is not difficult, but it is longer. The following exercises will prepare you for it.

Given this figure made of five straight lines in which $\angle A = \angle B$, AD bisects $\angle A$, and BE bisects $\angle B$.

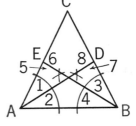

1. If $\angle A = \angle B$, $\angle 2$ is half of $\angle A$, and $\angle 4$ is half of $\angle B$, then $\angle 2 = \angle 4$. Why?

2. Prove that the overlapping triangles ABD and BAE are congruent.

3. Then $AD = BE$ and $\angle 7 = \angle 5$. Why?

4. $\angle 8 = \angle 6$. Prove it.

5. $\angle 1 = \angle 3$. Why?

6. Now prove that $\triangle ADC \cong \triangle BEC$.

7. $AC = BC$. Why?

You should now be able to understand easily the proof for Theorem 2 given in full on the next page.

If two angles of a triangle are equal, the sides opposite those angles are equal.

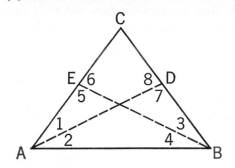

Given $\triangle ABC$ in which $\angle A = \angle B$.

To prove that $AC = BC$.

The *plan* is to bisect $\angle A$ and $\angle B$, to prove that $\triangle ABD \cong \triangle BAE$, and then prove that $\triangle ADC \cong \triangle BEC$.

Proof.

Draw AD and BE bisecting $\angle A$ and $\angle B$ respectively.

STATEMENTS	REASONS
In $\triangle ABD$ and $\triangle BAE$,	
1. $AB = AB$.	1. Identity.
2. $\angle ABD = \angle BAE$.	2. Given.
3. $\angle 2 = \angle 4$.	3. Ax. 6, page 84.
4. $\triangle ABD \cong \triangle BAE$.	4. $a.s.a. = a.s.a.$
5. $AD = BE$, $\angle 7 = \angle 5$.	5. $C.p.c.t.e.$
In $\triangle ADC$ and $\triangle BEC$,	
6. $\angle 8$ supp. to $\angle 7$, $\angle 6$ supp. to $\angle 5$.	6. Prop. 8, page 74.
7. $\angle 8 = \angle 6$.	7. Prop. 10, page 74.
8. $AD = BE$.	8. See Statement 5.
9. $\angle 1 = \angle 3$.	9. Reason 3.
10. $\triangle ADC \cong \triangle BEC$.	10. $a.s.a. = a.s.a.$
11. $AC = BC$.	11. $C.p.c.t.e.$

Note that here, as in Theorem 1, the proof is general. The proof is the same for any triangle if two of its angles are equal.

<u>COROLLARY TO THEOREM 2</u> **An equiangular triangle is also equilateral.**

(The proof uses Theorem 2.)

You can now prove that two sides of a triangle are equal if you can prove that the angles opposite those sides are equal (Theorem 2). Prove the following in good form.

1. If $DABE$ is a straight line and $\angle 1 = \angle 2$, then $AC = BC$.

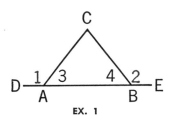

EX. 1

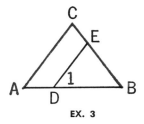

EX. 3

2. The bisectors of the base angles of an isosceles triangle form another isosceles triangle with the same base.

3. If $AC = BC$ and $\angle 1 = \angle A$, then $DE = BE$.

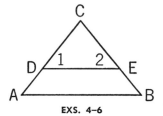

EXS. 4–6

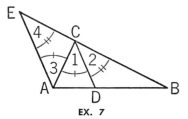

EX. 7

4. If $AC = BC$, $\angle 1 = \angle A$, and $\angle 2 = \angle B$, then $CD = CE$.

5. If ADC and BEC are straight lines, and $\angle ADE = \angle BED$, then $DC = EC$.

6. If $\angle 1 = \angle 2$, and D and E are the midpoints respectively of AC and BC, then $\triangle ABC$ is isosceles.

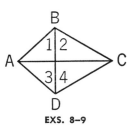

EXS. 8–9

EXTRA

7. If $\angle 3 = \angle 1$, $\angle 4 = \angle 2$, and $\angle 1 = \angle 2$, then $EC = AC$.

8. If $BC = DC$ and $\angle B$ and $\angle D$ are equal angles, then $AB = AD$.

9. If $BC = CD$ and $AB = AD$, then $\angle B = \angle D$.

■ Two Pairs of Congruent Triangles

As you have already seen, it is sometimes necessary to prove two pairs of triangles congruent in order to reach your conclusion. Consider first the pair of triangles whose corresponding parts you wish to prove equal. Then if they cannot be proved congruent, try to prove congruent a second pair of triangles whose corresponding parts will help you to prove the first pair congruent.

EXERCISES

Prove the following exercises in good form:

1. $AB = DE$, $BC = EF$, $AC = DF$, and $\angle 1 = \angle 2$. Prove that $CG = FH$.

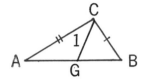

EXS. 1–3

2. If $AB = DE$, $BC = EF$, $AC = DF$, and G and H are the middle points of AB and DE respectively, then $CG = FH$.

3. If $AB = DE$, $BC = EF$, $AC = DF$, and CG and FH bisect $\angle C$ and $\angle F$ respectively, then $CG = FH$.

4. If $AC = BC$ and $AD = BD$, then $AO = BO$.

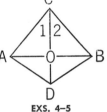

EXS. 4–5

EXTRA

5. If $AC = BC$, $AO = BO$ and $\angle O = 90°$, then $AD = BD$.

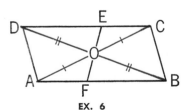

EX. 6

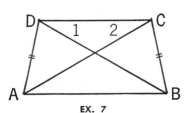

EX. 7

6. If AC and BD bisect each other, then any line through O and terminated by AB and DC is bisected at O.

7. If $AD = BC$ and $\angle BAD = \angle ABC$, then $\angle 1 = \angle 2$.

The bisector of the vertex angle of an isosceles triangle bisects the base and is perpendicular to it.

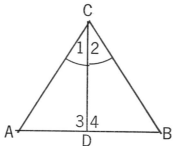

Given isosceles $\triangle ABC$ in which $AC = BC$ and CD bisects $\angle C$.

To prove that CD is the perpendicular bisector of AB.

The *plan* is to prove the two triangles congruent. What lines must you show to be equal before you can say that CD bisects AB? What do you prove to show that $CD \perp AB$?

The proof is left for you.

This theorem stated in the *if-then* form is:

If a line bisects the vertex angle of an isosceles triangle, then that line bisects the base and is perpendicular to it.

The line that connects the vertex of an isosceles triangle with the middle point of the base bisects the vertex angle and is perpendicular to the base.

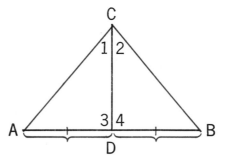

Given $\triangle ABC$ in which $AC = BC$ and D is the midpoint of AB.

To prove that CD bisects $\angle C$ and $CD \perp AB$.

The proof is left for you.

State this theorem as an *if-then* sentence.

■ Practical Use of Isosceles Triangles — *Optional*

Builders have used many forms of levels for determining horizontal and vertical lines. Some of the earliest were in the form of isosceles triangles. The use of such levels depends upon the relationships that you have proved in the theorems about isosceles triangles.

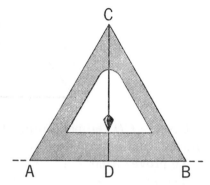

This instrument is so made that $AC = BC$ and $AD = DB$. A line with a weight at one end (plumb line) is attached at C so that it can swing freely. The plumb line will hang vertically, so when it hangs along the line CD, it is perpendicular to AB and AB is horizontal.

Can you prove that $CD \perp AB$?

The conditions are, "If a line connects the vertex of an isosceles triangle with the mid-point of the base." What is the conclusion?

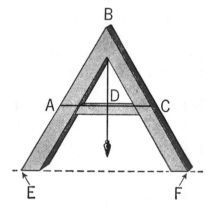

Another level using the same geometric relationship is the A-shaped level shown at the right.

The legs AE and CF are equal. $AB = BC$ and $AD = DC$. Then AC and EF are horizontal when the plumb line hangs along BD.

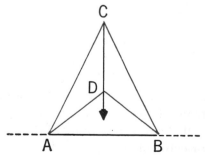

A third instrument is very much like the other two (see diagram). It is a wooden isosceles triangle with AD and DB painted on the wood. $AD = DB$. A plumb line is attached at C.

Can you prove that the line from C through D is perpendicular to AB?

**If lines are drawn from any point on the perpen-
dicular bisector of a line to the ends of the line,
they are equal.**

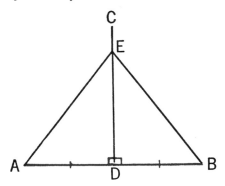

Given *CD* the perpendicular bisector of *AB* with *EA* and *EB*
drawn from any point *E* on *CD* to *A* and *B*.

To prove that *EA* = *EB*.

The *plan* is to prove that *ADE* and *BDE* are congruent.

Proof. The proof is left for you.

△ **The distance between two points** *is the length of the straight
line between them.* So Theorem 5 may be stated:

**Any point on the perpendicular bisector of a line is equally distant
from the ends of the line.**

Before you study Theorem 6

1. Draw a line *AB* 1 inch long. With your compass locate a
point $\frac{3}{4}$ in. from both *A* and *B*. Can you locate another point
$\frac{3}{4}$ in. from both *A* and *B*?

2. Locate two points each 1 in. from *A* and *B*.

3. Locate two points each 2 in. from *A* and *B*.

4. Locate two points each equally distant from *A* and *B*.

5. How many points are there each equally distant from *A*
and *B*?

6. All these points appear to lie in a straight line. What
relation does the line appear to have to *AB*?

7. How many points does it take to determine a line?

8. Given line *AB* and two points *C* and *D* each equally distant
from *A* and *B*. What relation does *CD* appear to have to *AB*?

9. Can you prove that in Exercise 8, *CD* is the perpendicular
bisector of *AB*?

If two points are each equally distant from the ends of a given line, a line connecting the two points is the perpendicular bisector of the given line.

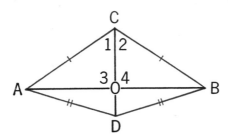

Given AB and points C and D so situated that $CA = CB$ and $DA = DB$.

To prove that CD is the perpendicular bisector of AB.

The *plan* is to prove that $\triangle CAD \cong \triangle CBD$ in order to get $\angle 1 = \angle 2$, then to use Theorem 3 *or* to prove that $\triangle CAO \cong \triangle CBO$.

Proof.

STATEMENTS	REASONS
1. $CA = CB$, $DA = DB$.	1. Given.
2. $CD = CD$.	2. Identity.
3. $\triangle CAD \cong \triangle CBD$.	3. $s.s.s. = s.s.s.$
4. $\angle 1 = \angle 2$.	4. $C.p.c.t.e.$
5. $CD \perp$ bisector AB.	5. Theorem 3.

This theorem may also be stated as:

Two points each equally distant from the ends of a line determine the perpendicular bisector of the line.

You can now prove that one line is the perpendicular bisector of another if you can show that it is determined by two points each equally distant from the extremities of the other.

EXERCISES

1. In a certain quadrilateral $AB = BC$ and $AD = DC$. Prove that DB is the perpendicular bisector of AC.

2. If the four sides of a quadrilateral are equal, each diagonal (line connecting opposite vertices) is the perpendicular bisector of the other.

◼ Congruent Right Triangles

Δ *In a right triangle the side opposite the right angle is the* **hypotenuse.**

The following exercises will suggest another proposition concerning congruent triangles.

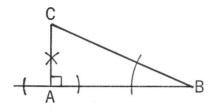 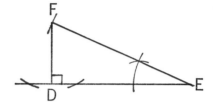

1. Construct any right triangle ABC. Construct $\angle E = \angle B$ and $EF = BC$. From F construct $FD \perp DE$.

2. Measure AB and DE, AC and DF, $\angle C$ and $\angle F$, and note that all the corresponding parts of these two triangles are equal. We see that the triangles are congruent.

3. What proposition is suggested by this construction?

The above is not a deductive proof and so we cannot call the proposition suggested a theorem. We shall, however, accept it as a postulate.

Postulate   **If two right triangles have the hypotenuse and an acute angle of one equal to the hypotenuse and an acute angle of the other, they are congruent.**

This postulate may be abbreviated as "right △ with *h.a.* = *h.a.*"

You can now prove that two triangles are congruent if you can show that the above conditions are fulfilled.

EXERCISES

1. Prove: If lines are drawn perpendicular to the equal sides of an isosceles triangle from the middle point of the base, they are equal.

2. Prove: The altitudes drawn from the vertices of the base angles of an isosceles triangle are equal.

THEOREM 7

If two right triangles have the hypotenuse and another side of one equal to the hypotenuse and a side of the other, they are congruent.

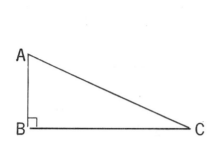

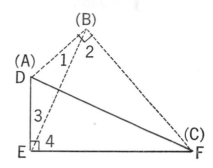

Given two right triangles ABC and DEF with right angles at B and E, $AC = DF$, and $AB = DE$.

To prove that $\triangle ABC \cong \triangle DEF$.

The *plan* is to place the triangles together as shown, then to prove that $\angle 1 = \angle 3$ and $\angle 2 = \angle 4$.

Proof. Place $\triangle ABC$ so that AC coincides with (fits on) its equal DF with A on D, C on F, and E and B on opposite sides of DF. Draw BE.

STATEMENTS	REASONS
1. $AB = DE$ (second figure).	1. Given.
2. $\angle 1 = \angle 3$.	2. Why?
3. $\angle B$ and $\angle E$ are rt. $\angle$s.	3. Given.
4. $\angle 2$ is comp. to $\angle 1$ and $\angle 4$ is comp. to $\angle 3$.	4. Prop. 9, page 74.
5. $\angle 2 = \angle 4$.	5. Prop. 11, page 74.
6. $BC = EF$.	6. Why?
7. $AC = DF$ (second figure).	7. Given.
8. $\triangle ABC \cong \triangle DEF$.	8. $s.s.s. = s.s.s.$

This theorem may be abbreviated as "right $\triangle$ with $h.s. = h.s.$"

You can now prove that two triangles are congruent if you can show that the conditions of the above theorem are fulfilled.

Note. The statement of Theorem 7 may be taken as a postulate after a discussion of the construction of the two triangles. (See the development on page 114.)

THEOREM 8

If lines are drawn from any point of the bisector of an angle, perpendicular to the sides of the angle, and terminated by the sides, they are equal.

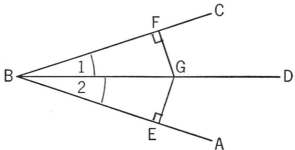

Given $\angle ABC$ and its bisector BD.   From any point G on BD, $GF \perp BC$ and $GE \perp AB$.

To prove   that $GF = GE$.

The proof is left for you.

EXERCISES

1. C is on the perpendicular bisector of AB. AC is 9 inches. How long is BC? What is your authority?

2. Prove: Two isosceles triangles are congruent if the base and one base angle of one are equal to the base and one base angle of the other.

3. Prove: If lines are drawn from any point on the bisector of the vertex angle of an isosceles triangle to the ends of the base, the lines are equal.

4. Prove: If lines are drawn from the middle points of the equal sides of an isosceles triangle to the middle point of the base, the lines are equal.

5. In $\triangle ABC$, the perpendicular bisectors of AB and BC meet at E. Prove that $EC = EB$.

6. In $\triangle ABC$, D is on AB, CD bisects AB, and $CD \perp AB$. Prove that $AC = BC$.

EXTRA

7. In the figure, $AB = CD$, $AD = BC$, $AE \perp DB$, and $CF \perp DB$. Prove that $AE = CF$. (First prove $\triangle ABD \cong \triangle CDB$.)

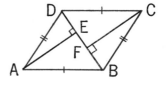

■ Proof of Construction Problems

In Chapter 1 you learned how to perform several constructions using only straightedge and compass. At that time you assumed that the results were correct or checked them by measurement. Now you will demonstrate their correctness by deductive reasoning.

Bisecting a given angle.

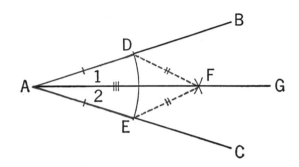

Given ∠BAC.
Required to bisect ∠BAC.
Construction. With A as center and any convenient radius draw an arc intersecting AB and AC at D and E respectively. With D and E as centers and the same radius for both, draw arcs intersecting at F. Draw AG through F. AG is the required bisector.

We wish to prove that what we have done is correct; that is, that ∠1 = ∠2.

The plan is to prove that the triangles are congruent.

Proof. Draw DF and EF.

STATEMENTS	REASONS
1. $AD = AE$.	1. Radii of same circle are equal.
2. $DF = EF$.	2. Radii of equal circles are equal.
3. $AF = AF$.	3. Identity.
4. $\triangle ADF \cong \triangle AEF$.	4. *s.s.s. = s.s.s.*
5. ∠1 = ∠2.	5. *C.p.c.t.e.*

Note the headings: Given, Required, Construction, Proof.

Constructing an angle equal to a given angle.

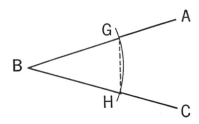 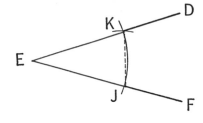

Given ∠*ABC*.
Required to construct an angle equal to *ABC*.
Construction (see page 19).
Proof. Draw *GH* and *KJ*.
The *plan* is to prove △*EJK* ≅ △*BHG*.
Write this problem in full with the proof.

Constructing a line perpendicular to a given line at a point on the line.

Given line *AB* with point *C* on it.

Required to construct a line perpendicular to *AB* at *C*.

Construction (see page 25).

Proof. Draw *DF* and *EF*.

If you prove that △*DCF* ≅ △*ECF*, you will know that ∠*FCD* = ∠*FCE* and so *GC* ⊥ *AB*.

Write this problem in full with the proof.

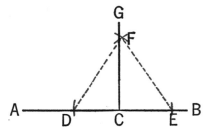

Bisecting a given line.

Given line *AB*.

Required to bisect *AB*.

Construction (see page 5).

Proof. Draw *CA*, *CB*, *DA*, and *DB*.

Note that *C* and *D* are each equally distant from *A* and *B*.

Write this problem in full with the proof.

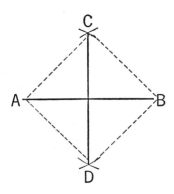

Constructing a line perpendicular to a given line from a point not on the line.

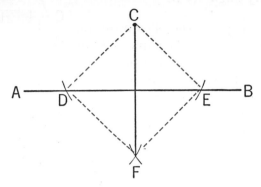

The *plan* is to use Theorem 6. Write this problem in full with the proof.

EXERCISES

1. Copy these designs, using straightedge and compass only.

2. Bring to class original designs similar to these.

■ Trisecting an Angle — *Optional*

For hundreds of years after the time of Plato mathematicians worked on the problem of trisecting an angle using only the straightedge and the compass. No solution has ever been found. As a matter of fact it has been proved that the construction, with these restrictions, cannot be done.

The problem can be solved by using other instruments. On page 120 is shown a way to trisect an angle using a draftsman's T-square. The proof that the angle is trisected is easily carried out by means of congruent triangles.

Procedure

1. Given any angle ACB.

2. Lay the arm of the T-square on side BC so that the center line EF of the T-square falls on BC. Use a corner of the T-head to mark points D and D' at equal distances from BC. Draw DD', which will be parallel to BC. (A proof of this last statement is given in Chapter 6.)

3. Lay the T-square so that one corner of the head meets AC at a point we shall call M and the opposite corner meets DD' at a point N. Also, EF must pass through C.

4. Draw FCE and CN.
Then $\angle ACE = \angle ECN = \angle NCB$ and the angle is trisected.

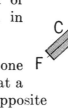

Construction 1

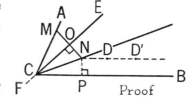

Construction 2

Proof

Proof. Draw MON. Draw NP the perpendicular distance from N to BC.

STATEMENTS	REASONS
1. $OM = ON$.	1. The center line of the T-square was used.
2. $\angle MOC = \angle NOC$.	2. Rt. $\angle$ made by the square.
3. $OC = OC$.	3. Identity.
4. $\triangle MOC \cong \triangle NOC$.	4. $s.a.s. = s.a.s.$
5. $\angle NOC$ and $\angle NPC$ are rt. $\angle$.	5. Made by the T-square and $NP \perp BC$.
6. $NP = ON$.	6. So made by the T-square.
7. $\triangle NOC \cong \triangle NPC$.	7. Rt. $\triangle$ with $h.s. = h.s.$
8. All three triangles are congruent and $\angle ACE = \angle ECN = \angle NCB$.	8. $C.p.c.t.e.$

Illustrating Two Ways of Attacking a Problem

John and Bill, while out hiking, reached the bank of a wide river. They decided to cross the river but the only way was to swim across. Both boys are good swimmers. John was all for jumping in and taking his chances of reaching the other side. Bill persuaded him, however, that they ought to have a method of attack.

Bill cautioned John that it would be a good thing to look at the goal first and then look back to see if there was some place in the river where they could rest, and from the resting place they could reach the goal. They saw such a place, a sand bar, not too far from the opposite bank.

They were confident they could easily swim to the opposite bank from the sand bar. The next step in the plan was to search out a place from which they could be sure they could swim to the sand bar. There it was, a large rock about one third of the way across. Finally, they decided they could reach the rock from where they were.

They then jumped in, swam to the rock, rested, and swam to the sand bar. From the sand bar they swam safely to the opposite bank.

John had looked at the goal and had wanted to try to reach the goal with no plan of attack. His way involved no planning — no orderly procedure. It was just a case of diving in and hoping to make the other shore with stamina and good luck. Bill's way illustrates a systematic method of looking step by step back from the goal to the starting point. He made a plan of attack before he started.

■ Analytic Method of Attack

The method used by Bill on the preceding page is here applied to geometry. Suppose you wish to prove this exercise:

Given   that $\angle 1 = \angle 2$ and $\angle 3 = \angle 4$.
To prove   that $AC = BC$.

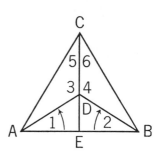

First you would look at the *hypothesis* — the *given* part — and get it firmly in mind. Next you would look at the *conclusion* — the *to prove* part — and ask yourself, "How can I prove that $AC = BC$?" Always look at the conclusion immediately after fixing the hypothesis in mind and ask, "How can I reach the conclusion?" In this case the answer is, "I can prove that $AC = BC$ if I can prove that $\triangle AEC \cong \triangle BEC$ or that $\triangle ADC \cong \triangle BDC$."

You next go back one step and ask, "How can I prove that these triangles are congruent?" Suppose you try $\triangle AEC$ and $\triangle BEC$ first. You know only that $CE = CE$ and cannot see how you can get any other parts equal. Then you try $\triangle ADC$ and $\triangle BDC$. Here you know two equalities: $\angle 3 = \angle 4$ and $CD = CD$.

Now you say, "Since I know that $\angle 3 = \angle 4$ and $CD = CD$, I can prove that $\triangle ADC \cong \triangle BDC$ if I can prove either that $\angle 5 = \angle 6$ or that $AD = BD$." You quickly see how to prove that $AD = BD$. (Why are they equal?)

This analysis gives you a complete plan. You have carried your thinking backward from the conclusion, making sure of each step until you arrived at something you can prove. By retracing your steps you have a logical demonstration or proof.

The point of departure in this method of analysis is the conclusion. Note the thinking in going from the conclusion to the hypothesis.

I can prove $AC = BC$ if I can prove $\triangle ADC \cong \triangle BDC$.

I can prove $\triangle ADC \cong \triangle BDC$ if I can prove $AD = BD$.

I can prove $AD = BD$, for I know $\angle 1 = \angle 2$ in $\triangle ADB$.

Each new step begins where the preceding step ends.

The method of discovering a proof which you have studied on this page is called *analytic*. It goes back from conclusion to hypothesis. In contrast, the method which proceeds from hypothesis to conclusion is termed *synthetic*. A written proof is usually given in the more concise synthetic form.

■ Lists of Methods of Proof

For convenience in your work, you should have lists of methods for proving important facts in geometry, such as the ways of proving that angles are equal, that lines are equal, that lines are perpendicular, or that triangles are congruent. You should write out these lists in a notebook or on cards that you can keep with your textbook. Whenever you accept a new postulate or prove a new theorem or corollary, you should make the proper additions to the lists. Copy the two sample lists given below and make other lists as suggested.

I. I can prove that two *lines are equal* if I can prove that —

1. They are equal to the same line or to equal lines.
2. They are the result of adding or subtracting equals.
3. They are doubles or halves of equals.
4. They are the parts of a bisected line.
5. They are the equal sides of an isosceles triangle.
6. They are opposite equal angles in a triangle.
7. They are corresponding sides of congruent triangles.
8. They are lines drawn from any point on the perpendicular bisector of a line to the extremities of the line.

II. I can prove that two *angles are equal* if I can prove that —

1. They are equal to the same angle or to equal angles.
2. They are the result of adding or subtracting equals.
3. They are doubles or halves of equals.
4. They are parts of a bisected angle.
5. They are the angles at the foot of a perpendicular.
6. They are right angles.
7. They are supplementary or complementary to the same angle or to equal angles.
8. They are vertical angles.
9. They are corresponding angles of congruent triangles.
10. They are opposite equal sides in a triangle.

■ Converse Theorems

Theorem 1 and Theorem 2 contain almost the same words. Yet they are different in meaning. One is the reverse of the other. The two theorems together are called **converse theorems.**

When a theorem has one condition and one conclusion, it has only one converse. The converse is formed by interchanging the hypothesis and the conclusion. The hypothesis and the conclusion of one theorem become, respectively, the conclusion and hypothesis of its converse.

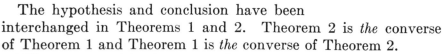

EXAMPLE: Theorem 1 says —

If AC = BC, then ∠B = ∠A.

Theorem 2 says —

If ∠B = ∠A, then AC = BC.

The hypothesis and conclusion have been interchanged in Theorems 1 and 2. Theorem 2 is *the* converse of Theorem 1 and Theorem 1 is *the* converse of Theorem 2.

When a proposition has more than one condition or more than one conclusion, a converse is obtained by interchanging any number of the conditions with the *same number* of the conclusions. Thus a theorem may have more than one converse.

EXAMPLE: Theorem 3 says —

If AC = BC and   then   CD bisects AB and
CD bisects ∠C,   CD ⊥ AB.

This theorem has two conditions and two conclusions. It will therefore have five converses as follows:

Converse 1. Interchanging the first condition with the first conclusion, you have —

If CD bisects AB and   then   AC = BC and
    CD bisects ∠C,   CD ⊥ AB.

Converse 2. Interchanging the first condition with the second conclusion, you have —

If CD ⊥ AB and   then   CD bisects AB and
    CD bisects ∠C,   AC = BC.

Converse 3. Interchanging the second condition with the first conclusion, you have —

If   AC = BC and   then   CD bisects ∠C and
CD bisects AB,   CD ⊥ AB.

Converse 4. Interchanging the second condition with the second conclusion, you have —

If   AC = BC and   then   CD bisects AB and
CD ⊥ AB,   CD bisects ∠C.

Converse 5. Interchanging both conditions with both conclusions, you have —

If   CD bisects AB and   then   AC = BC and
CD ⊥ AB,   CD bisects ∠C.

All of these five converses can be proved. Can you supply a word statement to fit each one? Converse 3 is Theorem 4. Can you prove Converses 2, 4, 5? You are not prepared at this time to prove Converse 1.

Note the system used above for interchanging conditions and conclusions. It is very important that you form your converses in a systematic manner, otherwise you may repeat or omit some.

A converse of a true statement is not necessarily true. Such a converse always requires proof before you know it to be true.

EXERCISES

In Exercises 1-4 each statement has one converse. State it. Which of the converses are true and which are false?

1. If a triangle is equilateral, it is also equiangular.

2. All bulldogs are short-haired.

It is usually easier to state a converse if the statement is in the form of a conditional sentence (an if-then sentence). The preceding statement written as a conditional sentence would be: If a dog is a bulldog, it is short-haired. The converse then is: If a dog is short-haired, it is a bulldog.

3. All right angles are equal.

4. If two angles are supplementary, their sum is 180°.

EXTRA

5. If two angles are supplementary to the same angle, they are equal.

6. If lines are drawn from any point on the perpendicular bisector of a line to the ends of the line, they are equal.

■ Multiconverse Statements—*Optional*

When a statement has more than one converse, it is called a multiconverse statement. Theorem 3 is a multiconverse statement and you have already studied its converses on page 124. The original statement and its converses are said to make up a "family" of converses. Theorem 3 is one of a family of six converses, since there are two conditions and two conclusions.

How large will a family of converses be if there are two conditions and one conclusion in the original? To answer this you can invent a statement to serve as a model while you count the converses:

1. Let your model be this statement: "If A, B, then X." A and B represent the two conditions in the if-clause, and X represents the conclusion. Write your model statement as shown below, then count the converses:

$$\text{If} \quad A \quad \text{then} \quad X$$
$$B$$

You will find that this family consists of three statements.

2. Count the converses and give the size of this family:

$$\text{If} \quad A \quad \text{then} \quad X$$
$$B \qquad\qquad Y$$
$$C$$

You are reminded to be systematic in making the exchanges. After you have interchanged X with each of A, B, and C, then interchange Y with each of A, B, and C. These exchanges give you six converses. Then interchange X and Y with each of A and B, B and C, and A and C. You should find a total of nine converses of the original, giving a family of ten.

3. How large is the family of converses when there are two conditions and three conclusions?

4. How large is the family of converses when there are three conditions and three conclusions?

There is a very good reason why such a process as this has been devised. If you can take one statement, form its converses, and end with six statements in all, then you may be able to prove some of the converses and thereby discover relationships you had not known at first. Thus, *multiconverse relationships* provide a method by which *new theorems* can be discovered.

You have practiced counting the converses to find the size of families of statements, but you have not learned just how a new theorem may result. There are four main steps in the discovery of a new theorem. They are:

Step 1. A representative figure is drawn and labeled to suit the original statement. The conditions in the if-clause and the conclusions in the then-clause are written in terms of the figure.

Step 2. All the converses are then formed.

Step 3. Each converse formed in Step 2 is changed into a general (word) statement.

Step 4. An attempt is made to prove each statement. Some of those statements which can be proved may not have been known before and are therefore new theorems.

EXAMPLE 1: Original theorem: If two angles are complementary to the same angle, then they are equal.

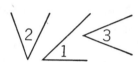

Step 1. If $\angle 1 + \angle 2 = 90°$ then $\angle 2 = \angle 3$
$\angle 1 + \angle 3 = 90°$

Step 2. **Converse 1:**
If $\angle 2 = \angle 3$ then $\angle 1 + \angle 2 = 90°$
$\angle 1 + \angle 3 = 90°$

Converse 2:
If $\angle 1 + \angle 2 = 90°$ then $\angle 1 + \angle 3 = 90°$
$\angle 2 = \angle 3$

Step 3. **Converse 1:** If two given angles are complementary and one of them is equal to a third angle, then the third angle and the other angle are complementary.

Converse 2: If two given angles are complementary and one of them is equal to a third angle, then the third angle and the other angle are complementary.

These two converses are alike when put into words.

Step 4. Can you tell whether these converses can be proved? Both of them can easily be proved. However, since they are alike when stated in words, only one new theorem results.

As you continue your study of geometry you will find many propositions that have multiple converses. Some of these propositions will be pointed out to you so that you will be able to form the converses and discover your own theorems.

Here is an example that shows how converse relationships can tie together statements which at first appear to have no connection at all.

EXAMPLE 2: Original statement: If the three sides of one triangle are equal to the corresponding three sides of another triangle, then the corresponding angles are equal.

$$
\begin{aligned}
\text{If} \quad x &= x' \quad \text{then} \quad \angle X = \angle X' \\
y &= y' \quad\quad\quad\quad \angle Y = \angle Y' \\
z &= z' \quad\quad\quad\quad \angle Z = \angle Z'
\end{aligned}
$$

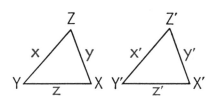

You can see there are three conditions and three conclusions to this statement. How many converses will there be? Can you carry out the exchanges and form the resulting word statements? Here is a partial summary of the results you should get. Three of the converses when put into words give you:

> If two triangles have two sides and the included angle of one equal respectively to two sides and the included angle of the other, then they are congruent.

Another three, when put into words give you:

> If two triangles have two angles and the included side of one equal respectively to two angles and the included side of the other, then they are congruent.

Six of the converses, when put into words give you:

> If two triangles have two angles and the side opposite one of them equal respectively to two angles and the corresponding side of the other, then they are congruent.

There are two more new statements which can be formed from the remaining converses. Can you discover what they are? Of this large family of twenty converses, seven are not true. Which ones are they?

■ Indeterminate Problems

In this triangle, $AC = BC$ and M is the middle point of BC. It appears that $\angle A$ is bisected. Is it?

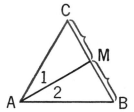

How would the analysis begin? "I can prove that $\angle 1 = \angle 2$ if I can prove that the triangles are congruent. If I try to prove that the triangles are congruent, I see that it cannot be done."

The triangles will not be congruent unless $AB = AC$. You do not know whether $AB = AC$ or not. Hence you must conclude that $\angle 1$ is *not necessarily* equal to $\angle 2$. When $AB = AC$ the angles will be equal. Otherwise they will not be equal.

As it stands, the problem is *indeterminate* — the answer to it cannot be determined. If you said "No," your answer would mean that the angles could not possibly be equal under the circumstances. If you said "Yes," it would mean that with the given conditions the angles would be equal in all cases. The answer is, therefore, "Not necessarily."

A good way to test a question of this kind is to draw a figure of a different shape, preferably exaggerated a little but still holding to the given conditions. For example, draw an isosceles triangle ABC, and then draw a line from A to the midpoint M of the side BC. You can easily see that in this case $\angle 1 \neq \angle 2$. ($\neq$ means "does not equal.") If an isosceles triangle can be drawn so that $\angle 1$ very obviously does not equal $\angle 2$, then of course it is useless to try to prove that $\angle 1 = \angle 2$. A proof must cover all cases.

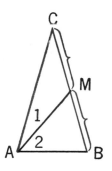

1. Does the bisector of an angle of a triangle bisect the opposite side?

2. Does the bisector of the vertex angle of an isosceles triangle bisect the base?

3. If a line is drawn from the vertex of an isosceles triangle to the middle point of the base, is it perpendicular to the base?

4. Is a point on a perpendicular to a line equally distant from the ends of the line?

EXERCISES

In some of the exercises that follow the question you will be asked cannot be answered by Yes *or* No. *In this case write,* Not necessarily. *If you can answer* Yes, *prove the exercise in good form. The method of analysis explained on page 122 will help you.*

1. If in $\triangle ABC$ $AC = BC$ and $\angle A = \angle B$, does $AD = BD$?

2. If in $\triangle ABC$ $AC = BC$ and $AD = BD$, does $\angle 1 = \angle 2$?

3. If $AC = BC$ and $\angle 3 = \angle 4$, does $\angle 5 = \angle 6$?

4. If $AC = BC$ and $AD = BD$, does $\angle 5 = \angle 6$?

5. If $\angle 1 = \angle 2$ and $AD = BD$, does $AC = BC$?

6. If $AC = BC$ and $\angle 3 = \angle 4$, does $\angle 1 = \angle 2$?

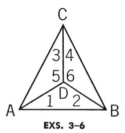

EXS. 1–2

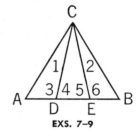

EXS. 3–6

In the figure for Exs. 7–9, ADEB is a straight line.

7. If $AC = BC$ and $\angle A = \angle B$, does $\angle 4 = \angle 5$?

8. If $AC = BC$ and $AD = BE$, does $\angle 4 = \angle 5$?

9. If $\angle 1 = \angle 2$ and $\angle 4 = \angle 5$, does $\angle A = \angle B$?

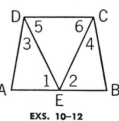

EXS. 7–9

In the figure for Exs. 10–12, AEB is a straight line.

10. If $AE = BE$ and $\angle A = \angle B$, does $DE = CE$?

11. If $AE = BE$, $\angle A = \angle B$, and $\angle 1 = \angle 2$, does $\angle 5 = \angle 6$?

12. If $AE = BE$, $AD = BC$, and $\angle 5 = \angle 6$, does $\angle A = \angle B$?

EXS. 10–12

CONGRUENT TRIANGLES

1. A circle whose center is O is drawn so that the circumference goes through the three vertices of the triangle ABC. AO, BO, and CO are extended to meet the circle in D, E, and F respectively. Prove that triangle DEF is congruent to triangle ABC.

2. From a point inside a right triangle lines are drawn perpendicular to the sides of the right angle. Each perpendicular is then extended its own length. Prove that the line joining the ends of the extended lines goes through the vertex of the right angle. (SUGGESTION. Connect the ends of the extended lines to the vertex of the right angle and prove that the sum of the angles formed there is 180°.)

3. D and E are the middle points of the equal sides AB and AC of the isosceles triangle ABC. BE and CD intersect in F. Prove that AF bisects angle BAC.

4. On the equal sides AB and AC of the isosceles triangle ABC equal segments AD and AE are taken. BE and DC are drawn and intersect in O. Prove that triangle BOC is isosceles. Also prove that AO extended to F on BC will be perpendicular to BC.

5. One diagonal of a quadrilateral $ABCD$ bisects two of its angles. Prove that this diagonal is the perpendicular bisector of the other diagonal.

6. Prove that the bisectors of a pair of corresponding angles of two congruent triangles are equal.

7. Triangle ABC is equilateral. D, E, and F are taken on AB, BC, and CA, respectively, so that AD equals BE equals CF. Prove that triangle DEF is equilateral.

8. At the midpoints of the equal sides of an isosceles triangle lines are drawn perpendicular to the equal sides and extended to meet the base. Prove that these lines are equal.

9. Given: $AF = AG$, $FO = OG$, $FC = GE$. $ADGE$, $ABFC$, BOE, DOC, and GOF are straight lines. Prove: $AB = AD$.

10. Given: $\angle AFG = \angle AGF$, $FC = GE$. Prove without using Theorem 2 that $AG = AF$. (SUGGESTION. Draw EF and CG. First prove $\triangle GEF \cong \triangle GCF$.)

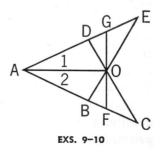

EXS. 9-10

■ Geometry of Three Dimensions — *Optional*

The figures you have studied have been *plane* (flat) ones. They have no thickness — only length and width. On the other hand, the **rectangular solid** (box) pictured at the right has thickness as well as length and width. It has three dimensions instead of two.

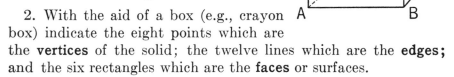

1. Make a drawing of a rectangular solid like the one at the right.

2. With the aid of a box (e.g., crayon box) indicate the eight points which are the **vertices** of the solid; the twelve lines which are the **edges**; and the six rectangles which are the **faces** or surfaces.

3. Does a line drawn on paper by means of a pencil have one, two, or three dimensions?

4. Can you think of three points so situated that they do not all lie in the same plane (flat surface)?

5. Indicate four points in the classroom that do not all lie in the same plane.

The points and lines of a plane can be represented very easily on paper, but it is often difficult to represent on paper the points, lines, and surfaces that occur in three-dimensional space. The illustration for the next exercise should help you to get a realistic view of a drawing of a three-dimensional object.

6. This is a picture of a tree standing upright on level ground, with three wires bracing it. Do you see from the picture that the tree (TA) is perpendicular to the plane MN representing the ground and that TA is perpendicular to AD and AC, the lines on the ground joining the foot of the tree with the stakes? If you measured angles TAD and TAC on the drawing, would they be right angles? The outdoor angles TAD and TAC are, of course, right angles.

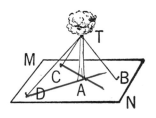

The study of relationships in three dimensions is called **solid geometry,** in contrast to that in two dimensions, which is **plane geometry.**

■ Lines and Planes—*Optional*

The conventional way to represent a plane is by a quadrilateral like the one in Figure 1. It is read "plane MN." TA represents a line perpendicular to MN, as you saw on page 132.

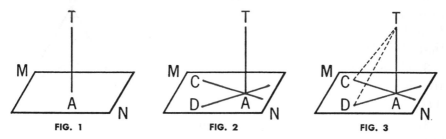

FIG. 1   FIG. 2   FIG. 3

Figure 2 represents a line TA perpendicular to a plane MN and two lines CA and DA in plane MN. (See the drawing on page 132.)

Figure 3 differs from the preceding one by the inclusion of the oblique lines TC and TD. Make a model of this figure so that you can see it in three dimensions.

The perpendicular TA intersects the plane MN in point A, called the *foot* of the perpendicular.

A line is said to be *perpendicular to a plane* if it is perpendicular to every line in the plane through its foot.

EXERCISES

1. AB is perpendicular to plane MN at B. BC and BD are two equal lines in MN. Prove that $\triangle ABD \cong \triangle ABC$. (Use a model if you need it.)

2. The point O is the center of a circle, drawn in plane MN. OC is perpendicular to plane MN. Prove that $CB = CA$.

3. Draw a figure like that for Ex. 1 and draw CD. Using the hypothesis of Ex. 1, prove that $AD = AC$ and $\angle ADC = \angle ACD$.

4. AB is perpendicular to the plane MN at the point B. AB is extended to C so that $BC = AB$. D is any point in the plane. Prove that $AD = DC$.

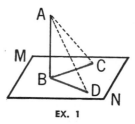

EX. 1

EX. 2

THREE DIMENSIONS

133

1. In $\triangle ABC$, R is the middle point of AC. BR is drawn and extended to S so that $RS = BR$. SC also is drawn. Prove that $\angle SCA = \angle A$.

2. Triangles ABC and ABD are two isosceles triangles on the same base AB. D and C are on the same side of AB. Prove that $\angle CAD = \angle CBD$.

3. In quadrilateral $ABCD$ all the angles are right angles and $AC = BD$. Prove that $AD = BC$.

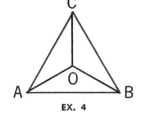

EX. 4

4. $AC = BC$, AO bisects $\angle A$, and BO bisects $\angle B$. Prove that CO bisects $\angle C$.

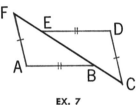

5. The pentagon $ABCDE$ is regular (five sides equal, five angles equal). Prove that the lines drawn from C and D to the middle points of AD and AC, respectively, are equal.

EX. 7

6. A and B are two points on a circle, not the ends of a diameter. Prove that a diameter perpendicular to the straight line AB bisects AB.

7. Prove: If $FA = DC$, $AB = ED$, and $\angle A = \angle D$, then $FE = BC$.

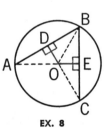

8. Points A, B, and C are on the circle and O is the center. $OD \perp AB$, $OE \perp BC$, and $OD = OE$. Prove that $AB = BC$.

EX. 8

Chapter Summary

I. Vocabulary.

    1. Use each of the following terms correctly in a sentence.
      a Base angles of an isosceles triangle
      b Corollary to a theorem
      c Hypotenuse of a right triangle
      d Analytic method of proof
      e Synthetic method of proof
      f Converse theorems

II. Hypothesis and Conclusion from Verbal Statements.

2. Construct a figure and write the hypothesis and conclusion for the following:

a If from any point on the bisector of an angle lines are drawn cutting off on the sides of the angle equal distances from the vertex, they are equal.

b The bisector of an angle, if extended, bisects the angle formed by continuing the sides of the angle through the vertex.

c Equal oblique (not perpendicular) lines, drawn from the same point on a perpendicular to a line, cut off on the line equal distances from the foot of the perpendicular.

III. Auxiliary Lines.

3. In each of the following, an auxiliary line is mentioned. Tell which lines have too many conditions placed upon them.

a D is the middle point of the base. CD is drawn from C to D.

b CD bisects $\angle C$.

c CD is drawn from C and is the perpendicular bisector of AB.

d CD is drawn from C and is perpendicular to AB.

e D is the middle point of AB. A perpendicular to AB at D passes through C.

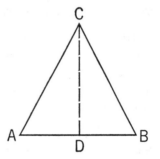

IV. Using Congruent Triangles.

4. State two ways of proving right triangles congruent and three ways of proving scalene triangles congruent.

V. Theorems.

5. State three theorems concerning isosceles triangles.

6. What is the theorem about any point on the bisector of an angle?

7. What is the theorem about any point on the perpendicular bisector of a line?

8. Draw a figure and write the plan of proof for each of the following theorems:

a If two sides of a triangle are equal, the angles opposite those sides are equal.

b Two points each equally distant from the extremities of a line determine the perpendicular bisector of the line.

c The bisector of the vertex angle of an isosceles triangle bisects the base and is perpendicular to it.

VI. Two Pairs of Congruent Triangles.

9. $AB = CD$, $AD = BC$, $AG = GC$, AGC and EGF are straight lines. Prove that $AE = CF$.

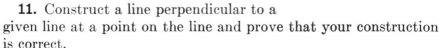

EX. 9

VII. Proof of Construction Problems.

10. What construction problems have you proved in this chapter?

11. Construct a line perpendicular to a given line at a point on the line and prove that your construction is correct.

VIII. Analytic Method of Attack.

12. $AD = DC$, $DE = EF$, $CE = EB$, DEF and CEB are straight lines. Prove that $BF = AD$.

You wish to prove that BF equals AD. You know that $AD = DC$. Hence you can prove that $BF = AD$ if you prove that $BF = \underline{\ ?\ }$. Prove the exercise in good form.

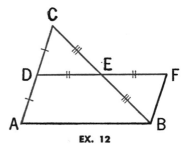

EX. 12

IX. Converse Theorems.

13. What are converse theorems?

14. What is the converse of this theorem? If a triangle has two equal sides, the angles opposite those sides are equal.

15. Is the converse of this statement true? The sum of the angles of a triangle is 180°.

TEST 1

Which of these statements are True *and which are* False?

1. If a statement is true, its converse is true.

2. The hypotenuse of a right triangle is the side opposite the right angle.

3. If a line bisects $\angle B$ of $\triangle ABC$, that line is the perpendicular bisector of AC.

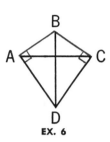

EX. 6

4. The bisector of any angle of an equilateral triangle (terminating on a side) is an altitude.

5. If $AB = AC$ in $\triangle ABC$, then $\angle A = \angle B$.

6. Angles A and C are right angles. If $AB = BC$, then $\triangle ABD \cong \triangle BCD$.

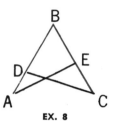

EX. 8

7. The propositions with which a deductive science begins cannot be proved.

8. If $AB = BC$, then $\angle A = \angle C$ because angles opposite equal sides are equal.

9. As soon as a proposition has been proved or otherwise accepted, it may be used as a reason in a deductive proof.

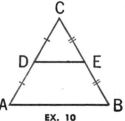

EX. 10

10. If $AD = DC$ and $BE = EC$, then $AC = BC$, because if equal quantities are added to equal quantities, the sums are equal.

11. In $\triangle ABC$, $\angle 1$ is opposite AB and $\angle 2$ is opposite BC.

12. If $AB = BC$ and $AD = EC$, then $BD = BE$.

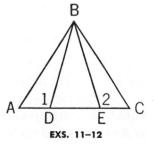

EXS. 11–12

13. If an exercise is stated in words, the hypothesis is always at the end.

TEST 2

Choose the best answer.

1. If a triangle is equiangular, it is also _?_.
 a isosceles **b** scalene **c** equilateral

2. These two triangles are congruent because _?_.
 a *s.a.s.* = *s.a.s.* **b** *rt.* △ with *h.a.* = *h.a.* **c** *rt.* △ with *h.s.* = *h.s.*

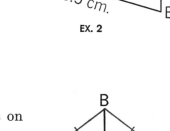

EX. 2

3. *CD* is the perpendicular bisector of *AB* if _?_ equally distant from *A* and *B*.
 a one point on *CD* is **b** two points on *CD* are

4. If *AB* = *BC* and *AE* = *EC*, the triangles I can prove congruent first are _?_.
 a △*ABE* and △*BCE* **b** △*ABD* and △*BDC* **c** △*AED* and △*DEC*

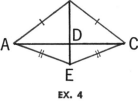

EX. 4

5. If *AC* = *BC*, *AD* and *BE* bisect ∠*A* and ∠*B*, then ∠1 = ∠3, because _?_.
 a equals subtracted from equals are equal **b** halves of equals are equal

6. If *E* and *D* are the middle points of equal sides *AC* and *BC*, respectively, in △*ABC*, then _?_.
 a *AE* is not equal to *BD* **b** *AE* = *BD* **c** relation between *AE* and *BD* is unknown

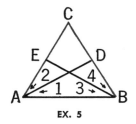

EX. 5

7. If *C* and *D* are each equally distant from *A* and *B*, then _?_.
 a *AC* = *AD* **b** *AC* does not equal *AD* **c** relation between *AC* and *AD* is unknown

8. If *AC* = *AD* and *BC* = *BD*, then ∠*CBE* = ∠*DBE* because _?_.
 a supplements of equal angles are equal **b** corresponding parts of congruent triangles are equal

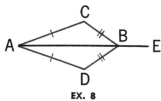

EX. 8

138

CONGRUENT TRIANGLES

CHAPTER **6** Parallel Lines

BEFORE YOU begin your study of parallel lines, it will be valuable for you to think again about the way a deductive science like demonstrative geometry is built up. You have started with certain undefined terms like *point* and *line*. These first terms cannot be defined because there are no simpler terms by which to define them. Then came terms which have been defined, then postulates, and then theorems.

The lines on your theme paper are parallel lines. The two rails of a straight, level railroad track are parallel lines. Give other illustrations of parallel lines.

△ *Parallel lines are straight lines in the same plane that do not meet however far extended.* The symbol for *parallel* or *is parallel to* is ‖.

It is possible for two straight lines not to intersect and yet not be parallel *if the lines are in different planes.* Consider, for example, a front vertical edge of a box and a back horizontal edge. Such lines are called **skew lines.**

Hold two yardsticks so that they represent parallel lines. Then hold them so that they will represent two skew lines.

The geometry that you are studying is called Euclidean geometry because it follows Euclid's postulate of parallel lines, which is —

Postulate **Through a given point not on a given line, one and only one line can be drawn parallel to the given line.**

There are other geometries based upon postulates that differ from this postulate or contradict it. Non-Euclidean geometries are studied in more advanced courses.

According to the postulate on the preceding page how many lines through P can be parallel to AB in this figure?

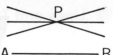

Perpendiculars to the same line. Draw a line AB and construct several lines perpendicular to it. They appear parallel. At this stage we shall assume that they are.

<u>Postulate</u>   **Two lines perpendicular to a third line, all in the same plane, are parallel.**

With three pencils illustrate how two lines can be perpendicular to the same line and not be parallel. Does your illustration contradict the postulate?

You can now prove that two lines are parallel if you can show that they are perpendicular to the same line and all are in the same plane. (In plane geometry all lines are in the same plane.)

Prove that lines perpendicular to a diameter of a circle at the extremities of the diameter are parallel.

△ The **distance from a point to a line** is measured on a perpendicular to the line from the point.

△ The **distance between two parallel lines** is measured on a line perpendicular to either of them.

Construction   Constructing a line parallel to a given line at a given
   Problem   distance from it.

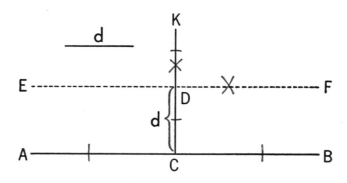

Given   line AB and a distance d.

Required   to construct a line parallel to AB at the distance d from it.

Construct $KC \perp AB$. Make $CD = d$. Construct $EF \perp KC$. The writing of the construction and proof is left for you.

■ Lines and Transversals

△ *A transversal is a line that intersects two or more lines.* *EF* in the figure is a transversal of *AB* and *CD*.

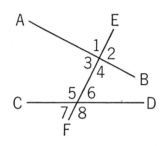

When two straight lines are cut by a transversal eight angles are formed. Four of them are *interior angles,* ∡3, 4, 5, and 6, and four of them are *exterior angles,* ∡1, 2, 7, and 8. There are two pairs of *alternate interior angles.* Angles 3 and 6 are one pair; ∡4 and 5 are the other. There are also two pairs of *alternate exterior angles,* ∠1 and ∠8, ∠2 and ∠7.

Angles on the same side of the transversal and on the same side of the lines cut by the transversal are *corresponding angles.* Pairs of corresponding angles are: ∠1 and ∠5, ∠2 and ∠6, ∠3 and ∠7, ∠4 and ∠8. There are four pairs of these angles. Corresponding angles are sometimes called *exterior-interior angles.* Can you tell why?

The pairs of angles, ∠3 and ∠5, ∠4 and ∠6, are called *interior angles on the same side of the transversal.* What would you call the pairs, ∠1 and ∠7, ∠2 and ∠8?

Follow the directions below to draw lines *AB* and *CD* cut by a transversal *EF* so that ∠1 = ∠2. These are a pair of alternate interior angles.

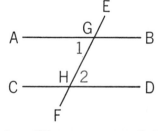

Draw the line *AB* and place a point *G* on it. Through *G* draw the line *EF*. Place a point *H* on *EF*. Measure ∠1 and at point *H* make ∠2 equal to ∠1 with your protractor. This gives you line *CD*.

If you have been accurate, you will see that *CD* appears parallel to *AB*.

For a minimum course in geometry you may accept the following statement as a postulate instead of proving it as shown in Theorem 9 on page 143.

Postulate   **If two straight lines are cut by a transversal so that two alternate interior angles are equal, the lines are parallel.**

Before you study Theorem 9

Read the statement of Theorem 9 on the next page.

You are to prove that two lines AB and CD are parallel if the alternate interior angles 1 and 2 are equal. This is proved by using the postulate on page 140 and showing that AB and CD are both perpendicular to the same line. Since there is no such line in the given figure, it must be drawn as an auxiliary line. The following paragraphs will help you to understand how this is done and how the two given lines are proved to be perpendicular to it.

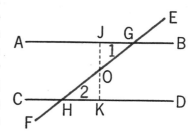

You know how to construct a line perpendicular to a given line at a point on the line and also from a point outside the line. You can therefore construct a line perpendicular to CD. You cannot, however, construct it perpendicular to AB also. If it *is* perpendicular to AB, that fact requires proof.

You have your choice as to where you will construct the perpendicular. It is wise, therefore, to place it at a point where you can make use of the fact that $\angle 1 = \angle 2$. Choose O the midpoint of HG, and from O construct JK perpendicular to CD.

If you prove that JK is not only perpendicular to CD (as it was constructed) but also perpendicular to AB, you will have two lines perpendicular to the same line and therefore parallel. You have then proved what you started to prove.

Study the following analytic approach to the proof of Theorem 9.

You can prove that $AB \parallel CD$ if you can prove that AB and CD are both perpendicular to the same line JK.

Since JK was constructed perpendicular to CD, you can prove AB and CD are both perpendicular to JK if you prove $JK \perp AB$.

You can prove that $JK \perp AB$ if you can prove that $\angle GJO$ is a right angle. (You know from the definition of perpendicular lines that the sides of a right angle are perpendicular lines.)

You can prove that $\angle GJO$ is a right angle if you can prove that it equals $\angle HKO$ which you know is a right angle.

You can prove that $\angle GJO = \angle HKO$ if you can prove that the two triangles are congruent.

You *can* prove that the two triangles are congruent because $a.s.a. = a.s.a.$ Explain.

If two straight lines are cut by a transversal so that two alternate interior angles are equal, the lines are parallel.

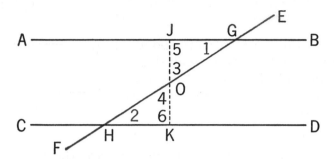

Given AB and CD cut by EF so that $\angle 1 = \angle 2$.

To prove   that $AB \parallel CD$.

The *plan* is to draw JK through the middle point of GH and perpendicular to CD, and to prove that AB and CD are both perpendicular to it.

Proof.   Bisect GH, and through O, the middle point, construct $JK \perp CD$.

STATEMENTS	REASONS
1. $GO = OH$.	1. A bisector divides a line into two equal parts.
2. $\angle 3 = \angle 4$.	2. Vertical angles are equal.
3. $\angle 1 = \angle 2$.	3. Given.
4. $\triangle JOG \cong \triangle KOH$.	4. *a.s.a.* = *a.s.a.*
5. $\angle 5 = \angle 6$.	5. *C.p.c.t.e.*
6. $\angle 6$ is a right angle.	6. A perpendicular to a line forms a right angle.
7. $\angle 5$ is a right angle.	7. Ax. 1, page 84.
8. $AB \perp JK$.	8. Two lines that form a right angle are perpendicular to each other.
9. $CD \perp JK$.	9. So constructed.
10. $AB \parallel CD$.	10. Postulate, page 140.

You can now prove that two lines are parallel by showing that the alternate interior angles made by a transversal are equal.

Before you study Theorems 10 and 11

Read the statements of Theorems 10 and 11 below so that you may know what you are given and what you are to prove.

Give a reason for each statement you make in these exercises.

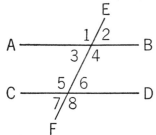

1. If ∠1 and ∠5 (two corresponding angles) are each 110°, how many degrees are there in ∠4? Do you now have two alternate interior angles equal? Are the lines parallel?

2. If ∠2 and ∠6 (two corresponding angles) are each 45°, how many degrees are there in ∠3? Do you now have a pair of alternate interior angles equal? Are the lines parallel?

3. Given ∠3 = ∠7 (these are two corresponding angles), prove that ∠3 = ∠6. (Both ∠3 and ∠6 are equal to ∠7.) Do you now have two alternate interior angles equal? Are the lines parallel?

4. Given ∠4 = ∠8, prove that ∠4 = ∠5 and hence AB ∥ CD.

5. If ∠3 = 40° and ∠5 = 140° (two interior angles on the same side of the transversal are supplementary), how many degrees are there in ∠6? Do you now have two alternate interior angles equal? Are the lines parallel?

6. Given ∠4 supplementary to ∠6, prove that ∠4 = ∠5 and hence AB ∥ CD. (Both ∠4 and ∠5 are supplementary to ∠6.)

THEOREM 10	*If two straight lines are cut by a transversal so that two corresponding angles are equal, the lines are parallel.*
THEOREM 11	*If two straight lines are cut by a transversal so that two interior angles on the same side of the transversal are supplementary, the lines are parallel.*

(In both Theorems 10 and 11 prove that two alternate interior angles are equal and hence the lines are parallel.)

■ Methods of Proving Lines Parallel

To your lists you should now add one that shows methods of proving that two lines are parallel. It should read as follows:

I can prove that two *lines are parallel* if I can prove that —

1. They are in the same plane and do not meet if extended.

2. They are in the same plane and are perpendicular to a third line in the same plane.

3. The alternate interior angles made by a transversal are equal.

4. The corresponding angles made by a transversal are equal.

5. The interior angles on the same side of a transversal are supplementary.

Note: Be sure to make additions to your lists of methods or to start a new list whenever you accept a postulate or prove a theorem or corollary. You must accept responsibility for your own lists. We shall only occasionally make one for you as we have done above.

Construction Problem   **Constructing a line parallel to a given line through a given point not on the line.**

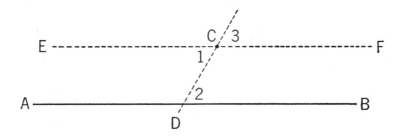

Given AB and point C *not* on it.
Required   to construct a line parallel to AB through C.
The *plan* is to draw a transversal through C and make $\angle 1 = \angle 2$ or $\angle 3 = \angle 2$. Here you will make $\angle 1 = \angle 2$.
Construction.   Through C draw a transversal CD. With C as a vertex and CD as a side construct $\angle 1 = \angle 2$ thus making $EF \parallel AB$.
Proof.   This is left for you.

■ Recognizing Alternate Interior and Corresponding Angles

It is not difficult to recognize alternate interior angles and corresponding angles in a figure made only of two straight lines and a transversal. When the figure is a bit more complex, however, recognition is more difficult.

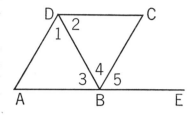

For example, in this figure are there any alternate interior angles? Are there any corresponding angles? If $\angle 1 = \angle 4$, what lines are parallel? If $\angle A = \angle 5$, what lines are parallel?

Can you tell what lines are parallel if $\angle 1 = \angle 5$? Are they either equal alternate interior angles or equal corresponding angles?

Can you tell what lines are parallel if $\angle C = \angle 3$? Are they either equal alternate interior angles or equal corresponding angles?

It will help you in recognizing such angles if you will note that alternate interior angles made by two lines and a transversal form a Z-type figure (Figs. 1 and 2) and corresponding angles form an F-type figure (Figs. 3 and 4).

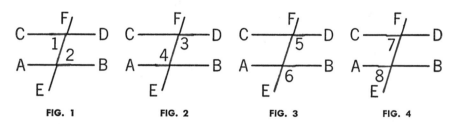

FIG. 1   FIG. 2   FIG. 3   FIG. 4

Note, in the quadrilateral $ABCD$, the alternate interior angles 1 and 2 made by DC and AB cut by DB. The dotted lines are drawn so that you may more easily see the two lines $EDCF$ and $GABH$ cut by the transversal $RDBS$. (Without the dotted lines this is DC and AB cut by the transversal DB.)

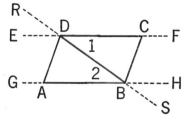

If $\angle 1 = \angle 2$, is $AD \parallel BC$, or is $DC \parallel AB$, or are both pairs parallel?

EXERCISES

In the following exercises copy the figures and draw in the Z's and the F's if you need to.

1. If ∠1 = ∠4, what lines are parallel? Why? Draw a sketch of this figure in which ∠1 = ∠4, but ∠2 is obviously not equal to ∠3.

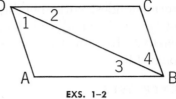

EXS. 1–2

2. In the same figure, if ∠2 = ∠3, what lines are parallel? Why? Draw a sketch of this figure in which ∠2 = ∠3, but ∠1 is obviously not equal to ∠4.

3. What lines are parallel if ∠A = ∠2? If ∠1 = ∠D? What line is the transversal?

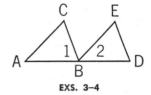

EXS. 3–4

4. In the same figure, what lines are parallel if ∠C = ∠CBE? Why? What line is the transversal?

5. If ∠A = ∠1, what lines are parallel? If ∠B = ∠2, what lines are parallel? In each case tell what line is the transversal.

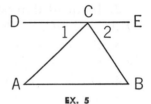

EX. 5

6. What lines are parallel if ∠C = ∠1? If ∠A = ∠2? Why?

7. Draw two straight lines cut by a transversal. Note that interior angles on the same side of the transversal form a figure like this ⌐ or this ⌐.

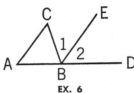

EX. 6

8. In this figure state four pairs of angles on the same side of the transversal. In each case tell what line is the transversal.

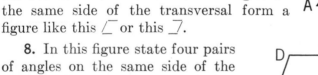

EXS. 8–10

9. If ∠A + ∠D = 180°, what lines are parallel? Why?

10. If ∠A + ∠B = 180°, what lines are parallel?

11. What lines are parallel if the following angles are equal?

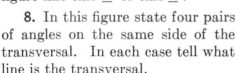

EX. 11

  a ∠2 = ∠6.   **c** ∠8 = ∠4.
  b ∠1 = ∠5.   **d** ∠3 = ∠7.

■ Proving Lines Parallel

Now that you have had practice in recognizing alternate interior angles, corresponding angles, and angles on the same side of the transversal you should be able to do the following exercises easily. Review the methods of proving lines parallel given on page 145.

EXERCISES

1. What lines are parallel in each of the following cases? Why?

a $\angle 1 = \angle 2$.　　　　**b** $\angle 2 = \angle 3$.

c $\angle 1 = \angle 3$.　　　　**d** $\angle 4 = \angle 5$.

e $\angle 5 = \angle 6$.　　　　**f** $\angle 4 = \angle 2$.

g $\angle 5 = \angle 3$.　　　　**h** $\angle 4 = \angle 3$.

EX. 1

2. In quadrilateral $ABCD$ with diagonal AC, $AB = CD$ and $\angle BAC = \angle DCA$. Prove that $AD \parallel BC$.

3. Prove: If the opposite sides of a quadrilateral are equal, they are also parallel.

4. Draw $\triangle ABC$ and extend AC to D. Through C construct a line parallel to AB.

5. On each side of a line AB construct a line parallel to it and 1 in. from it.

6. Through a circle whose radius is 1 in. construct two parallel lines each half an inch from the center.

EXTRA

7. Are AB and DC parallel if $\angle A = 80°$ and $\angle D = 100°$? if $\angle D = a°$ and $\angle A = 180° - a°$?

8. If $\angle A = 70°$, how many degrees must there be in $\angle B$ in order that AD be parallel to BC?

EXS. 7–9

9. If $\angle C = \dfrac{2a°}{3}$, how many degrees must there be in $\angle B$ in order that AB be parallel to DC?

10. $AB = CD$, $EC = BF$, $\angle 1 = \angle 2$. Prove that $AE \parallel DF$.

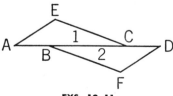

11. $AE = DF$, $AB = CD$, $EC = BF$. Prove that $EC \parallel BF$.

EXS. 10–11

■ Parallel Lines and Transversals

For a minimum course you may accept the next two statements as postulates. They are also given as Theorems 12 and 13.

Postulate 1   If a line is perpendicular to one of two parallel lines, it is perpendicular to the other also.

Postulate 2   If two parallel lines are cut by a transversal, the alternate interior angles are equal.

THEOREM
12

If a line is perpendicular to one of two parallel lines, it is perpendicular to the other also.

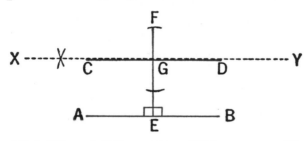

Given $AB \parallel CD$ and $FE \perp AB$. FE intersects CD at G.
To prove   that $FE \perp CD$.
The *plan* is to construct through G a line that we know is perpendicular to FE and then prove that this line is the same line as CD. (Then we shall know that $CD \perp FE$ or $FE \perp CD$.)
Proof.   Through G construct $XY \perp FE$.

STATEMENTS	REASONS
1. $FE \perp AB$ or $AB \perp EF$.	1. Given.
2. $XY \perp FE$.	2. So constructed.
3. $XY \parallel AB$ through G.	3. Why?
4. $CD \parallel AB$ through G.	4. Given.
5. CD and XY are the same straight line.	5. Postulate, page 139.
6. $CD \perp FE$ or $FE \perp CD$.	6. CD coincides with XY, and $XY \perp FE$.

This is a new kind of proof called *proof by coincidence*. It is discussed on page 316 under *Indirect Proof*.

If two parallel lines are cut by a transversal, the alternate interior angles are equal.

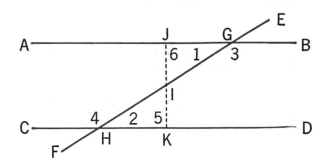

Given $AB \parallel CD$.

To prove that $\angle 1 = \angle 2$ and $\angle 3 = \angle 4$.

The *plan* is to prove that the triangles HIK and JIG are right triangles and congruent by $h.a. = h.a.$

Proof. Bisect GH and construct $JK \perp CD$ through I, the midpoint of GH.

STATEMENTS	REASONS
1. $AB \parallel CD$.	1. Given.
2. $JK \perp CD$.	2. Construction.
3. $JK \perp AB$.	3. Theorem 12.
4. $\angle 5$ and $\angle 6$ are rt. $\angle$.	4. Def. of $\perp$ line.
5. $HI = IG$.	5. Def. of bisector.
6. $\angle HIK = \angle JIG$.	6. Vertical angles.
7. $\triangle HIK \cong \triangle JIG$.	7. Postulate, page 114.
8. $\angle 1 = \angle 2$.	8. $C.p.c.t.e.$
9. $\angle 4$ supp. to $\angle 2$. $\angle 3$ supp. to $\angle 1$.	9. Prop. 8, page 74.
10. $\angle 3 = \angle 4$.	10. Prop. 10, page 74.

Before you study Theorems 14 and 15

If *two alternate interior angles are equal when a transversal cuts two straight lines*, then —

all pairs of alternate interior angles are equal,

all pairs of corresponding angles are equal, and

the interior angles on the same side of the transversal are supplementary.

You will see the truth of the statement at the bottom of page 150 from the results of the following exercises for discussion:

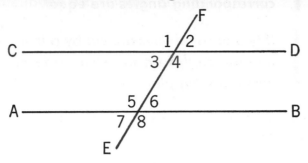

1. If ∠3 and ∠6 are each 50°, how many degrees are there in each of the following angles? Explain all of your answers.

   a ∠4 and ∠5   **b** ∠1 and ∠8   **c** ∠2 and ∠7

2. In Ex. 1 does ∠3 = ∠6? Did you find that ∠4 = ∠5? These are all the pairs of alternate interior angles.

3. From your answers to Ex. 1 do you find that ∠1 = ∠5? ∠2 = ∠6? ∠3 = ∠7? ∠4 = ∠8? These are all the pairs of corresponding angles.

4. From your answers to Ex. 1, what do you find to be the sum of ∠3 and ∠5? of ∠4 and ∠6? These are pairs of interior angles on the same side of the transversal.

5. Given that ∠3 = ∠6, prove that ∠2 = ∠6. (They are both equal to ∠3.)

6. Given that ∠3 = ∠6, prove that ∠1 = ∠5. (They are supplementary to equal angles.)

7. Given ∠3 = ∠6, prove that ∠3 = ∠7 and that ∠4 = ∠8.

8. Given *AB* ∥ *CD*, prove that ∠1 = ∠5.

9. Given *AB* ∥ *CD*, prove that ∠3 = ∠7.

10. Given *AB* ∥ *CD*, prove that ∠2 = ∠6.

11. Given *AB* ∥ *CD*, prove that ∠4 = ∠5.

12. Given *AB* ∥ *CD*, prove that ∠3 and ∠5 are supplementary. (If *AB* ∥ *CD*, you know that ∠3 = ∠6. You know also that ∠6 is supplementary to ∠5. Substitute ∠3 for ∠6.)

13. Given that *AB* ∥ *CD*, prove that ∠4 and ∠6 are supplementary.

THEOREM 14	**If two parallel lines are cut by a transversal, the corresponding angles are equal.**

THEOREM 15	**If two parallel lines are cut by a transversal, the interior angles on the same side of the transversal are supplementary.**

The *plan* for proving Theorems 14 and 15 is to use Theorem 13. No auxiliary lines are necessary.

EXERCISES

1. Given $AB \parallel CD$ in Fig. 1. Is $\angle 1 = \angle 2$ or is $\angle 3 = \angle 4$? Why?

2. Given $AD \parallel BC$ in Fig. 1. Is $\angle 1 = \angle 2$ or is $\angle 3 = \angle 4$? Why?

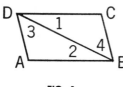

FIG. 1

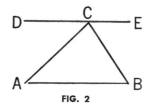

FIG. 2

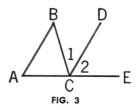

FIG. 3

3. Given $DE \parallel AB$ in Fig. 2. How many transversals are there? Name them. There are two pairs of alternate interior angles. Name them. Name two pairs of interior angles on the same side of the transversal. The angles of each pair are supplementary.

4. $AB \parallel CD$ in Fig. 3. Name one pair of alternate interior angles and one pair of corresponding angles. The angles of each pair are equal.

5. $AE \parallel BD$. Which of the following statements are true?

$\angle 1 = \angle E$, $\angle E = \angle 5$, $\angle 4 = \angle 5$, $\angle 1 = \angle 4$

6. Prove: If two parallel lines are cut by a transversal, the alternate exterior angles are equal.

7. Prove: If two parallel lines are cut by a transversal, the exterior angles on the same side of the transversal are supplementary.

EX. 5

Two straight lines parallel to the same straight line are parallel to each other.

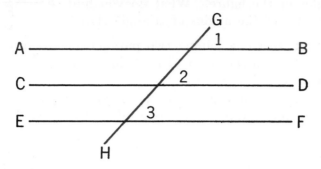

Given $AB \parallel EF$ and $CD \parallel EF$.
To prove that $AB \parallel CD$.
The *plan* is to prove that $\angle 1 = \angle 2$.
Proof. The proof is left for you.

EXERCISES

1. If $\angle 4 = 125°$ and $\angle 6 = 55°$, is $AB \parallel CD$?

2. If $\angle 2 = 60°$ and $\angle 6 = 62°$, is $AB \parallel CD$?

3. Will AB and CD extended meet if $\angle 3 = 70°$ and $\angle 6 = 65°$? If $\angle 3 = 40°$ and $\angle 5 = 140°$? (If they did not meet, what would be true?)

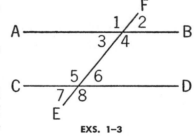

EXS. 1–3

4. If AB and CB intersect as shown, is it possible that $\angle 1 = 85°$ and $\angle 2 = 85°$? (If the two angles were equal, what would be true of AB and BC?)

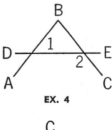

EX. 4

5. $AB \parallel DE$, $\angle 1 = 60°$, and $\angle 2 = 80°$. Evaluate all the other angles of the figure. What do you find to be the sum of the angles of the triangle?

6. Prove: If $DE \parallel AB$ and $\angle 1 = \angle 2$, then $\triangle ABC$ is isosceles.

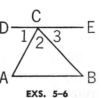

EXS. 5–6

7. DA, CE, and FB are each perpendicular to AB, $\angle 1 = 60°$, $\angle 2 = 70°$. Evaluate all the other angles of the figure. What do you find to be the sum of the angles of triangle ABC?

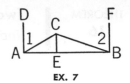

EX. 7

8. Prove: If a line joining two parallel lines is bisected, any line drawn through the point of bisection and terminated by the parallels is bisected by the point.

9. Prove: If a line is drawn through any point on the bisector of an angle and parallel to one side of the angle, the triangle formed is isosceles.

10. Prove: If a line is drawn parallel to the base of an isosceles triangle and it intersects the other two sides, the triangle formed is isosceles.

11. $BE \parallel AC$. Prove that $\angle A + \angle C = \angle CBD$.

12. $AF = EB$, $AC \parallel ED$, $FC \parallel BD$, and $AEFB$ is a straight line. Prove that $FC = BD$.

EX. 11

13. Prove: If in quadrilateral $ABCD$, $AB = CD$, $AC = BD$, and AC and BD meet at O, then $\angle BAO = \angle CDO$.

14. Prove: If the opposite sides of a quadrilateral are parallel, they are also equal.

15. Prove: If two sides of a quadrilateral are parallel and equal, the other two sides are parallel and equal.

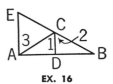

EX. 12

EXTRA

16. $AE \parallel CD$, CD bisects $\angle ACB$. Prove that in $\triangle ACE$ $AC = EC$.

EX. 16

17. Prove: If two circles intersect, the line connecting their centers is the perpendicular bisector of the line connecting the points of intersection.

18. Prove: If the diagonals of a quadrilateral bisect each other, the opposite sides are parallel.

19. Prove: If the opposite sides of a quadrilateral are parallel, the diagonals bisect each other.

20. Form all the converses of the proposition in Ex. 15. How many are there? Is the proposition in Ex. 14 one of these converses?

1. $\angle ABC$ and $\angle DEF$ are both acute. $AB \parallel DE$ and $BC \parallel EF$. Prove that $\angle ABC = \angle DEF$.

2. $\angle ABC$ is acute and $\angle DEF$ is obtuse. $AB \parallel DE$ and $BC \parallel EF$. Prove that $\angle ABC$ is supplementary to $\angle DEF$.

3. Triangle ABC lies entirely within $\triangle DEF$ in such a way that $AB \parallel DE$, $BC \parallel EF$, and $AC \parallel DF$. Prove that $\angle A = \angle D$, $\angle B = \angle E$, and $\angle C = \angle F$.

4. Prove: Two lines that are perpendicular respectively to the sides of a right angle are perpendicular to each other.

5. In $\triangle ABC$, $AC = BC$. AC is extended to D and BC is extended to E so that $ED \parallel AB$. Prove that $CE = CD$.

6. In the quadrilateral $ABCD$, $AB \parallel CD$. AE is drawn through the middle point E of BC and extended until it meets DC (extended) at F. Prove that $\triangle ABE \cong \triangle FCE$.

7. In $\triangle ABC$, E and F are the middle points of AC and BC respectively. EF is extended to G so that $FG = EF$. Prove that $BG \parallel AE$.

8. In $\triangle ABC$, $AC = BC$. AC is extended to some point D. Prove that $\angle A = \frac{1}{2}\angle DCB$.

9. Prove: If through a point halfway between two parallel lines, two lines are drawn cutting the parallels, they intercept equal segments on the parallels.

10. $ABCD$ is a quadrilateral in which AB and DC are parallel and equal. Prove that the diagonals of this quadrilateral bisect each other.

11. In quadrilateral $ABCD$, AB is longer than DC, $AB \parallel DC$, $\angle A = \angle B$. CE is drawn so that it is parallel to AD. E is on AB. Prove that $CE = BC$.

12. In triangle ABC, AB is extended to some point D. Prove that $\angle CBD = \angle A + \angle C$.

13. Side AB of $\triangle ABC$ is extended to E. BA is extended in the opposite direction to D. AF is drawn so that $\angle FAC = \angle CAB$ and BG is drawn so that $\angle ABG$ is twice $\angle ABC$. If $\angle 1$ is complementary to $\angle 2$, prove that $BG \parallel AF$.

■ Non-Euclidean Geometry — *Optional*

The geometry of Euclid is based upon several postulates, among them the parallel postulate which you accepted in this chapter; namely, *through a point outside a line only one line can be drawn parallel to the given line.* This was Euclid's fifth postulate. There is evidence that he himself was suspicious of it. Mathematicians for centuries found fault with it. They thought it was not as evident as the other postulates and they considered it more complex. They tried to deduce it from the other postulates. They believed it could be proved as a theorem.

There were several supposedly successful attempts to prove the postulate but in all cases there were flaws in the argument. Saccheri, a mathematician of the eighteenth century, tried to show by assuming it false that he would come to some contradiction in his geometry. He found no contradiction but his deductions became so involved he was led to believe he had found one. By the nineteenth century mathematicians began to believe that Euclid's fifth postulate was entirely independent of the other postulates and could not be deduced from them.

Now a postulate is merely an assumption. It does not necessarily have to describe the physical property of things. Once mathematicians grasped the idea that this postulate was independent of the others, there was nothing to prevent them from attempting to build up a geometry with contradictory postulates. That is exactly what did happen.

Lobachevski (lō′bȧ-chĕf′skĭ), early in the eighteen hundreds, produced a geometry based on the postulate that through a point outside a line an infinite number of lines can be drawn parallel to a given line. His other postulates were the same as those of Euclid. Lobachevskian geometry is also known as *hyperbolic geometry*.

Riemann, in 1854, published a geometry in which he assumed that through a point outside a line no line can be drawn parallel to a given line. Riemannian geometry is also known as *elliptic geometry* and is the forerunner of a present-day higher mathematics called *topology*. These other geometries are called non-Euclidean geometries.

Most of the theorems of Euclidean geometry can be deduced from the postulates in either of the systems just mentioned. However, all the theorems whose proofs in Euclidean geometry depend upon the postulate of parallels are necessarily replaced by others. One may ask, "Are these non-Euclidean geometries mere speculations or are they true to the world as we know it, and will they supersede Euclidean geometry?"

Before attempting to answer this question of replacement, we ought to ask, "What is meant here by *true?*" Are the Euclidean postulates true? Do they describe the nature of things? We answer these questions by saying that a mathematical science is not involved with the physical nature of objects. Where, in the material world, is there a point or straight line in the geometric sense? But the facts of this world approximate the conclusions of Euclidean geometry. As closely as we can measure with our most accurate instruments, it seems true that the sum of the angles of any triangle is 180° (proved in the next chapter as an outcome of Euclid's postulate). However, no instruments are fine enough to measure angles as small as those that we can imagine in our logical deductions and we know that all measurements are approximate.

The other theorems seem to be borne out in the same way. The result is that for all practical purposes of carpentry, architecture, engineering, and the like, we continue to use Euclidean geometry. For some aspects of astronomy (cosmological research), where we are dealing with distances in light years and speeds as fast as the speed of light, it is another story.

The non-Euclidean geometry of Riemann, as has been said, assumes that through a point outside a line there can be no line parallel to a given line. From this he deduces the statement that the sum of the angles of a triangle is greater than 180° but approaches 180° as the triangle becomes smaller. It would seem that this statement could not be true. How can we tell? We cannot get out into space and measure the angles with a protractor. It is interesting to note that calculations based upon the geometry of Riemann have predicted the movement of some of the heavenly bodies better than old calculations based upon Euclidean geometry.

Although there are other non-Euclidean geometries, those of Lobachevski and Riemann are the most famous. Some of you may wish to read more about the contributions of such men as Saccheri, Bolyai, and Beltrami to this field of geometry. You may be surprised to learn that philosophical considerations enter into the development of mathematics.

■ Parallel Lines and Planes — *Optional*

A line and a plane are parallel if they do not meet, however far extended; two planes likewise are parallel if they do not meet, however far extended.

1. Point out some parallel planes in the classroom.
2. Point out lines parallel to the plane of the floor.
3. Hold a yardstick to represent a line parallel to the plane of the blackboard.
4. With two pieces of cardboard represent two parallel planes.

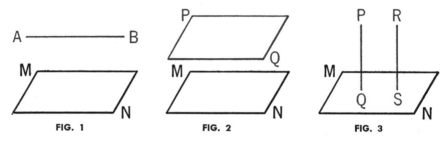

FIG. 1   FIG. 2   FIG. 3

Figure 1 represents a line *AB* parallel to a plane *MN*.
Figure 2 represents two parallel planes.
Figure 3 represents two lines perpendicular to a plane.

EXERCISES

No proofs are required:

1. Are two lines perpendicular to a plane parallel?

2. Is any line in one of two parallel planes parallel to the other plane?

3. Is any line in one of two parallel planes parallel to any line in the other plane?

4. Is it true that only one line can be drawn parallel to a plane through a point outside the plane?

5. Through a given point outside a given plane can there be more than one plane parallel to the given plane?

6. Are two planes perpendicular to the same line parallel?

7. If a line is perpendicular to one of two parallel planes, what is its relation to the other?

1. Given a quadrilateral with the opposite sides parallel. Prove that a diagonal divides it into two congruent triangles.

2. Draw $\triangle ABC$. Through B construct a line parallel to AC.

3. Draw $\triangle ABC$ and bisect $\angle B$. Through A construct a line parallel to the bisector. Extend CB until it meets the parallel at F. Prove that $FB = AB$.

4. $FA = DC$, $FA \parallel DC$, $FE = BC$. $FEBC$ is a straight line. Prove that $AB \parallel ED$.

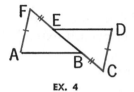

EX. 4

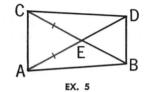

EX. 5

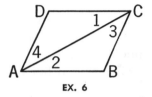

EX. 6

5. $AC \parallel BD$ and $AE = CE$. AED and CEB are straight lines. Prove that $AB = CD$.

6. $AB \parallel CD$ and $AD \parallel BC$. Prove that the total angle at A equals the total angle at C.

7. In $\triangle ABC$, $\angle A = 30°$, $\angle B = 50°$, and $\angle C = 100°$. $FD \parallel BC$, $DE \parallel AC$, and $FE \parallel AB$. How many degrees are there in $\angle D$, $\angle E$, and $\angle F$?

8. In quadrilateral $ABCD$, $\angle A + \angle B = 180°$ and $\angle A + \angle D = 180°$. Prove that $AB = DC$ and $AD = BC$.

9. If the opposite sides of quadrilateral $ABCD$ are equal, then lines BE and DF drawn perpendicular to the diagonal AC from the vertices B and D are equal (E and F are on AC).

10. $AB \parallel DC$, $AD \parallel BC$, BF bisects $\angle B$, DE bisects $\angle D$. Prove that $BF = DE$.

11. From a point D outside of acute $\angle ABC$ lines DE and DF are drawn perpendicular to the sides AB and BC of the angle. Prove that $\angle EDF$ is equal to $\angle ABC$.

I. Vocabulary.

1. Illustrate each of the following terms by drawing a figure.

Parallel lines   Alternate exterior angles
Transversal   Corresponding angles
Interior angles   Interior angles on the same side of
Exterior angles   the transversal
Alternate interior angles

II. Methods of Proving Lines Parallel.

2. You can prove that two lines are parallel if you can prove that they are in the same plane and do not meet even if extended indefinitely.

Give four other methods of proving lines parallel.

III. Theorems.

3. State either four theorems or one postulate and three theorems concerning parallel lines.

Testing Your Understanding

Which of these statements are true and which are false?

1. If straight lines AB and CD never meet, they are parallel.

2. If a point C is not on AB, the distance from C to AB is the length of any line drawn from C to AB.

3. ABC is a triangle. Through C only one straight line can be drawn parallel to AB.

4. Alternate interior angles are always equal.

5. If, in Fig. 1, $AB \parallel CD$, then $\angle 3 = \angle 4$.

6. If, in Fig. 2, $AB \parallel CD$, they are cut by a transversal, and $\angle 1 = 90°$, then $\angle 2 = 90°$.

7. $AB \parallel CD$ in Fig. 3. If $\angle A = 50°$, then $\angle ACD = 130°$.

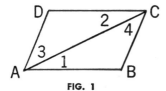

FIG. 1

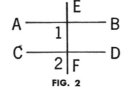

FIG. 2

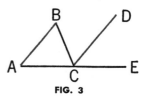

FIG. 3

CHAPTER **7** Polygons—Triangles and Parallelograms

In THIS chapter you start with the undefined term, *straight line*, and, by means of a series of definitions, build a family of terms involving polygons. You will also prove several theorems.

△ A ***broken line*** *is a succession of different straight lines. ABCDE* is a broken line.

△ A ***polygon*** *is a closed broken line in a plane. ABCDE* at the right is a polygon. The points *A, B, C,* etc., are the ***vertices;*** ∠*A,* ∠*B,* ∠*C,* etc., are the ***angles;*** *AB, BC, CD,* etc., are the ***sides;*** and a line such as *AC* is a ***diagonal.***

△ *The portion of the plane enclosed by a polygon is the* ***interior of the polygon.*** It is common usage to refer to the surface bounded by the broken line as the polygon.

△ *A polygon no side of which extended will enter the interior of the polygon is* ***convex;*** *otherwise it is* ***concave*** (or ***re-entrant***). *ABCDE* above is a convex polygon. *GHIJK* at the right is a concave polygon.

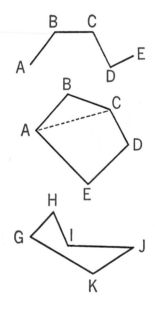

The word "polygon" in this book will always refer to a *convex polygon.*

The names of certain polygons classified according to the number of sides are as follows:

Three — Triangle	Five — Pentagon	Eight — Octagon
Four — Quadrilateral	Six — Hexagon	Ten — Decagon

■ Sum of Angles of Triangle

The next theorem is one with which you are probably familiar. You learned about it in earlier grades by means of measuring. Now, by deduction, you can show from the preceding theorems and definitions that it is true. Many geometric relationships which you have known before as isolated (separate) facts can be shown by reasoning to fit into one system.

THEOREM 17 | *The sum of the angles of a triangle is 180°.*

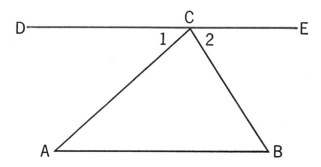

Given △ABC.
To prove that ∠A + ∠B + ∠C = 180°.
Proof. Through C draw DE ∥ AB.

STATEMENTS	REASONS
1. ∠1 + ∠ACB + ∠2 = a straight angle, or 180°.	1. Ax. 8, page 84.
2. DE ∥ AB.	2. So drawn.
3. ∠A = ∠1, ∠B = ∠2.	3. Why?
4. ∠A + ∠C + ∠B = 180°.	4. Ax. 1, page 84.

1. How do you find the number of degrees in one angle of a triangle if the number of degrees in each of the other two angles is given?

2. How many degrees are there in one angle of an equilateral triangle?

3. If one acute angle of a right triangle is 25°, how many degrees are there in the other?

EXERCISES

1. In $\triangle ABC$, $\angle A = 50°$ and $\angle B = 80°$. How many degrees are there in $\angle C$?

Do you see that when the number of degrees in each of two angles of a triangle is given, you can find the number of degrees in the third angle by _?_ the number of degrees in the two angles and _?_ the result from _?_?

2. In two triangles ABC and DEF, $\angle A + \angle B = \angle D + \angle E$. Does $\angle C = \angle F$? (Experiment with various numbers of degrees. For example, let $\angle A + \angle B = 150°$, then $\angle D + \angle E = $ _?_ °. Then $\angle C$ would equal _?_ ° and $\angle F$ would equal _?_ °.)

3. In $\triangle ABC$, $AC = BC$ and $\angle A = 50°$. How many degrees are there in $\angle C$?

4. In $\triangle ABC$, $AC = BC$ and $\angle C = 40°$. How many degrees are there in $\angle A$ and in $\angle B$?

5. $\triangle ABC$ is equilateral. How many degrees are there in each angle?

You see that in an equilateral triangle each angle will always be _?_ °.

6. In $\triangle ABC$, $AB = BC$ and $\angle A = 60°$. How many degrees are there in $\angle C$ and in $\angle B$? Is the triangle equilateral?

7. In $\triangle ABC$, $AB = BC$ and $\angle B = 60°$. How many degrees are there in $\angle A$ and in $\angle C$?

You see that when two sides of a triangle are equal and the included angle is 60°, the triangle is _?_ .

8. In $\triangle ABC$, $\angle C = 90°$ and $\angle A = 40°$. How many degrees are there in $\angle B$? What is the sum of $\angle A$ and $\angle B$?

You see that in a right triangle the sum of the acute angles is _?_ °.

9. In $\triangle ABC$, $\angle C = 90°$ and $AC = BC$. How many degrees are there in $\angle A$ and in $\angle B$?

You see that each acute angle of an isosceles right triangle is _?_ °.

10. In $\triangle ABC$ and $\triangle DEF$, $\angle C$ and $\angle F$ are each 90°. $\angle B$ and $\angle E$ are each 40°. How many degrees are there in $\angle A$ and in $\angle D$?

You see that if two right triangles have an acute angle of one equal to an acute angle of the other, the other acute angles are _?_ .

11. In $\triangle ABC$, AB is extended to D, $\angle A = 30°$, and $\angle C = 80°$. How many degrees are there in $\angle CBD$? In this case is $\angle CBD = \angle A + \angle C$?

Try other values for $\angle A$ and $\angle C$ and then evaluate $\angle CBD$. Do you find that in all these cases $\angle CBD = \angle A + \angle C$?

You see that if one side of a triangle is extended, the exterior angle thus formed is equal to the _?_ of the two remote interior angles (the angles not adjacent to the exterior angle).

12. In these two triangles $AB = DE$, $\angle A$ and $\angle D$ are each 30°, and $\angle C$ and $\angle F = 110°$. Does $\angle B = \angle E$?

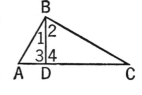

Did you originally have *a.s.a.* of one triangle equal to *a.s.a.* of the other triangle?

Since you now know that $\angle B = \angle E$, do you have *a.s.a.* = *a.s.a.*? Are the triangles congruent?

13. If in the same figures you know that $AB = DE$, $\angle A = \angle D$, and $\angle C = \angle F$, can you find that $\angle B = \angle E$? Are the triangles congruent?

14. $\angle ABC$ is a right angle, $BD \perp AC$, and $\angle 1 = 30°$. Evaluate the other angles of the figure.

15. BD bisects $\angle B$ of $\triangle ABC$, D is on AC, $\angle A = 25°$, $\angle C = 45°$. Evaluate the other angles of the figure.

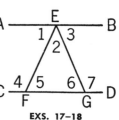

EX. 14

EX. 15

16. The side AC of $\triangle ABC$ is extended to D, $\angle A$ and $\angle BCD$ are bisected, and the bisectors meet at E. If $\angle B = 100°$ and $\angle A = 50°$, how many degrees are there in $\angle E$?

17. $AB \parallel CD$. If $\angle 2 = 80°$ and $\angle 4 = 140°$, how many degrees are there in the other angles?

18. $AB \parallel CD$. If $\angle 2 = 70°$ and $\angle 5 = 30°$, how many degrees are there in the other angles?

EXS. 17–18

■ Corollaries to Theorem 17

There are several corollaries to Theorem 17. They all depend upon the fact that the sum of the angles of a triangle is 180°. Study the corollaries below and be able to give numerical examples.

COROLLARY 1 **If two angles of one triangle are equal to two angles of another triangle, the third angles are equal.**
(See Exs. 1 and 2, page 163.)

COROLLARY 2 **A triangle can have but one right angle or one obtuse angle.**
(If it had two such angles, the sum of the angles would be more than 180°.)

COROLLARY 3 **If two right triangles have an acute angle of one equal to an acute angle of the other, the other acute angles are equal.**
(See Corollary 1 above.)

COROLLARY 4 **The acute angles of a right triangle are complementary.**
(See Ex. 8, page 163.)

COROLLARY 5 **Each angle of an equilateral triangle is 60°.**
(See Ex. 5, page 163.)

COROLLARY 6 **When two sides of a triangle are equal and the included angle is 60°, the triangle is equilateral.**
(See Ex. 7, page 163.)

COROLLARY 7 **If two triangles have two angles and a side of one equal respectively to two angles and the corresponding side of the other, they are congruent.**
Abbreviation: $a.a.s. = a.a.s.$ or $a.s.a. = a.s.a.$ (See Exs. 12 and 13, p. 164.)

COROLLARY 8 **If one side of a triangle is extended, the exterior angle thus formed is equal to the sum of the two remote interior angles.**
(See Ex. 11, page 164.)

◼ Early Proofs of Theorem 17—*Optional*

The theorem that the sum of the angles of a triangle is equal to two right angles (180°) was probably proved very early by the Greeks. It is believed that the theorem was at first proved separately for three different kinds of triangles — the equilateral, the right, and then the scalene triangle.

There is no record of the early proofs but references to the theorem by later Greek writers suggest what the proofs may have been. Proofs for the three types of triangle follow:

1. Equilateral triangle

From inspection of Egyptian floors paved with tiles, Thales (about 600 B.C.), or some other mathematician, would have seen that six equilateral triangles could be placed around a common vertex. Then assuming the angles of an equilateral triangle to be equal, he would have the sum of all the angles at the center equal to 4 right angles (360°), so the sum of three of them, $\angle 6 + \angle 1 + \angle 2 = 2$ rt. $\angle$. But $\angle 7 = \angle 6$ and $\angle 8 = \angle 2$, so $\angle 7 + \angle 1 + \angle 8 = 2$ rt. $\angle$.

2. Right triangle

The Greeks knew that each angle of a rectangle is a right angle. They placed two congruent right triangles together to form a rectangle as shown.

Since the sum of the angles of the rectangle is 4 rt. $\angle$, the sum of the angles of each triangle is 2 rt. $\angle$.

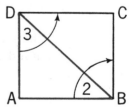

3. Scalene triangle

In a scalene triangle ABC they drew the perpendicular CD as shown. The sum of the angles of the two right triangles is 4 rt. $\angle$. So, subtracting $\angle 2 + \angle 5$ (180°) because $\angle 2$ and $\angle 5$ are not angles of the given triangle, $\angle A + \angle B + \angle C = 2$ right angles.

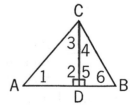

EXERCISES

1. AB in $\triangle ABC$ is extended to D. If $\angle A = 30°$ and $\angle C = 25°$, how many degrees are there in $\angle CBD$? (See Corollary 8 to Theorem 17.)

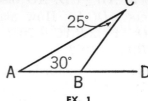

EX. 1

2. O is the center of the circle and BOC is a straight line. How many degrees are there in $\angle COA$ if $\angle B = 35°$? (Get the result without finding the number of degrees in $\angle BOA$.)

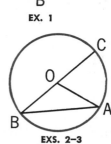

3. In the figure for Ex. 2, how many degrees are there in $\angle B$ if $\angle COA = 100°$?

EXS. 2–3

4. ABC and EDC are straight lines. How many degrees are there in $\angle C$ if $\angle ABE = 65°$ and $\angle E = 27°$? (Get the result without evaluating any other angle.)

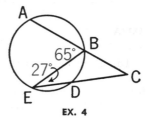

EX. 4

5. O is the center of the circle, DCB and AOB are straight lines, and $BC = OC$. How many degrees are there in $\angle AOD$ if $\angle B = 40°$?

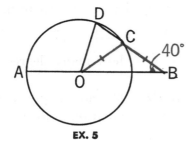

EX. 5

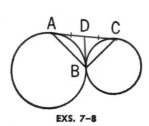

EXS. 7–8

6. How many degrees are there in $\angle AOD$ if $\angle B = 34°$? Use the hypothesis of Ex. 5. (Draw a new diagram.)

7. $AD = DC = DB$. ADC is a straight line. How many degrees are there in $\angle ABC$ if $\angle A = 20°$?

8. How many degrees are there in $\angle ABC$ if $\angle A = 30°$?

9. $AB \parallel CD$, AO bisects $\angle BAC$, and CO bisects $\angle DCA$. How many degrees are there in $\angle O$ if $\angle BAC = 70°$? if $\angle BAC = 80°$? if $\angle BAC = 50°$?

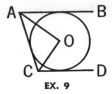

EX. 9

10. In quadrilateral $ABCD$, $AB \parallel DC$, $AD \parallel BC$, and $\angle A$ and $\angle B$ are bisected. The bisectors meet at E. How many degrees are there in $\angle E$ if $\angle D = 140°$? if $\angle C = 60°$?

11. AE bisects $\angle A$, BE bisects $\angle B$, and $DEF \parallel AB$. How many degrees are there in each angle if $\angle A = 40°$ and $\angle B = 60°$?

12. AE bisects $\angle A$, BE bisects $\angle B$, and $DEF \parallel AB$. How many degrees are there in each angle if $\angle C = 110°$ and $\angle CDF = 50°$?

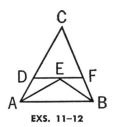

EXS. 11–12

EXTRA

13. If in the figure for Ex. 1 (page 167), $\angle A = \dfrac{a°}{2}$ and $\angle C = a°$, how many degrees are there in $\angle CBD$?

14. If in the figure for Ex. 2, $\angle B = a°$, $\angle COA = \underline{}°$.

15. If in the figure for Ex. 3, $\angle COA = a°$, $\angle B = \underline{}°$.

16. In the figure for Ex. 4, $\angle ABE = \dfrac{a°}{2}$ and $\angle E = \dfrac{b°}{2}$. How many degrees are there in $\angle C$?

17. In $\triangle ABC$, $AC = BC$. How many degrees are there in $\angle C$ in terms of a if $\angle A = a°$? if $\angle A = 2a°$? if $\angle A = \dfrac{a°}{2}$?

18. If in the figure for Ex. 5, $\angle B = a°$, how many degrees are there in $\angle AOD$?

19. If in the figure for Ex. 5, $\angle AOD = 90°$, how many degrees are there in $\angle B$? (Let $\angle B = x°$, form an equation, and solve it.)

20. If in the figure for Ex. 7, $\angle A = a°$, how many degrees are there in $\angle ABC$?

21. $AB \parallel CD$. How many degrees are there in each angle in terms of a and b if $\angle 2 = a°$ and $\angle 4 = b°$? if $\angle 2 = a°$ and $\angle 5 = b°$?

22. If in the figure for Ex. 9, $\angle BAC = a°$, how many degrees are there in $\angle O$?

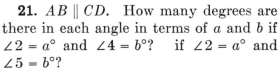

EX. 21

■ Trisecting an Angle — *Optional*

Here is another method of trisecting an angle using an instrument attributed to Blaise Pascal, a famous French mathematician, who lived in the seventeenth century. Even as a small boy Pascal liked to work problems while the other boys were playing games. His adding machine was the forerunner of today's speedometer, fare register, and mechanical adding machine.

The trisector is made of three bars, AB, CE, ED, as shown below at the left. $AC = CE$ and $CE = ED$. CE is hinged at C. CE and DE are hinged at E. D can move in a groove in bar AB.

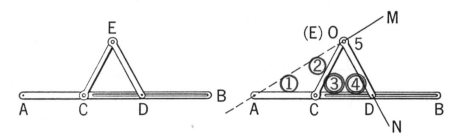

In the figure above at the right $\angle MON$ is trisected by the instrument; that is, $\angle MAB = \frac{1}{3}\angle MON$.

The pivot at E is placed at O, the vertex of the angle. ED lies along ON and A is on the extension of MO.

Proof. Point E is on vertex O of $\angle MON$.

STATEMENTS	REASONS
1. $AC = CO = OD$.	1. Instrument so made.
2. $\angle 1 = \angle 2$.	2. Theorem 1.
3. $\angle 3 = \angle 1 + \angle 2$.	3. The exterior angle of triangle, etc.
4. $\angle 3 = 2\angle 1$.	4. Substituting $\angle 1$ for $\angle 2$.
5. $\angle 5 = \angle 4 + \angle 1$.	5. Exterior angle of $\triangle AOD$.
6. $\angle 3 = \angle 4$.	6. Theorem 1.
7. $\angle 5 = \angle 3 + \angle 1$.	7. Substituting $\angle 3$ for $\angle 4$.
8. $\angle 5 = 2\angle 1 + \angle 1$ or $3\angle 1$.	8. Substituting $2\angle 1$ for $\angle 3$.

This is the same as $\angle MON = 3\angle A$ or $\angle A = \frac{1}{3}\angle MON$.

■ Inductive Approach to Theorem 18

1. Draw a quadrilateral and one diagonal. How many triangles are formed? What is the sum of the angles of one triangle? What is the sum of the angles of the polygon?

2. Draw a pentagon and all possible diagonals from one vertex. Answer the questions in Ex. 1.

3. Make a table like the following and fill in the blanks.

NO. OF SIDES OF POLYGON	NO. OF TRIANGLES FORMED BY DRAWING ALL DIAGONALS FROM ONE VERTEX	SUM OF THE ANGLES OF THE POLYGON
4	2	360°
5	3	540°
6	?	?
7	?	?
8	?	?
9	?	?
10	?	?

4. Do you see that there are always two triangles less than the number of sides? How many triangles would there be for a polygon of 20 sides? What is the sum of the angles of a 20-sided polygon?

5. State a rule for finding the sum of the angles of a polygon of any number of sides.

The proof of the statement you made for Exercise 5 follows on the opposite page as Theorem 18. For a minimum course, you will omit the theorem and accept the statement as a postulate.

Postulate **The sum of the angles of a polygon of n sides is $(n-2)180°$.**

△ An **equilateral polygon** *is one with all sides equal.*
△ An **equiangular polygon** *is one with all angles equal.*
△ A **regular polygon** *is one that is both equilateral and equiangular.*

The sum of the angles of a polygon of n sides is $(n-2)180°$.

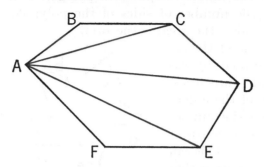

Given a polygon of n sides. $ABCDEF$ represents this polygon.

To prove that the sum of the angles is $(n-2)180°$.

Proof. Draw all possible diagonals from A. Then $(n-2)$ triangles are formed, one for each side of the polygon except AB and AF. The sum of the angles of one triangle is $180°$. Hence the sum of the angles of $(n-2)$ triangles is $(n-2)180°$. Since the sum of the angles of all the triangles is the same as the sum of the angles of the polygon, the sum of the angles of the polygon is $(n-2)180°$.

Note that the proof of this theorem is general for polygons of any number of sides. The proof would be the same, word for word, no matter how many sides the polygon has.

Using this theorem to find the sum of the angles of a particular polygon, you will subtract 2 from the number of sides and then multiply by 180.

To find the number of degrees in one angle of a *regular* polygon, divide the sum of all the angles by the number of angles.

Written as a formula Theorem 18 states, $S = (n-2)180°$. As it stands it is solved for S. When n is known S can be found. When S is known n can be found.

EXERCISES

1. Find the sum of the angles of a pentagon, a hexagon, an octagon, and a decagon.

2. How many degrees are there in one angle of a regular pentagon, a regular hexagon, a regular octagon, and a regular decagon?

▪ Exterior Angles of a Polygon

The sum of the *interior angles* of a polygon is a variable and depends upon the number of sides of the polygon. The greater the number of sides, the greater the sum.

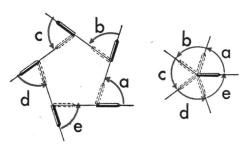

This is not true of the *exterior angles* formed by extending the sides in succession. The sum of these does not depend upon the number of sides, but is a constant (always the same). This can be seen easily by noting that a pencil rotated through the exterior angles in succession makes one complete revolution. (Study the figure.) The sum is therefore 360°.

COROLLARY **The sum of the exterior angles of a polygon made by extending each of its sides in succession is equal to 360°.**

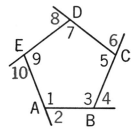

Outline of proof. The sum of the two angles (such as interior ∠1 and exterior ∠2) at any vertex, as A, B, C, etc., is 180°. If the polygon has n sides, the sum of the exterior and interior angles is therefore $n \times 180°$ or $180n°$. The sum of the interior angles is $(n-2)180°$ or $180n° - 360°$. The sum of the exterior angles, by subtraction, is $180n° - (180n° - 360°)$, or 360°. See Exercises 1 and 2.

1. *ABCDE* above is a pentagon. What is the sum of angles 1, 3, 5, 7, and 9? What is the sum of angles 1 and 2? of angles 3 and 4? of angles 5 and 6? of angles 1, 2, 3, 4, 5, 6, 7, 8, 9, and 10? From this last sum subtract the sum of the interior angles to find the sum of the exterior angles. What is this sum?

2. Draw any polygon of six sides *ABCDEF* and extend each of the sides in succession to make the exterior angles. What is the sum of the six interior angles? of the two angles at A? at B? of all the exterior and interior angles together? of the exterior angles? (Find the sum of the exterior angles by subtraction to check the fact that the sum is 360°.)

EXERCISES

1. Find the sum of the interior angles of polygons of the following number of sides:

Four	Five	Twenty
Eight	Twelve	Fifteen
Ten	Sixteen	Six

2. What is the sum of the interior angles of a regular pentagon? Since it has five equal angles, how many degrees are there in one angle?

3. How many degrees are there in one interior angle of a regular hexagon? a regular octagon? a regular decagon? a regular polygon of 15 sides?

4. What is the sum of the exterior angles of a regular hexagon? Since there are six equal exterior angles, how many degrees are there in one exterior angle?

5. How many degrees are there in one exterior angle of a regular pentagon? a regular octagon? a regular decagon?

6. How many sides has a polygon if the sum of its interior angles is 1800°? Note that $(n - 2)180 = 1800$.

7. How many sides has a polygon if the sum of its interior angles is 2160°?

EXTRA

8. Could the sum of the interior angles of a polygon be 1350°? Explain.

9. How many sides has a regular polygon if each of its interior angles is 144°? First find the number of degrees in one exterior angle.

10. The formula for the number of degrees in one interior angle of a regular polygon is $\dfrac{180(n - 2)}{n}$. Explain.

11. Given $S = (n - 2)180$. Solve for n, then find the value of n when $S = 3600$.

12. Solve $S = \dfrac{180(n - 2)}{2}$ for n.

Parallelograms

△ A **parallelogram** *is a quadrilateral with its opposite sides parallel.* The symbol for parallelogram is □.

The opposite sides of a parallelogram are also *equal*, but this is not part of the definition. You will deduce the fact that these sides are equal from the fact that they are parallel. There is no such figure as a quadrilateral with opposite sides parallel and unequal.

You will also prove that in a parallelogram:

The opposite angles are equal.

Any two successive angles are supplementary.

The diagonals bisect each other.

THEOREM 19	The opposite sides of a parallelogram are equal.

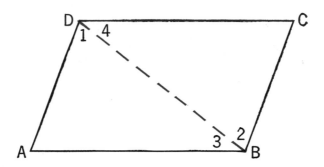

Given □*ABCD*.

To prove that *AB* = *CD* and *AD* = *BC*.

The *plan* is to prove that the triangles are congruent.

Proof. Draw the diagonal *BD*.

STATEMENTS	REASONS
1. *ABCD* is a □.	1. Given.
2. *AB* ∥ *CD*.	2. Def. of □.
3. ∠3 = ∠4.	3. Why?
4. *AD* ∥ *BC*.	4. Why?
5. ∠1 = ∠2.	5. Why?

The rest of the proof is left for you.

COROLLARY 1 A diagonal of a parallelogram divides it into two congruent triangles.

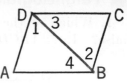

COROLLARY 2 The opposite angles of a parallelogram are equal.

($\angle A = \angle C$ because they are corresponding parts of congruent triangles. If $\angle 1 = \angle 2$ and $\angle 3 = \angle 4$, $\angle 1 + \angle 3 = \angle 2 + \angle 4$.)

COROLLARY 3 Parallel lines are at all points the same distance apart.

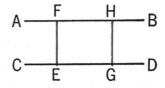

(From any two points on one line draw perpendiculars to the other. The figure formed is a parallelogram. Prove that the perpendiculars are equal.)

COROLLARY 4 The successive angles of a parallelogram are supplementary.

THEOREM 20 | *The diagonals of a parallelogram bisect each other.*

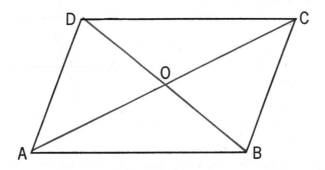

Given   □$ABCD$ with the diagonals AC and BD.

To prove   that $AO = OC$ and $BO = OD$.

The *plan* is to prove $\triangle DOC \cong \triangle AOB$. (Use Theorem 19 and *a.s.a.* = *a.s.a.*)

Proof. The proof is left for you.

EXERCISES

1. Which of the following statements are true and which are false? In $\square ABCD$ (Fig. 1 and Fig. 2) $\angle A$ does not equal $\angle B$.

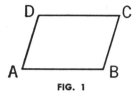

FIG. 1

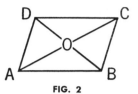

FIG. 2

a $AB = CD$ by definition of a parallelogram. (Fig. 1)

b If $AD = 6$ in., then $BC = 6$ in. (Fig. 1)

c $\angle A$ and $\angle C$ are both supplementary to $\angle B$. (Fig. 1)

d If $\angle B = 110°$, $\angle D$ can equal $100°$. (Fig. 1)

e $AO = OC = BO = OD$. (Fig. 2)

f If $AO = 3$ in., then $CO = 3$ in. (Fig. 2)

g $\triangle ABC$ can be proved congruent to $\triangle ABD$. (Fig. 2)

h $\triangle DOA$ can be proved congruent to $\triangle COB$. (Fig. 2)

i $\triangle ABD \cong \triangle CDB$. (Fig. 2)

2. In $\square ABCD$, $\angle A = 2 \angle B$. How many degrees are there in each angle?

3. $AB \parallel CD$ and $EF \parallel GH$. Prove that $RS = VT$ and $ST = RV$.

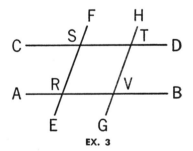

EX. 3

4. One angle of a parallelogram is $42°$. How many degrees are there in each of the other angles?

5. The perimeter of a parallelogram is 50 in. and one side is 15 in. How long is each of the other sides?

6. Prove: Any line drawn through the middle point of a diagonal of a parallelogram and terminated by the sides is bisected at the point.

7. Prove: If two parallel lines are cut by a transversal so that two alternate interior angles are equal, the bisectors of those angles are parallel.

■ Is It a Parallelogram?

Now turn to the converses of some previous statements.

1. What is the definition of a parallelogram? Its converse, of course, is true just as it is with all definitions. The converse is:

> If the opposite sides of a quadrilateral are parallel, the figure is a parallelogram.

2. What is the converse of Theorem 19? of its second corollary? of Theorem 20?

3. The following converses are true.

a If the opposite sides of a quadrilateral are equal, the figure is a parallelogram. (This is Theorem 21.)

b If the opposite angles of a quadrilateral are equal, the figure is a parallelogram. (This statement can be proved. Try it.)

c If the diagonals of a quadrilateral bisect each other, the figure is a parallelogram. (This is Theorem 23.)

4. It is also true that —

> If two sides of a quadrilateral are parallel and equal, the figure is a parallelogram. (This is Theorem 22.)

■ Methods of Constructing a Parallelogram

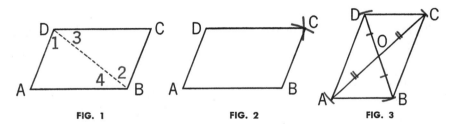

FIG. 1   FIG. 2   FIG. 3

Construct a parallelogram by making the opposite sides parallel. To do this, make $\angle 1 = \angle 2$ and $\angle 3 = \angle 4$. (Fig. 1)

Construct a parallelogram by making the opposite sides equal. This method is suggested by Figure 2.

Construct a parallelogram by making two sides parallel and equal. Make $AB = DC$ and $\angle 3 = \angle 4$. (Fig. 1)

Construct a parallelogram by making the diagonals bisect each other. Draw two intersecting lines AC and BD and mark off $OD = OB$ and $OA = OC$. (Fig. 3)

If the opposite sides of a quadrilateral are equal, the figure is a parallelogram.

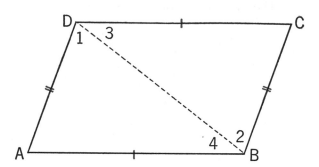

Given quadrilateral $ABCD$ with $AB = CD$ and $AD = BC$.
To prove that $ABCD$ is a parallelogram.
Show that $\triangle ABD \cong \triangle CDB$. Then $\angle 3 = \angle 4$ and $AB \parallel CD$.
The proof is left for you.

If two sides of a quadrilateral are parallel and equal, the figure is a parallelogram.

Given quadrilateral $ABCD$ with $AB = CD$ and $AB \parallel CD$.
To prove that $ABCD$ is a parallelogram.
Show that $\triangle ABD \cong \triangle CDB$. Then $\angle 1 = \angle 2$ and $AD \parallel BC$.

If the diagonals of a quadrilateral bisect each other, the figure is a parallelogram.

Prove two triangles congruent. Use Theorem 22.

▪ Rectangle, Rhombus, and Square

△ *A **rectangle** is a parallelogram with one right angle.*

You might think from this definition that a rectangle has only one right angle. This is **not** true. If $ABCD$ is a rectangle, it is a parallelogram. If one angle, $\angle A$, $= 90°$, then $\angle C = 90°$. Why?

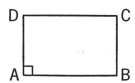

Also $\angle A + \angle B = 180°$. Why? So $\angle B = 90°$ and $\angle D = 90°$. Thus, you have the following corollary to the definition.

COROLLARY 1   **Each angle of a rectangle is a right angle.**

1. Are all rectangles parallelograms?
2. Are all parallelograms rectangles?

This is another example of the fact that not all converses of true statements are true.

Since a rectangle is a parallelogram, all the properties of a parallelogram are also properties of a rectangle. For example, the opposite sides are equal and the diagonals bisect each other. A rectangle has, in addition, special properties not true of parallelograms in general. For one thing, all the angles are equal.

COROLLARY 2   **The diagonals of a rectangle are equal.**

What two triangles should you prove congruent?

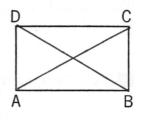

COROLLARY 3   **If the diagonals of a parallelogram are equal, it is a rectangle.**

You must prove that one angle is a right angle. Prove $\triangle ABD \cong \triangle BAC$ and get $\angle A = \angle B$. Then, since $\angle A + \angle B = 180°$, each angle equals 90°.

△ A *rhombus is a parallelogram with two adjacent sides equal.*

In the figure below, $ABCD$ is a parallelogram with $AB = AD$. It is a rhombus.

COROLLARY 4   **All four sides of a rhombus are equal.**

1. Are all rhombuses parallelograms?
2. Are all parallelograms rhombuses?

Since a rhombus is a parallelogram, all properties of a parallelogram are also properties of a rhombus. A rhombus, in addition, has special properties.

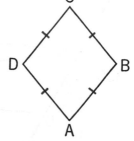

COROLLARY 5   **The diagonals of a rhombus are perpendicular to each other.**

(Use Theorem 6.)

COROLLARY 6 **The diagonals of a rhombus bisect its angles.**

To prove that $\angle 1 = \angle 2$ and $\angle 3 = \angle 4$, prove that $\triangle DBA \cong \triangle DBC$. In a similar manner, show that $\angle A$ and $\angle C$ are bisected. Find another way of proving this corollary.

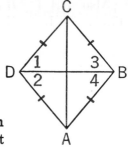

COROLLARY 7 **If the diagonals of a parallelogram are perpendicular to each other, it is a rhombus.**

$CA \perp DB$ (given) and CA bisects DB (Theorem 20), hence $DC = BC$ (Theorem 5).

$\triangle$ *A square is a rectangle with two adjacent sides equal.*

From this definition you see that a square is a rhombus with right angles. All the properties of parallelograms and the special properties of rectangles and rhombuses are also properties of squares. The diagonals are equal and perpendicular to each other and they bisect the angles of the square.

■ Parallelogram of Forces — *Optional*

A plane is headed in the direction AP, 85° from a north-south line, and is flying at the rate of 180 miles per hour through the air. The wind is blowing from 330° at 45 m.p.h.

The wind, of course, will change the direction in which the plane flies and its rate over the ground. What *are* the course and the ground speed? This problem can be solved graphically.

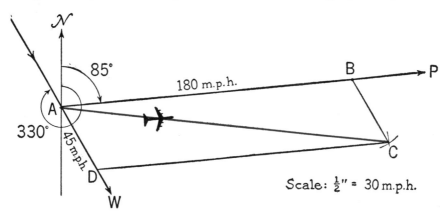

Scale: $\frac{1}{2}'' = 30$ m.p.h.

In the diagram AB represents both the plane's *heading* (direction headed) and its *air speed* (speed through the air). It is drawn at an angle of 85° from the north-south line and its length represents 180 m.p.h. (scale $\frac{1}{2}''$ = 30 m.p.h.). It is called a **vector.**

The line AD is a vector that represents the velocity and direction of the wind. It is drawn at an angle of 330° from the north-south line and is $\frac{3}{4}''$ long (45 m.p.h.).

Using AB and AD as sides, a parallelogram is constructed as shown. (What method was used to make the parallelogram?) The plane will move along the diagonal in a direction of about 98° (measure the angle with a protractor) with a ground speed of about 200 m.p.h. (AC measures about 3.4″ and $3.4 \times 2 \times 30$ = 204.)

■ Necessary and Sufficient Conditions — *Optional*

You have learned about converse theorems and know that you should not assume the truth of a converse theorem just because you know the theorem itself to be true. A converse of a true statement is not necessarily true. Another way to talk about a theorem and a converse is to speak about *necessary* and *sufficient* conditions. You know, for instance, that if a triangle is equilateral, it has two equal sides. Is the converse statement true? If a triangle has only two equal sides, is it equilateral? It is not.

Having two sides equal is a necessary condition for an equilateral triangle. You cannot have an equilateral triangle unless two sides are equal. But having two equal sides is not a sufficient condition. An equilateral triangle must have three equal sides.

Is it necessary for the opposite sides of a quadrilateral to be equal to have a parallelogram? Yes. You cannot have a parallelogram unless the opposite sides are equal. There is no such thing as a parallelogram without opposite sides equal. You proved this in Theorem 19. Is it sufficient for the opposite sides of a quadrilateral to be equal to have a parallelogram? The answer to this question is also "Yes," because the converse of Theorem 19 is true. Having the opposite sides equal is a necessary and sufficient condition for a quadrilateral to be a parallelogram.

Having one angle a right angle is a necessary condition for a rectangle. You would not have a rectangle without one of the angles being a right angle. It is not a sufficient condition, as is shown by the figure $ABCD$. In the figure you have a quadrilateral with one right angle at D but the figure is obviously not a parallelogram.

Being born a citizen of the United States is a necessary condition for being president. You cannot be president unless you are born a citizen of the United States. But there are other conditions. It is not a sufficient condition.

■ Organizing Your Knowledge

In order to make the best use of your knowledge of geometric relationships, you should organize related theorems into groups. You should be able to answer readily such questions as:

How can you prove lines parallel if they are cut by a transversal?

What theorems have you had that relate to parallel lines?

What are the properties of a parallelogram?

How can you prove that a quadrilateral is a parallelogram?

If your knowledge is organized, the pertinent facts will come easily to mind when you are asked to prove an exercise.

EXERCISES

1. What are the properties of a parallelogram? (Begin with the definition.)

2. In what ways may a quadrilateral be proved to be a parallelogram?

3. What are the special properties of a rectangle, a rhombus, and a square?

4. Name two special kinds of parallelogram that are equilateral and two that are equiangular.

5. What kind of parallelogram is equilateral and equiangular?

6. Name the equiangular parallelogram that is not necessarily equilateral.

7. Is a square always a rectangle? always a rhombus?

8. What common properties do a square and a rectangle have?

9. A square and its diagonal are drawn. Find the number of degrees in each angle of the figure.

■ Checking Proofs for Errors

This proof was taken from a student's paper.   Check it and discuss the errors.   Are the statements with the reason "Given" actually given? Are the other reasons "acceptable" ones and do they apply?   Are their conditions fulfilled?

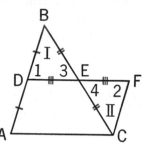

Given $\triangle ABC$ with D and E the middle points of AB and BC, respectively. DEF is a straight line and $DE = EF$.

To prove   that $AB \parallel CF$ and $AD = CF$.

Attempted proof.

STUDENT'S STATEMENTS	STUDENT'S REASONS
1. $\angle 1 = \angle 2$.	1. When two parallel lines are cut by a transversal, the alternate interior angles are equal.
2. $AB \parallel CF$.	2. When two straight lines are cut by a transversal so that the alternate interior angles are equal, the lines are parallel.
3. D and E are the middle points of AB and BC.	3. Given.
4. $BE = EC$.	4. Halves of equals are equal.
5. $\angle 3 = \angle 4$.	5. Vertical angles are equal.
6. $DE = EF$.	6. Given.
7. $\triangle I \cong \triangle II$.	7. *s.a.s. = s.a.s.*
8. $DB = CF$.	8. *C.p.c.t.e.*
9. $DB = AD$.	9. Same as Reason 4.
10. $AD = CF$.	10. If equals are subtracted from equals, the remainders are equal.

Reasoning in a circle

To get $\angle 1 = \angle 2$, the student assumed the lines to be parallel before he had proved them parallel.   Then, using the statement that $\angle 1 = \angle 2$, he proved them parallel.   This is reasoning in a circle.   It is as useless as the following: "Where is John?" "He's with Fred." "Where is Fred?" "He's with John."

■ Inductive Approach to Theorems 24, 25, 26

For a minimum course you will accept as postulates the statements given in Theorems 24, 25, and 26. The proofs are given on the following pages. On this page you will experiment with a special case of each relationship.

Postulate 1 If a line joins the middle points of two sides of a triangle, it is parallel to the third side and equal to half of it.

Read the postulate and explain what it means.

Refer to page 29. You will find there a figure constructed according to the conditions of the postulate above. Do this experiment again, this time making *AB* equal to 6 inches. Is *DE* equal to 3 inches and does it appear to be parallel to *AB*?

△ *A **trapezoid** is a quadrilateral with two and only two sides parallel. The parallel sides are **bases** of the trapezoid.*

△ *An **isosceles trapezoid** is one whose nonparallel sides are equal.*

△ *The **median of a trapezoid** is a line joining the middle points of the nonparallel sides.*

Postulate 2 The median of a trapezoid is parallel to the bases and equal to one half their sum.

Can you explain what the postulate means?

Make a trapezoid as shown using the lines on ruled paper. Make *AB* 4 inches and *DC* 3 inches. *EF* is the median. How long is *EF*? Is this half the sum of *AB* and *CD*? Try this same experiment with *AB* = 5 in. and *DC* = 4 in.

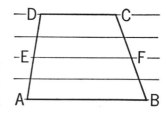

Postulate 3 If three or more parallel lines cut off equal segments on one transversal, they cut off equal segments on every transversal.

Can you explain what Postulate 3 means?

On a piece of paper ruled with parallel lines note that the parts of AB on the edge are equal. Draw three other lines as CD, EF, and GH. The parts of these lines are also equal.

This does not mean that the parts of AB are equal to the parts of CD or that the parts of CD are equal to the parts of GH.

■ Analytic Approach to Theorem 24

Given $\triangle ABC$ with D and E the middle points of AC and BC, respectively. DEF is a straight line. $EF = DE$.

To prove that $DE \parallel AB$ and $DE = \frac{1}{2}AB$.

In any exercise first ask, "How can I prove the conclusion?" In this case you ask, "How can I prove that $DE \parallel AB$ and $DE = \frac{1}{2}AB$?"

You know that $DE = \frac{1}{2}DF$, hence you can prove that $DE = \frac{1}{2}AB$, if you can prove that $AB = DF$.

DE is a part of DF, hence you can prove that $DE \parallel AB$ if you can prove that $DF \parallel AB$.

You would like to prove that AB is equal and parallel to DF. That suggests that you try to prove that $ABFD$ is a parallelogram.

You can prove that $ABFD$ is a parallelogram, if you can prove __?__. (Think over all the ways you know of proving that a quadrilateral is a parallelogram.) Finally, you will eliminate all but the following: You can prove that $ABFD$ is a parallelogram if you can prove that AD is parallel and equal to BF.

AD is a part of AC. You can prove $AC \parallel BF$ if you can prove that $\angle 1 = \angle 2$.

Since $AD = DC$, you can prove that $AD = BF$ if you can prove that $DC = BF$.

You can prove that $\angle 1 = \angle 2$ and $DC = BF$ if you can prove $\triangle I \cong \triangle II$. You *can* prove that $\triangle I \cong \triangle II$. How?

Now by retracing your steps you will prove the exercise.

If a line joins the middle points of two sides of a triangle, it is parallel to the third side and equal to half of it.

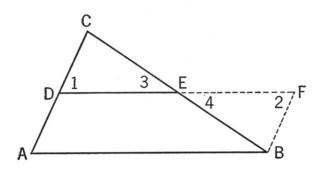

Given $\triangle ABC$ with D and E the middle points of AC and BC respectively.

To prove   that $DE \parallel AB$ and $DE = \frac{1}{2}AB$.

The *plan* is to continue DE its own length to F and prove that $ABFD$ is a parallelogram.

Proof.   Continue DE so that $EF = DE$.   Draw BF.

STATEMENTS	REASONS
1. $BE = EC$.	1. Given.
2. $DE = EF$.	2. So drawn.
3. $\angle 3 = \angle 4$.	3. Why?
4. $\triangle DEC \cong \triangle FEB$.	4. Why?
5. $\angle 1 = \angle 2$.	5. Why?
6. $AD \parallel BF$.	6. Theorem 9.
7. $DC = BF$.	7. Why?
8. $AD = DC$.	8. Given.
9. $AD = BF$.	9. Substituting AD for DC.
10. $ABFD$ is a $\square$.	10. Theorem 22.
11. $DE \parallel AB$.	11. Why?
12. $DF = AB$.	12. Why?
13. $DE = \frac{1}{2}DF$.	13. So drawn.
14. $DE = \frac{1}{2}AB$.	14. Substituting AB for DF.

The proof of Theorem 24 illustrates a method of proving that one quantity is equal to one half of another quantity. The smaller quantity was doubled and the resulting quantity proved equal to the larger quantity. Another way is to halve the larger quantity and prove the half equal to the smaller quantity.

EXERCISES

1. The sides of a triangle are 8, 6, and 5 inches. If lines join the middle points of the sides, how long are the sides of each of the four triangles formed? Are the four triangles congruent?

2. The triangle ABC is equilateral with each side 10 inches long. D, E, and F are the middle points of AB, BC, and CA respectively. What is the perimeter of $\triangle DEF$?

3. The diagonals of quadrilateral $ABCD$ are 6 inches and 10 inches long. The middle points of AB, BC, CD, and DA are connected in order. How long are the sides of the new quadrilateral? Is it a parallelogram? Do you believe you would get a parallelogram regardless of the quadrilateral you used?

4. $ABCD$ is a rectangle. E, F, G, and H are the middle points of AB, BC, CD, and DA respectively. Is $EFGH$ a rhombus? Prove your answer.

5. Construct a rhombus with one angle 30° (make the angle with a protractor), bisect the sides, and join in succession the middle points. Evaluate the angles of the new quadrilateral. What kind of quadrilateral is it?

If you let the angle be $a°$ instead of 30° and go through your evaluation again, you will have proved a *general* relationship.

6. Prove: The lines joining the middle points of three sides of a triangle form four congruent triangles.

7. Prove: If, from the point where the bisector of an angle of a triangle meets the opposite side, parallels to the other sides are drawn, a rhombus is formed.

8. Each side of an equilateral triangle is 12 inches. If lines connect in succession the middle points of the sides, what is the perimeter of each triangle formed?

9. Is the relationship you found in Ex. 8 true for all lengths of the given side?

■ Some Interesting Applications—*Optional*

1. The basis of this figure is the parallelogram *ABCD*. The sides *AB*, *BC*, *CD*, and *DA* are extended in succession and the exterior angles are bisected and the bisectors extended. *EFGH* appears to be a rectangle. Is it? Can you prove that it is?

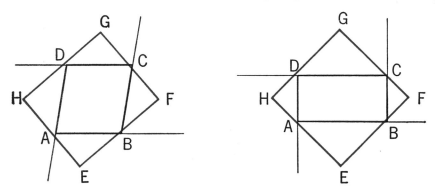

2. *ABCD* is a rectangle with exterior angles bisected in succession. Is *EFGH* a square? Can you prove it?

3. In quadrilateral *ABCD*, *AB* ∥ *DC*, *AD* = *BC*, ∠*A* = ∠*B*, and the exterior angles are bisected in succession. In the quadrilateral *EFGH*, prove that ∡*E* and *G* are right angles, ∡*F* and *H* are supplementary, *EF* = *FG*, and *GH* = *HE*.

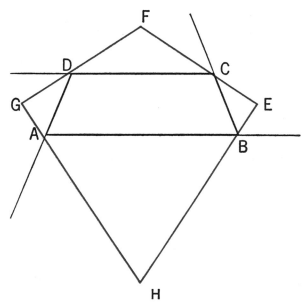

The median of a trapezoid is parallel to the bases and equal to one half their sum.

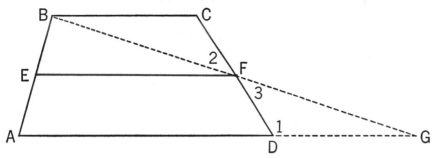

Given trapezoid $ABCD$ with median EF.

To prove that $EF \parallel AD \parallel BC$ and $EF = \frac{1}{2}(AD + BC)$.

Proof. Draw BF and continue it until it meets AD at G.

STATEMENTS	REASONS
Consider $\triangle BCF$ and GDF.	
1. $CF = FD$.	1. Given.
2. $BC \parallel ADG$.	2. Def. of trapezoid.
3. $\angle C = \angle 1$.	3. Why?
4. $\angle 2 = \angle 3$.	4. Why?
5. $\triangle BCF \cong \triangle GDF$.	5. Why?
In $\triangle ABG$	
6. $BF = FG$.	6. Why?
7. $BE = EA$.	7. Given.
8. $EF \parallel AD$,	8. Theorem 24.
$\quad EF = \frac{1}{2}(AD + DG)$.	
9. $BC = DG$.	9. Why?
10. $EF = \frac{1}{2}(AD + BC)$.	10. Substituting BC for DG.
11. $EF \parallel AD \parallel BC$.	11. Theorem 16.

In proving that the median equals one half the sum of the bases, you are really finding a *formula for the median* in terms of the bases. You found that the auxiliary line which was introduced aided you in developing the desired formula, but that no part of the auxiliary line itself remained as a permanent part of the formula. This situation will occur rather frequently as you progress in this course. Remember that, although auxiliary lines are necessary for the development, no parts of these lines will appear in the final results.

If three or more parallel lines cut off equal segments on one transversal, they cut off equal segments on every transversal.

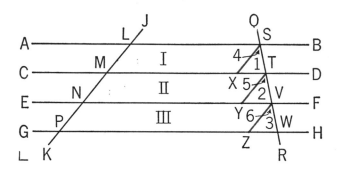

Given $AB \parallel CD \parallel EF \parallel GH$ cutting transversal JK so that $LM = MN = NP$ and any other transversal QR.

To prove   that $ST = TV = VW$.

The *plan* is to draw SX, TY, and VZ parallel to JK and to prove that they are equal. ST, TV, and VW may then be proved equal by congruent triangles.

Proof.   Draw SX, TY, and VZ parallel to JK.

STATEMENTS	REASONS
1. $AB \parallel CD \parallel EF \parallel GH$.	1. Given.
2. SX, TY, $VZ \parallel JK$.	2. So drawn.
3. Quadrilaterals I, II, and III are parallelograms.	3. The opposite sides are parallel.
4. $SX = LM$, $TY = MN$, and $VZ = NP$.	4. Theorem 19.
5. $LM = MN = NP$.	5. Given.
6. $SX = TY = VZ$.	6. Axiom 2, page 84.
7. $\angle 1 = \angle 2 = \angle 3$.	7. Theorem 14.
8. $SX \parallel TY \parallel VZ$.	8. Theorem 16.
9. $\angle 4 = \angle 5 = \angle 6$.	9. Theorem 14.
10. $\triangle SXT \cong \triangle TYV \cong \triangle VZW$.	10. *a.a.s.* = *a.a.s.*
11. $ST = TV = VW$.	11. *C.p.c.t.e.*

Are the segments on QR equal to those on JK?   Might they be equal for some positions of QR and JK?

If a line is parallel to one side of a triangle and bisects another side, it bisects the third side also.

(Draw $XY \parallel DE$ through C. Use Theorem 26.)

If a line is parallel to the bases of a trapezoid and bisects one of the nonparallel sides, it bisects the other also.

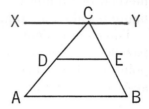

■ Dividing a Line into Equal Parts

You know how to divide a line into two equal parts. How would you divide a line into 4, 8, or 16 equal parts? Would you know how to divide a line into 3 or 5 equal parts?

Construction Problem Dividing a line into any number of equal parts.

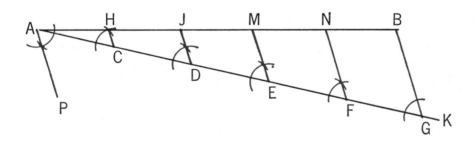

Given line AB.

Required to divide AB into any number of equal parts (for example, five).

Construction.

Draw AK at any convenient angle with AB. From A with any radius mark off five equal parts in succession on AK so that $AC = CD = DE = EF = FG$. Draw BG and through F, E, D, C, and A construct lines parallel to BG. H, J, M, and N are the required points of division.

Proof. The proof is left for you. (Use Theorem 26.)

■ Finding an Average Graphically

Here is an interesting application of Theorems 25 and 26, a method of finding the average of two numbers graphically. The figure is called an **alignment chart**.

Three equivalent scales are drawn as shown. The scales are on parallel lines and the lines are so placed that E is the middle point of AD. Then, if any other transversal is drawn, it will also be bisected by the middle line. Why? $ADCB$ is a trapezoid

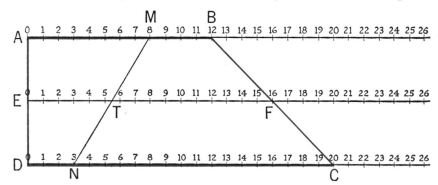

and EF is its median. AB is 12 units and DC is 20 units. When the length of EF is read, it is found to be 16, the average of 12 and 20. $\left(\dfrac{12 + 20}{2} = 16\right)$

To find the average of 8 and 3, lay a ruler from the point 8 on the upper scale to the point 3 on the lower scale. This is the line MN in the figure. The average is the length of ET on the middle scale. It is $5\frac{1}{2}$. $\left(\dfrac{8 + 3}{2} = 5\frac{1}{2}\right)$

Why does this method always work?

Of course, with such small numbers there is little advantage in this graphical method. The average of these numbers can be found mentally. What is the average of 354 and 375? Could this be done by starting each of the scales at 350? Try it and see.

1. Find the average of 19 and 19 using the chart. (Lay a straightedge from 19 on the top scale to 19 on the bottom scale and read the number indicated on the middle scale.) Is your answer sensible?

2. Use a straightedge to find the average of 13 and 25. Check your answer by using the formula: Average $= \dfrac{a + b}{2}$.

1. The base of an isosceles triangle ABC is AC. Through point E on AC a line is drawn to point D on the extension of BC so that CD equals CE. DE is extended to F on AB. Prove that angle BFE equals three times angle CDE.

2. In the equilateral triangle ABC the bisectors of angle A and the exterior angle at B meet in E. AE intersects BC at F. ED is perpendicular to AB extended. Prove DE equals AF.

3. On the diagonal AC of the square $ABCD$, E is taken so that AE equals AD. EF is perpendicular to AC and meets CD in F. Prove that FD equals EF equals EC.

4. The diagonal AC is drawn in the parallelogram $ABCD$. The bisectors of angle ABC and angle ADC meet AC at E and F respectively. Prove BF equals ED.

5. The line that connects the middle points of the diagonals of a trapezoid is parallel to the bases and equal to one half their difference. (SUGGESTION. Draw a line from the middle point of one diagonal parallel to the bases.)

6. E and F are the middle points of AB and CD respectively of parallelogram $ABCD$. Prove that DE and BF trisect AC.

7. On the sides AC and BC of any triangle ABC, equilateral triangles ACE and BCD are constructed externally. Prove that DA equals BE.

8. Through vertices A and C of quadrilateral $ABCD$, draw lines parallel to diagonal DB. Similarly, through vertices B and D draw lines parallel to diagonal AC. Prove the resulting quadrilateral is a parallelogram twice as large as the original quadrilateral.

9. Angle B of rhombus $ABCD$ is a $60°$ angle. The bisectors of angles BCA and ACD meet AB and AD in E and F, respectively. Prove that triangle CEF is equilateral.

10. Parallel lines are drawn from the vertices B and D of parallelogram $ABCD$ to intersect AC at E and F respectively. Prove that BF equals ED.

11. AB is parallel to CD. BD is a straight line. A line through B and a line through D meet at E. Angle 1 equals angle 2, and angle 3 equals angle 4. Find the number of degrees in angle E.

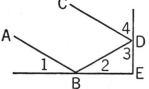

■ More about Converses — *Optional*

Some of the theorems in this chapter belong to interesting families of converses. One theorem of each of two families is set down for you in symbols. You should be able to form the converses by the usual method. (See page 124.)

1. The opposite sides of a parallelogram are equal.

    If $\quad a \parallel b \quad$ then $\quad a = b$
    $\qquad c \parallel d \qquad\qquad\ c = d$

    The distinct converses stated in words are:

    a If two sides of a quadrilateral are equal and parallel, then the other two sides are equal and parallel (in other words, it is a parallelogram).

    b If the opposite sides of a quadrilateral are equal, then it is a parallelogram.

    c If two sides of a quadrilateral are equal and the other two sides are parallel, then the first two sides are parallel and the second two are equal.

    Converses **a** and **b** can be proved, but converse **c** cannot. Draw a figure showing that **c** is not true.

2. The line joining the midpoints of two sides of a triangle is parallel to the third side and equal to half of it.

    If $\quad BD$ bisects $AC \quad$ then $\quad BD \parallel CE$
    $\qquad BD$ bisects $AE \qquad\qquad BD = \frac{1}{2}CE$

    The distinct converses stated in words are:

    a A line parallel to one side of a triangle and bisecting one of the other sides is equal to half the first side and is the bisector of the third side.

    b A line bisecting one side of a triangle and equal to half of the second side is parallel to the second side and bisects the third side.

    c If a line intersects two sides of a triangle and is both parallel to and equal to one half of the third side, it bisects the first two sides.

    Are all three of these converses true?

■ What Do You Mean by That?
Definitions — *Optional*

In discussions of general matters, the reasoning often goes astray because the terms are not used with exactitude. In geometry you have been able to draw valid conclusions because the terms were defined precisely. To draw valid conclusions in other fields of thought, you must use this same exactness of terms.

While you are studying various subjects in high school, you will often have opportunity to hear definitions of terms in biology, physics, chemistry, history, economics, government, and in other fields of study. If, at any time, definitions of key words are omitted, be sure to ask for them. Discussions using such terms as species, speed, molecular theory, isolationism, or extrapolation would have little meaning to a person not knowing the definitions of those terms.

If a term is not defined, different people may interpret it differently. If you keep this in mind, you may be able to avoid difficulty. Yet, it is not always a simple matter. What, for instance, does *excessive* mean in the following statement?

Excessive talking will not be allowed in the school library.

Suppose the librarian reprimands Mary and Eva for talking. They can answer "Yes, we were talking, but not excessively." The librarian disagrees. It is not easy to define excessive in this situation so that all parties will agree to the definition. Can you define it? Or would you prefer to omit the word?

Note the ambiguous words (uncertain meanings) in the following statements. Can you make the sentences more exact by defining these words?

1. Just mail us $5.98 each month and soon this lovely sewing machine will be yours.
2. Elect candidate Jones and get a square deal.
3. The speed limit is 55 miles per hour at night.
4. Good paint lasts considerably longer than inferior paint.
5. Faulty judgment causes many serious auto accidents.
6. Our services are quick, dependable, and economical.
7. Poor families can get financial relief from the state.
8. Driving speeds inside the city shall be reasonable and proper.
9. Comic books are not allowed in study halls.

■ Classes: The Basis of Deduction — *Optional*

The idea of class is at the basis of deduction. A **class** is a group of objects or persons which contain some common characteristic. For example, each of the following is a class.

1. All the persons who bought two pairs of shoes last year
2. Products not manufactured in this country
3. Christmas cards received after December 25

Can you name the common characteristic in each of the examples above? Give three more examples of this kind of expression.

One class is often included within another. The statement "automobiles are vehicles" states "the class of objects called automobiles is included in the larger class of objects called vehicles." Name the two classes in each of the following examples and tell which class is larger:

1. Fox terriers are dogs.
2. Olympic runners are excellent athletes.
3. Engineers are college graduates.

The foregoing gives a clue as to why some converses are not true. Form the converses of the above examples. Do you see that these converses must be false because they state that the larger class is included in the smaller class?

The principle illustrated in these examples is known as *class inclusion* because the members of the smaller class are included among the members of the larger class. This principle can be visualized by means of circles. To represent statement 3 above, draw a circle which represents all college graduates. Within this circle draw a smaller one to represent all engineers. (See Fig. 1.)

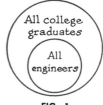

FIG. 1

Draw circles for the other statements to illustrate the inclusion principle.

Definitions do not come under the class-inclusion idea. A definition is a statement which concerns classes of equal size; its converse must be true. In the definition *triangles are three-sided polygons* the class of *all triangles* has the same size as the class of *three-sided polygons*. Each class includes the other, so to speak.

Figures 2 and 3 illustrate two more ways circles may be used to diagram the class relationship of a statement.

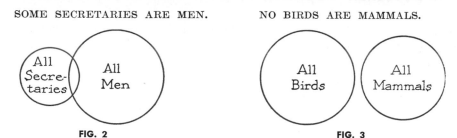

SOME SECRETARIES ARE MEN.

NO BIRDS ARE MAMMALS.

FIG. 2

FIG. 3

The principle illustrated in Figure 3 is known as the *class exclusion* principle. Can you see why?

Can you explain the diagrams shown below?

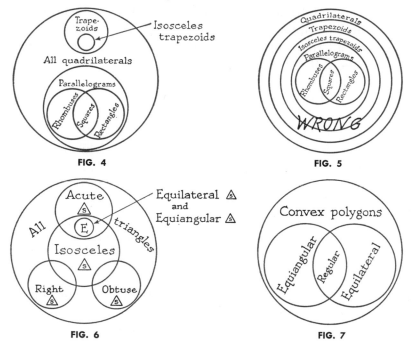

FIG. 4

FIG. 5

FIG. 6

FIG. 7

Figure 4 shows the relationships among the various kinds of quadrilaterals you have defined. Can you explain the diagram?

Can you explain the errors in Figure 5?

Can you explain the meanings of Figures 6 and 7?

Circles such as these are called Euler's (oiler's) Circles after the brilliant Swiss mathematician, Leonhard Euler (1708–1783), who was the first person to use them in this way.

■ Using Euler's Circles
in Deduction — *Optional*

Euler's circles are very helpful in visualizing deductive reasoning, especially in geometry. The circles provide a quick way for establishing the proper conclusion in a reasoning process, and a means of checking to see if a stated conclusion is the right one.

EXAMPLE:

All right angles are equal angles.
$\angle A$ and $\angle B$ are right angles.
$\angle A = \angle B$.

When the first statement is diagramed, you see the large circle representing all equal angles and within it the smaller circle representing all right angles. But the second statement tells you that $\angle A$ and $\angle B$ belong to the class of right angles, so a third circle is made within the circle representing right angles. This third circle represents $\angle A$ and $\angle B$. The conclusion stated is correct because the smallest circle is entirely within the medium-sized circle and the medium-sized circle is entirely within the largest circle. So the smallest circle is entirely within the largest.

When two statements lead directly to a necessary conclusion, then all three statements are an example of deductive reasoning. This type of deduction involving three statements is called a **syllogism.** The first statement is called the **major premise,** the second statement is called the **minor premise,** and the third statement is the **conclusion.**

Here is another example of a syllogism:

1. If two sides of a triangle are equal, then the angles opposite those sides are equal. (General statement or major premise)
2. $\angle B$ and $\angle C$ are opposite the equal sides of $\triangle ABC$. (Specific statement or minor premise)
3. $\angle B = \angle C$. (Conclusion)

If the minor premise *exactly* fulfills all of the conditions in the if-clause of the major premise, then the conclusion must follow the then-clause of the major premise *exactly.*

Euler's circles will help you to make sure your syllogisms are examples of exact deductive reasoning.

■ The Syllogism and Deductive Proof — *Optional*

You know that syllogisms are used in geometric proofs. You may not recognize them readily, but this is merely because the three parts of the syllogism are not in order. A geometric proof is usually made up of *chains of syllogisms* in which the conclusion of one syllogism constitutes the minor premise of a syllogism to follow. This relation continues throughout the proof.

On page 79 you saw a specimen geometric proof. This proof is shown below written in syllogistic form. Note how much the two proofs are alike.

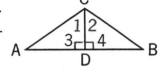

Given this figure, in which CD bisects AB and $CD \perp AB$.

To prove that $AC = BC$.

If a line is bisected, it is divided into two equal parts.
CD bisects AB.
$AD = DB$.
A perpendicular to a line forms equal adjacent angles with it.
$CD \perp AB$.
$\angle 3 = \angle 4$.
If there is a quantity, then it equals itself. (Abbr. *Identity.*)
CD is a quantity.
$CD = CD$.
If two triangles have two sides and the included angle of one equal respectively to two sides and the included angle of the other, they are congruent.
$AD = DB$, $\angle 3 = \angle 4$, $CD = CD$.
$\triangle ADC \cong \triangle BDC$.
Corresponding parts of congruent triangles are equal.
AC, BC are corresponding parts of triangles ADC and BDC, which are congruent.
$AC = BC$.

The minor premises in the last two syllogisms require you to refer to the figure to make sure $\angle 3$ and $\angle 4$ are *included* angles and AC and BC are *corresponding* parts of the triangles. Note that the conclusions of the first three syllogisms make up the minor premise of the fourth syllogism. Then the conclusion of the fourth syllogism makes up part of the minor premise of the last syllogism.

■ Polygons in Solids — *Optional*

△ *A solid completely bounded by planes is a **polyhedron**.* The portions of the planes bounding the polyhedrons are called **faces.** Every face of a polyhedron is a polygon. It may be a triangle, a quadrilateral, a pentagon, and so forth.

△ *A **regular polyhedron** is one all of whose faces are congruent regular polygons and all of whose polyhedral angles* (angles made by the planes coming together) *are equal.*

There are just five regular polyhedrons as pictured below.

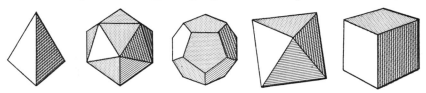

REGULAR POLYHEDRONS

In order from left to right their names are —

Regular tetrahedron: Four faces each an equilateral triangle.
Regular icosahedron: Twenty faces each an equilateral triangle.
Regular dodecahedron: Twelve faces each a regular pentagon.
Regular octahedron: Eight faces each an equilateral triangle.
Regular hexahedron or *cube:* Six faces each a square.

The figure below at the left is a ***right square prism.*** The upper and lower faces are congruent squares and the lateral (side) faces are congruent rectangles.

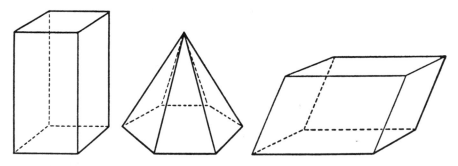

The central figure is a ***regular hexagonal pyramid.*** Its base is a regular hexagon and its lateral faces are congruent triangles.

The figure above at the right is a ***parallelepiped.*** Its opposite faces are parallelograms in parallel planes.

1. In $\triangle ABC$, $\angle A = 90°$ and $\angle B = 60°$. How many degrees are there in $\angle C$?

2. One angle of a parallelogram is 43°. Evaluate the other angles.

3. AOB and COD are straight lines. If $\angle 1 = \angle 3 = 40°$, how many degrees are there in $\angle 2$, $\angle 4$, and $\angle 5$?

EX. 3

4. Draw any line AB. Find by construction the difference between one third and one half of AB.

5. Four angles of a pentagon are 90°, 100°, 120°, and 110°. How many degrees are there in the fifth angle?

6. $ABCDE$ is a regular pentagon. How many degrees are there in $\angle ADB$?

7. How many sides has a polygon if the sum of the interior angles is 3240°?

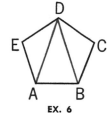

EX. 6

8. Can one exterior angle of some regular polygon be 13°? Explain.

9. Prove: AB and CD intersect at E, and AD and BC are drawn. If $\angle A = \angle B$, then $\angle C = \angle D$.

10. Prove: If two triangles have two angles and the bisector of one of these angles equal, respectively, to two angles and the corresponding bisector of the other, they are congruent.

11. Prove: If two base angles of a trapezoid are equal, the trapezoid is isosceles.

12. In $\triangle ABC$, AD bisects $\angle A$, BD bisects $\angle B$, a line through D is parallel to AB and intersects AC and BC at E and F respectively. Prove that $EF = AE + BF$.

13. Prove: In an isosceles triangle, the bisector of the exterior angle formed by extending one of the equal sides beyond the vertex angle is parallel to the base.

14. One base of a trapezoid is 10 in. and the other is 8 in. How long is the median?

15. The median of a trapezoid is 7 in. and one base is 9 in. How long is the other base?

16. Construct an equilateral triangle. Divide the base into three equal parts and connect the points of division with the opposite vertex. Are the three triangles thus formed congruent?

17. Prove: If the diagonal of a parallelogram bisects an angle, the figure is a rhombus.

18. Prove: If lines from the extremities of one diagonal of a parallelogram are drawn perpendicular to the other diagonal and terminated at that diagonal, the lines are equal.

19. $ABCD$ is a parallelogram, and E and F are the middle points of BC and AD respectively. Prove that $BFDE$ is a parallelogram.

20. $ABCD$ is a parallelogram, $BE \perp AD$, and $CF \perp AD$. E and F are on AD or AD extended. Prove that $BEFC$ is a rectangle. Prove that $\triangle ABE \cong \triangle DCF$.

21. $ABCD$ is a parallelogram. Points E, F, G, and H are taken on sides AB, BC, CD, and DA, respectively, so that $AE = BF = CG = DH$. Prove that $EFGH$ is a parallelogram.

22. Each half of the diagonals of a parallelogram is bisected and the points of division are joined by straight lines. Prove that the figure thus formed is a parallelogram.

23. D and E are the middle points of AC and BC in $\triangle ABC$. AE and BD intersect at O. F and G are the middle points of AO and BO respectively. Prove that $FG = DE$.

24. Prove: Lines joining the extremities of two diameters of a circle form a rectangle.

25. Prove: The base angles of an isosceles trapezoid are equal angles.

I. Vocabulary.

1. Illustrate each of the following terms by drawing a figure.

Polygon

Equilateral polygon

Equiangular polygon

Regular polygon

Convex polygon

Quadrilateral

Pentagon

Hexagon

Octagon

Decagon

Interior angles of a polygon

Exterior angles of a polygon

Parallelogram

Rectangle

Rhombus

Square

Trapezoid

Bases of trapezoid

Isosceles trapezoid

Median of trapezoid

II. Parallelograms.

2. Prove that the opposite sides and the opposite angles of a parallelogram are equal and that the diagonals bisect each other.

3. Prove that a quadrilateral is a parallelogram if the opposite sides are equal, if two sides are parallel and equal, or if the diagonals bisect each other.

4. Prove that the diagonals of a rectangle or a square are equal.

5. Prove that the diagonals of a rhombus or a square are perpendicular to each other and that they bisect the angles to which they are drawn.

III. Other Theorems (or Postulates).

Complete the following:

6. The sum of the angles of a triangle is _?_, the sum of the interior angles of a polygon of n sides is _?_, and the sum of the exterior angles is _?_.

7. The acute angles of a right triangle are _?_.

8. An exterior angle of a triangle equals the sum of _?_.

9. If a line joins the middle points of two sides of a triangle, _?_.

10. The median of a trapezoid is parallel _?_.

11. If three or more parallel lines cut off equal segments on one transversal, _?_.

TEST 1

Write the numbers 1 to 20 in a column. After each number write True *or* False *to indicate that the corresponding statement on this page is true (under all conditions) or false.*

1. The sum of the exterior angles of a hexagon is the same as the sum of the interior angles of a pentagon.

2. The successive angles of a parallelogram are equal.

3. The diagonals of a parallelogram bisect the angles.

4. If in $\triangle ABC$, $\angle B = \angle A + \angle C$, then $\angle B = 90°$.

5. One angle of a regular decagon contains 144°.

6. The diagonals of a parallelogram are equal.

7. If $\angle 1 = \angle 2$ and $\angle B = \angle D$, then $\triangle ACD \cong \triangle ACB$.

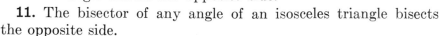

8. In a rhombus each diagonal is the perpendicular bisector of the other.

9. A line that bisects one side of a triangle bisects the other side also.

10. The bisector of any angle of an equilateral triangle bisects the opposite side.

EX. 7

11. The bisector of any angle of an isosceles triangle bisects the opposite side.

12. The bisector of any angle of an isosceles triangle meets the opposite side at right angles.

13. The bisector of any angle of an equilateral triangle meets the opposite side at right angles.

14. Two isosceles triangles are congruent if they have equal vertex angles.

15. If a line through the vertex of a triangle and perpendicular to the base also bisects the base, the triangle is isosceles.

16. The diagonals of a rectangle are perpendicular.

17. A quadrilateral with equal diagonals is a rhombus.

18. An equilateral quadrilateral has perpendicular diagonals.

19. The adjacent sides of a rectangle are equal.

20. If the opposite angles of a quadrilateral are supplementary, the figure is a parallelogram.

TEST 2

Be ready to give reasons for your answers:

1. If $ABCD$ is a rectangle, $\angle A = \underline{\ ?\ }°$.
2. $\triangle ABC$ is isosceles. If $\angle B = 90°$, $\angle C = \underline{\ ?\ }°$.
3. $ABCD$ is a parallelogram. If $\angle A = 37°$, $\angle B = \underline{\ ?\ }°$.
4. $ABCD$ is a rhombus. If $AB = 6''$, $BC = \underline{\ ?\ }''$.
5. If I draw all possible diagonals from one vertex of a decagon, $\underline{\ ?\ }$ triangles will be formed.
6. The sum of the angles of a polygon of 14 sides is $\underline{\ ?\ }°$.
7. One angle of a regular polygon of 20 sides is $\underline{\ ?\ }°$.

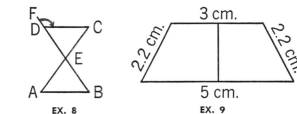

EX. 8   EX. 9

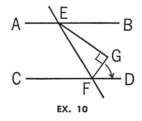

EX. 10

8. $AB \parallel CD$. If $\angle A = 75°$ and $\angle AEB = 40°$, then $\angle FDC = \underline{\ ?\ }°$.

9. The median of this trapezoid equals $\underline{\ ?\ }$ cm.

10. $AB \parallel CD$. EG bisects $\angle BEF$, $\angle G = 90°$. If $\angle GEF = 25°$, $\angle GFD = \underline{\ ?\ }$.

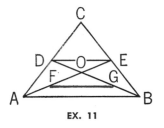

EX. 11

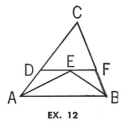

EX. 12

11. D and E are the middle points of AC and BC. F and G are the middle points of AO and BO. If $DE = 2''$, then $FG = \underline{\ ?\ }''$.

12. AE bisects $\angle A$, BE bisects $\angle B$, and $DEF \parallel AB$. If $AD = 1''$ and $DF = 1\frac{1}{2}''$, then $BF = \underline{\ ?\ }''$.

13. The line joining the midpoints of the bases of an isosceles trapezoid is $\underline{\ ?\ }$ to the bases.

TESTING YOUR UNDERSTANDING   **205**

CHAPTER **8** The Circle — A Unique Geometric Figure

THE CIRCLE has many characteristics that are possessed by no other plane figure. It is the only figure that can be rotated about a point without changing its apparent position. It is the only figure that is symmetrical with respect to an infinite number of axes of symmetry. It is the only continuous curved line of definite length such that any portion of it can be made to coincide with any other portion of equal length. It encloses more surface than any other figure or curve having the same length. The circle is important in art, and is necessary to industry.

In starting this new topic, you must again have definitions and postulates. The terms *circle, center, radius, diameter, arc,* and *semicircle* have already been defined (see pages 2 and 3).

△ *The* **circumference** *of a circle is the length of the circle.*

△ *A* **minor arc** *is an arc less than a semicircle.* Arc AB in Fig. 1 below is a minor arc. Arc AB is often written $\overset{\frown}{AB}$. *A* **major arc** *is an arc greater than a semicircle.* Arc $CDEF$ in Fig. 1 is a major arc.

△ **Concentric circles** *are circles with the same center.* (See Fig. 2.)

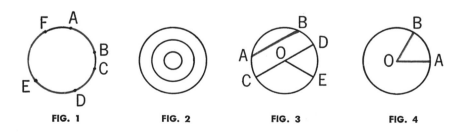

FIG. 1   FIG. 2   FIG. 3   FIG. 4

△ A **chord** is a line joining any two points on a circle. The straight line *AB* in Fig. 3 is a chord. *CD* is a *diameter*. *OC*, *OD*, and *OE* are *radii*.

△ A **central angle** of a circle is an angle with its vertex at the center and with radii for its sides. ∠*AOB* in Fig. 4 is a central angle. Arc *AB*, cut off by ∠*AOB*, is said to be **intercepted** by ∠*AOB*. (*Intercepted* means *cut off*.)

Postulates

1 Two circles are equal if their radii or their diameters are equal.
2 A diameter bisects a circle.
3 If a line bisects a circle and is terminated by the circle, it is a diameter.
4 A straight line cannot intersect a circle in more than two points.
5 If the distance from a point to the center of a circle is equal to a radius, the point lies on the circle. If the distance from a point to the center of a circle is greater than a radius, the point lies outside the circle. If the distance from a point to the center of a circle is less than a radius, the point lies within the circle.
6 In the same circle or in equal circles, equal central angles have equal arcs. (If ∠*AOB* = ∠*COD*, then arc *AB* = arc *CD*.)
7 In the same circle or in equal circles, equal arcs have equal central angles. (If arc *AB* = arc *CD*, then ∠*AOB* = ∠*COD*.)

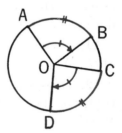

EXERCISES

1. Draw a figure for each of the postulates above and, using the figure, explain what the postulate means.

2. *O* is the center of the circle. Name the chords, the minor arcs intercepted by the chords, the central angles, and the arcs intercepted by the central angles.

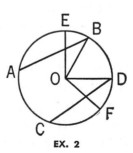

EX. 2

3. O and O' are the centers of two circles as shown. Are the circles equal? Why?

4. AB is a diameter and arc ACB is 7 inches long. How long is arc ADB? Why?

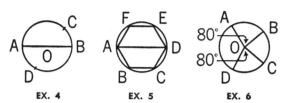

EX. 4   EX. 5   EX. 6

5. Arc $ABCD$ = arc $DEFA$. Is AD a diameter? Why?

6. In the figure, O is the center of the circle, $\angle AOB$ and $\angle COD$ are each 80°. What arcs are equal? Why?

7. Complete: A circle is determined (definitely located) if its _?_ and its _?_ are known.

8. Draw two circles having **a** no points in common, **b** one point in common, **c** two points in common. In **c** draw the common chord.

9. Are all diameters chords? Are all chords diameters?

10. Four points A, B, C, and D are placed in succession on a circle so that arc AB = arc CD and arc BC = arc DA. Is AC a diameter? Why?

11. Does the bisector of a central angle bisect the intercepted arc? Why?

12. Does a line connecting the middle point of an arc with the center of the circle bisect the central angle that intercepts the arc? Why?

13. Prove: Two intersecting diameters intercept two equal pairs of arcs.

14. Prove: If three diameters divide a circle into six equal arcs, the six angles at the center contain 60° each.

15. Construct two equal circles and draw central angles of 90° in each. Draw the chords of these central angles. How do they compare in length?

16. CD is perpendicular to the radius OA at its outer extremity A. OB is any other line from O meeting CD at B. Prove that B lies outside the circle.

17. Prove: Equal arcs of the same circle have equal chords.

18. In a circle draw a diameter and construct a diameter perpendicular to it. Prove that the circle is divided into four equal parts.

19. Draw a large circle and divide it into eight equal parts. Prove that your construction is correct.

20. Prove: If AB and CD are diameters of the same circle, then arc AC = arc BD.

EXTRA

21. Prove: If a radius bisects an arc, it bisects the chord of the arc and is perpendicular to it.

22. Prove: A line through the center of a circle and perpendicular to a chord bisects the arc of the chord.

23. AO and BO are two radii. At A and B lines are drawn perpendicular to AO and BO, intersecting at C. Prove that CO bisects arc AB.

THEOREM
27 | *In the same circle or in equal circles, equal chords have equal arcs.*

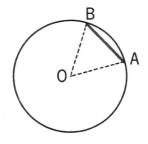 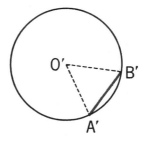

Given ⊙O = ⊙O' with chord AB = chord $A'B'$.
To prove that arc AB = arc $A'B'$.
The *plan* is to prove that the triangles are congruent and then use Postulate 6, page 207.
Proof. The proof is left for you.

THEOREM 27   **209**

<table>
<tr><td>THEOREM
28</td><td>|</td><td>*In the same circle or in equal circles, equal arcs have equal chords.*</td></tr>
</table>

Use Postulate 7, page 207, and then prove that the triangles are congruent.

EXERCISES

1. How can you prove that two arcs are equal?

2. How can you prove that two chords are equal?

3. Is the chord of a central angle of 120° twice as great as the chord of a central angle of 60°?

4. Compare the chord of a 60° central angle with the radius of the circle.

5. How large is the central angle of a chord that is equal to the radius of a circle?

6. Two equal circles intersect at A and B. Prove that the two arcs AB are equal.

<table>
<tr><td>THEOREM
29</td><td>|</td><td>*If a line through the center of a circle is perpendicular to a chord, it bisects the chord and its arc.*</td></tr>
</table>

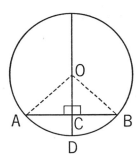

Given ⊙O with $OCD \perp AB$.

To prove that arc AD = arc DB and that $AC = CB$.

The *plan* is to prove that the triangles are congruent.

Proof. The triangles are congruent. (Rt. △ with $h.s. = h.s.$)

COROLLARY **A line through the center of a circle and bisecting a chord (not a diameter) is perpendicular to it.**

EXERCISES

1. A circle is divided into three equal parts and lines are drawn connecting the points of division. Prove that an equilateral triangle is formed.

2. $\triangle ABC$ is inscribed in a circle (all three vertices are on the circle) and has $\angle A = \angle C$. Prove that arc AB = arc BC.

3. In $\odot O$, OB is a radius perpendicular to chord AC. Prove that $\angle CAB = \angle ACB$.

4. The point P on a circle is equally distant from the radii OA and OB. Prove that P is the middle point of arc AB.

5. Prove: Two equal chords that are drawn from one end of a diameter of a circle make equal angles with the diameter.

Before you study Theorems 30 and 31

Theorem 30 reads: *In the same circle or in equal circles equal chords are equally distant from the center.* What is given and what is to be proved?

In $\odot O$, $AB = CD$, $OE \perp AB$, and $OF \perp CD$. You are to prove that $OE = OF$.

Look at your conclusion. You can prove that $OE = OF$ if you can prove that _?_.

What kind of triangles are $\triangle AOE$ and $\triangle COF$? State two methods of proving right triangles congruent.

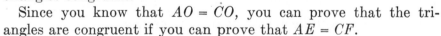

Since you know that $AO = CO$, you can prove that the triangles are congruent if you can prove that $AE = CF$.

You know that $AE = \frac{1}{2}AB$ and $CF = \frac{1}{2}CD$. Why?

$AE = CF$. Why? The triangles are congruent and $OE = OF$.

Theorem 31 reads: *In the same circle or in equal circles, chords equally distant from the center are equal.* What are the hypothesis and the conclusion?

Use the above figure. In $\odot O$, $OE \perp AB$, $OF \perp CD$, and $OE = OF$. You are to prove that $AB = CD$.

This is a converse of what you have already done on this page and requires much the same kind of proof in *reverse order*.

To prove $AB = CD$ note that $AB = 2AE$ and $CD = 2CF$.

You can prove that $AB = CD$ if you can prove that $AE = CF$.

You *can* prove that $AE = CF$ because $\triangle AEO \cong \triangle CFO$.

THEOREM 30

In the same circle or in equal circles, equal chords are equally distant from the center.

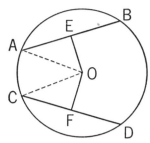

Given $\odot O$ with $AB = CD$, $OE \perp AB$, and $OF \perp CD$.

To prove that $OE = OF$.

The *plan* is to prove that the triangles are congruent.

Proof. Draw OA and OC.

STATEMENTS	REASONS
1. $AB = CD$, $OE \perp AB$, $OF \perp CD$.	1. Given.
2. $AE = \frac{1}{2}AB$, $CF = \frac{1}{2}CD$.	2. Why?
3. $AE = CF$.	3. Halves of equals are equal.

Now prove that $\triangle AOE \cong \triangle COF$. The rest is left for you.

THEOREM 31

In the same circle or in equal circles, chords equally distant from the center are equal.

Use the figure above.

Given $\odot O$ with $OE \perp AB$, $OF \perp CD$, and $OE = OF$.

To prove that $AB = CD$.

Outline of proof. Draw OA and OC.

First prove that $\triangle AOE \cong \triangle COF$.

Then $AE = CF$. *C.p.c.t.e.*

$AB = 2AE$ and $CD = 2CF$. (Theorem 29)

So $AB = CD$. Doubles of equals are equal.

You can now prove that two chords are equal if you can prove that they are equally distant from the center. This means that you must prove that the *perpendiculars* from the center to the chords are equal.

212   THE CIRCLE

EXERCISES

1. ABC is an equilateral triangle. O is the center of the circle. $OD \perp BC$, $OE \perp CA$, $OF \perp AB$. If $OD = 7''$, how long are OE and OF?

2. If in the same figure, instead of having $OD = 7$ inches you have $CD = 7''$, what is the perimeter of the triangle?

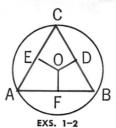

EXS. 1–2

3. O is the center. $OE \perp AB$, $OF \perp CD$, $OE = 3''$, and $OF = 3''$. If $AB = 10''$, how long is CD?

4. In the same figure, arc AB = arc CD, $OE \perp AB$, $OF \perp CD$, and $OE = 5''$. How long is OF?

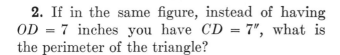

EXS. 3–4

5. $ABCDEF$ is a regular hexagon with its vertices on the circle. O is the center. OG, OH, OK, OM, ON, and OP are equal and perpendicular to the sides. Show that a circle with radius OG will pass through the points H, K, M, N, and P.

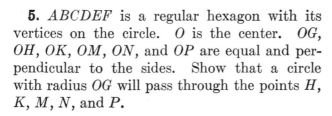

EX. 5

6. O is the center of the circle. $OD \perp AB$, $OE \perp BC$, OD and OE are each $5''$ and $BE = 12''$. How long is AB?

7. O is the center of the circle, $OE \perp AB$, $OF \perp CD$, and $\angle 1 = \angle 2$. Prove that $AB = CD$.

8. In the same figure, O is the center of the circle, $OE \perp AB$, $OF \perp CD$, and $AB = CD$. Prove that $\angle 1 = \angle 2$.

EX. 6

9. Chords AB and BC make equal angles with the diameter drawn to the point B. Prove the chords equal.

10. AB and BC are equal chords. Prove that the diameter BD bisects $\angle B$.

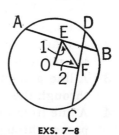

EXS. 7–8

USING THEOREMS 30 AND 31

■ Tangent to a Circle

In the figure the line RS touches the circle at only one point S and it has no other point in common with the circle even when extended. Line XY also has only one point Z in common with the circle.

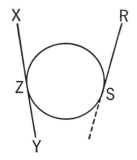

△ *A line which touches a circle at only one point, even when extended, is called a* **tangent** *to the circle.* The circle is also tangent to the line.

Lines RS and XY are tangent to the circle at points S and Z, respectively.

△ *The point that a tangent and a circle have in common is called the* **point of tangency** *or the* **point of contact.**

1. Draw a circle and a radius OC. At C *draw* a line perpendicular to OC. Does the line seem to be tangent to the circle?

2. Draw a circle and lay your ruler against it as shown. Draw AB which will have only one point C in common with the circle. Draw the radius OC. What kind of angle does $\angle OCB$ appear to be?

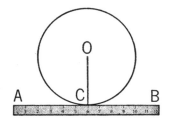

3. Draw a circle and a line which appears to be tangent to it. Draw a line perpendicular to the tangent at the point of contact. Does this line go through the center of the circle?

4. Draw a circle and a line which appears to be tangent to it. From the center of the circle, draw a line perpendicular to the tangent. Does this line pass through the point of contact?

Postulates

1 A straight line perpendicular to a radius at its outer extremity is tangent to the circle.
2 A tangent to a circle is perpendicular to the radius drawn to the point of contact.
3 A line perpendicular to a tangent at its point of contact passes through the center of the circle.
4 A line from the center of a circle and perpendicular to a tangent passes through the point of contact.

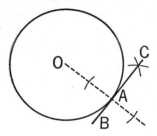

Given $\odot O$ with point A on it.

Required to construct a tangent to $\odot O$ at A.

The construction and proof are left for you. (Remember that
you can prove that a line is tangent to a circle if you can prove
that it is perpendicular to a radius at its outer extremity.)

△ The **length of a tangent from a point to a circle** *is the
length of the segment of the tangent from the given point to the point
of contact.* AB (shown below) is the length of the tangent from A.

**THEOREM
32**

**The tangents to a circle from a point outside the
circle are equal.**

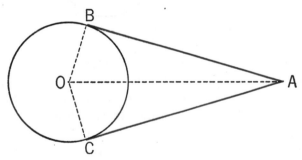

Given $\odot O$ with tangents AB and AC.

To prove that $AB = AC$.

The *plan* is to draw lines as indicated and prove that $\triangle ABO$
and $\triangle ACO$ are congruent. (What kind of triangle is each?)

Proof. The proof is left for you.

COROLLARY **If two tangents are drawn to a circle from an outside
point, the line from the point to the center bisects the
angle between the tangents.**

■ Tangent Circles

△ *Two circles are said to be **tangent to each other** if they are both tangent to the same line at the same point. They are tangent internally if one circle lies within the other (⊙O and ⊙O'). They are tangent externally if each circle lies outside the other (⊙O and ⊙O'').*

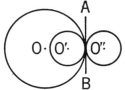

△ *The **line of centers** of two circles is the line joining their centers.*

THEOREM 33	*If two circles are tangent to each other, their line of centers passes through the point of contact.*

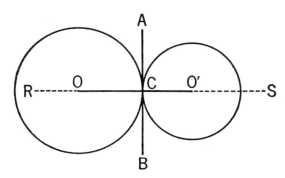

Given   ⊙O and ⊙O', both tangent to AB at C.

To prove   that OO' passes through C.

The *plan* is to draw a line that we know passes through C and then prove that OO' is in this same straight line.

Proof.   At C draw RS ⊥ AB.

STATEMENTS	REASONS
1. AB is tangent to ⊙O and ⊙O'.	1. Given.
2. RS ⊥ AB at C.	2. Construction.
3. RS passes through O and O'.	3. Postulate 3, page 214.
4. OO' and RS are the same straight line.	4. Postulate 3, page 89.
5. OO' passes through C.	5. It is also line RS.

EXERCISES

1. AC is tangent to $\odot O$ and OB is a radius. If $\angle C = 40°$, how many degrees are there in $\angle O$? Explain.

2. In the same figure OB is a radius and $AC \perp OB$ through B. How many points has AC in common with the circle? Explain.

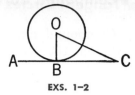

EXS. 1–2

3. How would you construct two lines tangent to a given circle and parallel to each other?

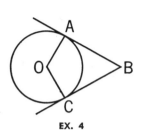 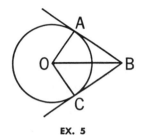 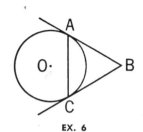

EX. 4   EX. 5   EX. 6

4. AB and BC are tangents to $\odot O$. O is the center. If $\angle B = 60°$, how many degrees are there in $\angle O$? (Hint. What is the sum of the angles of $ABCO$?)

5. AB and BC are tangents to $\odot O$. O is the center. If $\angle ABO = 35°$, how many degrees are there in $\angle AOC$?

6. AB and BC are tangents to circle O. If $\angle B = 55°$, how many degrees are there in $\angle BAC$ and in $\angle BCA$?

7. Prove: If two tangents from a point outside a circle form an angle of 60°, the chord joining the points of contact makes with them an equilateral triangle.

EXTRA

8. Isosceles triangle ABC in which $AB = BC$ is drawn around a circle in such a way that its sides are all tangent to the circle. Prove that AC is bisected at the point of contact.

9. If the angle between two tangents to a circle is as follows, how many degrees are there in the angle formed by each tangent and the chord joining the points of contact?

$$a° \qquad\qquad b° \qquad\qquad a° + b° \qquad\qquad a° - b°$$

$$\frac{a° + b°}{2} \qquad\qquad a° + \frac{b°}{2} \qquad\qquad 180° - \frac{a°}{2} \qquad\qquad 90° + \frac{a°}{3}$$

USING TANGENTS

▪Compound Curves — *Optional*

Compound curves are made by joining two arcs of tangent circles at their point of contact.

Circles O and O' are externally tangent at B. The arcs AB and BC form a compound curve. The arcs are not necessarily as long as the semicircles in Fig. 1.

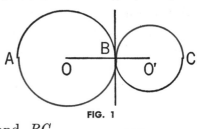

FIG. 1

Circles O and O', Fig. 2, are internally tangent at B. Arcs AB and BC form a compound curve.

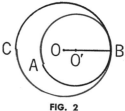

FIG. 2

Fig. 3 is a compound curve used by architects in the design for a molding. The height AD is divided into three equal parts. The first point of division, O, is used as center and OD as radius of the larger circle. The small figure $OO'BA$ is a square. $\odot O'$ is drawn with O' as center and OO' as radius. $\odot O$ is drawn with O as center and OD as radius. Since $OD = 2(OO')$, the circles are tangent internally and $DCBO$ is a compound curve.

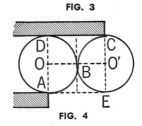

FIG. 3

Fig. 4 shows another compound curve used in architecture. $AECD$ is a square. O and O' are the mid-points of sides. Tangent circles are drawn with O and O' as centers and half the height AD as radius. The resulting compound curve for the design is shown in color.

FIG. 4

Fig. 5 shows part of a pattern for a plywood wing tip for the wing of an airplane. The height AD is divided into 6 equal parts at R, O, S, O', and T. Circles O and O' are drawn with OA as radius. The point P is one of the intersections of the two circles. A circle is drawn with P as center and POB as radius. The compound curve is shown in color. Arc AB is a part of $\odot O$, arc BC is a part of $\odot P$, and arc CD is a part of $\odot O'$.

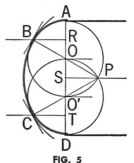

FIG. 5

THE CIRCLE

■ Common Tangents

△ *A line tangent to each of two circles is called a **common tangent.*** If the circles lie on opposite sides of the tangent, it is a ***common internal tangent,*** *as AB.*

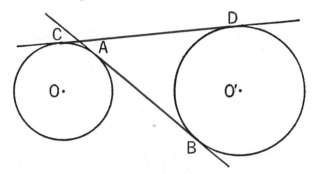

If the circles lie on the same side of the tangent, it is a ***common external tangent,*** *as CD.* The length of these tangents is the length of the segment between the points of contact.

1. Draw two circles that have two common external tangents and two common internal tangents.

2. Draw two circles that have one common internal tangent and two common external tangents.

3. Draw two circles that have two common external tangents and no common internal tangent.

4. Draw two circles that have one common external tangent and no common internal tangent.

5. Draw two circles that have no common tangents.

6. Prove: If two circles are so situated that they have one common internal tangent and two common external tangents, the part of the internal tangent between the other two tangents is one half the sum of the external tangents.

△ *A polygon is said to be **circumscribed about a circle** if all its sides are tangent to the circle. In this case the circle is **inscribed** in the polygon.*

△ *A polygon is said to be **inscribed in a circle** if all its vertices lie on the circle. In this case the circle is said to be **circumscribed** about the polygon.*

EXERCISES

1. In each figure below AB is a common tangent to two circles. In which figure is it a common internal tangent? In which figure is it a common external tangent?

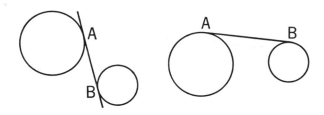

2. In both of the figures below the circles are tangent to each other. In which figure are they tangent internally? In which figure are they tangent externally?

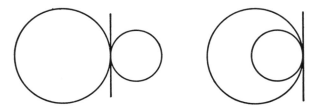

3. Two circles are tangent externally. The radius of the larger circle is 7″ and the radius of the smaller circle is 5″. How long is the line of centers? Explain.

4. If the circles in Ex. 3 are tangent internally, how long is their line of centers?

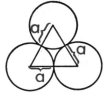

5. Three circles, whose radii are each a inches, are tangent externally as shown. Prove that the lines of centers form an equilateral triangle.

6. An inscribed triangle ABC has $AB = BC$. Through B a diameter BD is drawn. Prove that arc AD = arc DC.

7. Prove: If two circles are tangent externally, the tangents drawn to each from any point in the common internal tangent are equal.

8. Prove: If two circles are tangent externally, the common internal tangent bisects their common external tangent.

1. If from any point A on one of two equal chords a line is drawn through the center O to B on the other chord and AO equals OB, then the equal chords will also be parallel.

2. AB and AC, two tangents to circle O from a point A, make an angle of 60° with each other. Prove that the circle bisects AO.

3. AOB is a diameter of a circle whose center is O. Chord AC is drawn. A line tangent to the circle at C meets a line through O parallel to AC at D. Prove that DB is tangent to the circle.

4. Two radii, AO and BO, are perpendicular to each other. A tangent to the circle at some point on arc AB meets OA and OB extended in C and D respectively. Prove that the two tangents to the circle drawn from the points C and D are parallel.

5. Three equal circles are tangent to each other so that each circle touches the other two. Prove that the three common internal tangents meet at a point which is equally distant from the centers of the circles.

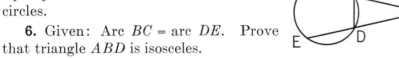

6. Given: Arc BC = arc DE. Prove that triangle ABD is isosceles.

7. Two externally tangent circles are each tangent internally to a third circle. Prove that the perimeter of the triangle formed by joining the centers of the three circles is equal to the diameter of the outer circle.

8. From any point B on the common internal tangent of two equal circles that are tangent externally at A, BO and BO' are drawn to the centers of these circles. If BO and BO' intersect the circles at C and D, prove that BC equals BD.

9. Lines are drawn from the vertices of a circumscribed quadrilateral to the center of the circle. Prove that any central angle is supplementary to the central angle that is not adjacent to it.

10. Two tangents AB and BC are drawn from a point B outside of a circle, touching the circle at A and C. A third tangent DE is drawn through any point of the intercepted arc. Prove that the perimeter of the triangle formed by the three tangents is equal to the sum of AB and BC.

In Exs. 1–4, AB is a diameter and O is the center of the circle. Show that the following statements are true:

1. If $\angle ACD = \angle ADC$, then arc AC = arc AD.

2. If $AB \perp CD$, then $AC = AD$.

3. If arc CB = arc DB, then $AC = AD$.

4. If $\angle COB = \angle DOB$, then $AC = AD$.

EXS. 1–4

5. Prove: If a diameter bisects the angle between two chords intersecting within a circle, the chords are equal.

6. Prove: If two equal chords intersect within a circle, the diameter through the point of intersection bisects the angle between them.

7. AB and AC are respectively a chord and a diameter of a circle. Prove that a radius parallel to AB bisects arc BC.

8. CD is a chord parallel to a diameter AB. Prove that arc AC = arc BD.

9. In the figure, AC is a diameter, OD is a radius, and arc BD = arc DC. Prove that AB is parallel to OD.

10. Construct a line that will be tangent to a given circle and parallel to a given line.

11. Construct a chord equal to a given chord and parallel to a given line. Prove that your construction is correct.

12. In a given circle construct two parallel and equal chords. Prove that your construction is correct.

13. AB and AC are tangent to $\odot O$ at B and C. Prove that OA bisects BC and is perpendicular to it.

14. Prove: The sum of one pair of opposite sides of a quadrilateral circumscribed about a circle is equal to the sum of the other pair.

THE CIRCLE

15. Prove: An angle formed by two tangents is supplementary to the angle between the radii drawn to the points of contact.

16. *AP* and *BP* are tangents with *A* and *B* the points of tangency, and *AOC* is a diameter. Prove that *OP* ∥ *CB*.

17. *AB* and *CD* are parallel tangents; *FG* is a tangent from any point *F* on *AB* meeting *CD* at *G*; and *O* is the center of the circle. Prove that ∠*FOG* is a right angle.

18. Prove: If a line is drawn through the point of contact of two externally tangent circles and is terminated by the two circles, the radii drawn to its extremities are parallel.

19. Prove: A radius that bisects an arc bisects the chord of the arc.

20. Prove: The common internal tangents of two circles are equal.

21. Prove: The common external tangents of two circles are equal.

22. *CD* is tangent to circle *O* at *A* and *BA* is a diameter. *RS* is a chord parallel to *CD*. Prove that *BA* bisects *RS*.

23. *ABCD* is any circumscribed quadrilateral. Prove that ∠*DOC* + ∠*AOB* = 180°.

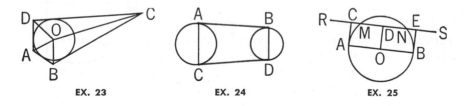

EX. 23   EX. 24   EX. 25

24. *AB* and *CD* are common external tangents. Prove that *AC* ∥ *BD*.

25. *AB* is a diameter. *RS* cuts the circle at *M* and *N*. *O* is the center of the circle. *AC*, *OD*, and *BE* ⊥ *RS*. Prove that *CM* = *NE*.

■ Solid Geometry — *Optional*

1. When you fold over a piece of paper and make a crease, could this crease ever be a curved line? When you look at Figure 1, do you "see" the three-dimensional figure formed by a folded sheet of paper?

When two planes intersect, the intersection is a straight line. In Figure 1 the planes are AC and BD. Their intersection is the line AB.

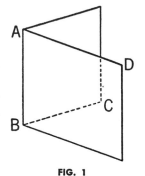

FIG. 1

△ *The figure formed by two intersecting planes is a **dihedral angle**.* AB is the **edge,** and planes AC and BD are the **faces.**

2. Make a copy of Figure 1. Then choose any point E on AB. Represent a line $EF \perp AB$ in plane AC and a line $EG \perp AB$ in plane BD.

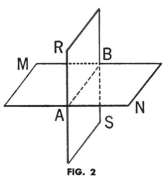

FIG. 2

3. Figure 2 represents a horizontal plane intersecting a vertical plane in the line AB. How many dihedral angles do you see? Draw this figure. Take any point C on AB and represent a line CD perpendicular to plane MN. Do you think that CD lies in the plane RS?

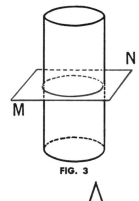

FIG. 3

4. Figure 3 at the right represents a **cylinder.** The upper and lower bases are circles in parallel planes. The plane MN is a plane parallel to the planes of the bases. What do you think is the nature of the intersection of the plane and the surface of the cylinder?

5. Figure 4 represents a **cone** with a circular base. Draw this figure and represent a plane parallel to the base of the cone and intersecting its curved surface. What is the nature of the intersection?

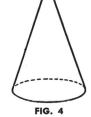

FIG. 4

THE CIRCLE

■ Spheres — *Optional*

Spheres in space correspond to circles in a plane.

△ *A **sphere** is a surface any point of which is at a given distance from a point within it called the **center**.* A baseball or a basketball is an illustration of a sphere. Figure 1 represents a sphere. *O* is the center, *BC* is a diameter, and *OA* is a radius.

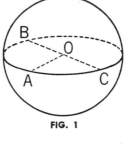

FIG. 1

1. Figure 2 represents a sphere cut by a plane. What is the nature of the intersection of the plane and the surface of the sphere? (Think of an orange with part of it sliced off.)

The intersection of a plane and a sphere is always a circle, the largest possible circle being made by a plane which contains the center of the sphere. A circle formed by the intersection of a sphere and a plane through its center is called a **great circle**.

Circle *ABC* (Fig. 1) is a great circle.

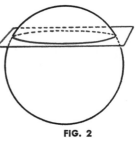

FIG. 2

2. Figure 3 represents the earth. The equator *WE* is a great circle. The other circles of latitude are made by planes parallel to the plane of the equator. Are these circles as large as the equator? The meridians are great circles made by planes passing through the diameter *NS* from north pole to south pole. Considering the earth to be spherical, are all these circles the same size?

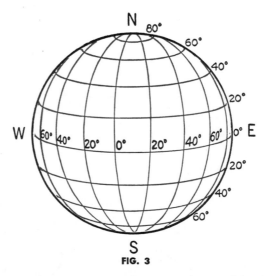

FIG. 3

*The **shortest distance between any two points on the surface of a sphere** is the minor arc of the great circle passing through them.*

I. Vocabulary.

1. Draw a figure to help you show the meaning of each of the following terms:

Circle   Major arc   Lines of centers
Center of circle   Concentric circles   Inscribed polygon
Radius   Chord   Circumscribed polygon
Diameter   Central angle   Inscribed circle
Semicircle   Intercepted arc   Circumscribed circle
Arc   Tangent   Tangent circles
Minor arc   Point of tangency   External tangent
                 Internal tangent

II. Postulates.

2. State the postulates suggested by these figures:

  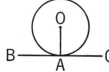 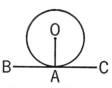

$\angle AOB = \angle COD$ Arc AB = Arc CD OA is a radius. OA is a radius.
                                    BC is tangent at A. $BC \perp AO$ at A.

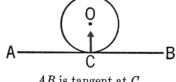 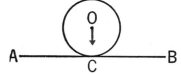

AB is tangent at C. AB is tangent at C.
$AB \perp CO$ at C. $OC \perp AB$

III. Theorems.

3. State the theorems suggested by these three figures:

$AB = CD$ Arc AB = Arc CD $OA \perp DC$

4. State the theorems suggested by the following figures:

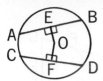

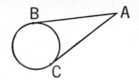

$AB = CD$
$OE \perp AB$
$OF \perp CD$

$OE \perp AB$
$OF \perp CD$
$OE = OF$

AB and AC are tangents.

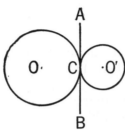

$\odot O$ and $\odot O'$ are both tangent to AB at C.

Testing Your Understanding

TEST 1

Give an authority for each of the following statements. In case more than one reason is necessary, give the final one.

1. If BC is tangent to a circle at A and OA is a radius, $\angle OAB = 90°$.

2. If arc ABC is a semicircle, AC is a diameter.

3. O is the center of a circle and A, B, and C are on the circle. If $\angle AOB = 65°$ and $\angle BOC = 65°$, then arc AB = arc BC.

4. O is the center of a circle and A, B, and C are on the circle. If $OC \perp AB$, then arc AC = arc CB.

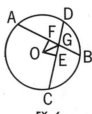

EX. 6

5. $\triangle ABC$ inscribed in a circle is equilateral. Therefore arc AB = arc BC = arc AC.

6. $OF \perp AB$, $OE \perp CD$, $AB = 5$ cm., $CD = 5$ cm. Therefore $\triangle OGE \cong \triangle OGF$.

7. If AB and BC are tangents and O is the center of the circle, $\angle 1 = \angle 2$.

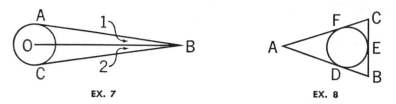

EX. 7   EX. 8

8. ABC is a circumscribed triangle. Therefore $AF = AD$, $BE = BD$, and $CE = CF$.

9. If AB and CD are tangents to a circle at points P and Q and PQ is a diameter, then $AB \parallel CD$.

10. If two circles are tangent externally, their line of centers is equal to the sum of the radii.

11. In order to bisect a given arc, I can draw the chord of the arc and construct a perpendicular to it from the center, then extend the perpendicular until it meets the arc.

12. If arc AB = arc BC = arc CD = arc DE = arc EA, then $ABCDE$ is an equilateral pentagon.

TEST 2

Be ready to give reasons for your answers.

1. OA is a radius of a circle and AB is a chord equal to OA. If the circumference of the circle is 24 in., the arc AB is _?_ in.

2. A, B, C, and D are points on a circle in that order. If $\angle AOB = \angle COD$ and arc AC = 6 in., then arc BD = _?_ in. (O is the center of the circle.)

3. In circle O, the radius OA is perpendicular to the chord CD and COE is a diameter. If $\angle COA = 40°$, then $\angle DOE$ = _?_°.

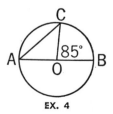

4. AOB is a diameter and AC is a chord. If $\angle COB = 85°$, $\angle CAB$ = _?_°.

EX. 4

5. $AB = CD$ in circle O. If $\angle AEO = 55°$, then $\angle BED = \underline{\ ?\ }°$.

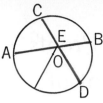

EX. 5

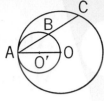

EX. 6

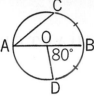

EX. 9

6. O is the center of one circle and O' is the center of a circle tangent to it. If $AC = 5$ in., $AB = \underline{\ ?\ }$ in.

7. AB and CD are diameters of the same circle. If $AC = 2$ in., then $BD = \underline{\ ?\ }$ in.

8. AB is a diameter perpendicular to chord CD. If $\angle ACD = 70°$, then $\angle BAD = \underline{\ ?\ }°$.

9. AB is a diameter and arc $CB =$ arc BD. O is the center of the circle. If $\angle BOD = 80°$, $\angle CAB = \underline{\ ?\ }°$.

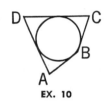

EX. 10

10. $ABCD$ is a circumscribed quadrilateral. $DC = 4$ cm., $BC = 2.3$ cm., $AB = 2.2$ cm., $AD = \underline{\ ?\ }$ cm.

CHAPTER **9** Algebra in Proofs — Measurement of Angles

Euclid, whose monumental work in geometry has been followed for centuries, did not have at hand the algebraic symbolism you have today. If he had known algebra, the chances are that he would have used it in many of his proofs. Algebra is a powerful mathematical tool which simplifies the proofs you will study in this chapter.

However, the chapter is written so that the algebra may be omitted if your teacher so directs.

Before you begin algebra in proofs

Here you will review the algebra you will need in this chapter. Note how simple it is.

1. If $\angle A = 50°$, what is the supplement of $\angle A$? How did you get it?

2. If $\angle A = a°$, what is the supplement of $\angle A$?

3. Write the supplement of each of the following angles.

$$2a° \qquad 3b° \qquad 5x° \qquad 7y°$$

4. Write the complement of each angle in Ex. 3.

5. Write $\frac{1}{2}a$ as a fraction with denominator 2. $\left(\text{Answer } \frac{a}{2}\cdot\right)$

6. Write each of the following as a fraction with denominator 2.

$$\tfrac{1}{2}b \qquad \tfrac{1}{2}(a-b) \qquad \tfrac{1}{2}(180-a) \qquad \tfrac{1}{2}(90-a)$$

7. Write the sum of $\frac{a}{2}$, $\frac{b}{2}$, and $\frac{c}{2}$ as a single fraction.

8. Write each of the following expressions as a single fraction.

$$\frac{x}{3}+\frac{y}{3}; \qquad \frac{2a}{5}+\frac{3b}{5}; \qquad \frac{5a}{6}-\frac{7b}{6}$$

9. If $\angle A = a°$, how many degrees are there in twice $\angle A$?

10. In the equation $2x = a$, solve for x.

11. Solve each equation for x:

$$2x = 4 \qquad\qquad 3x = 12 \qquad\qquad 5x = a \qquad\qquad 7x = b$$

12. Show by adding that $\dfrac{b}{2}+\dfrac{a-b}{2}=\dfrac{a}{2}$.

13. Combine as indicated:

$$\frac{3b}{2}+\frac{a-3b}{2}; \quad \frac{b}{3}+\frac{a-b}{3}; \quad \frac{3y}{5}+\frac{2x-3y}{5}; \quad \frac{4c}{7}+\frac{5x-4c}{7}.$$

14. Is $90°$ when changed to halves equal to $\dfrac{45°}{2}$ or $\dfrac{180°}{2}$?

15. Show by combining that $90-\dfrac{180-a}{2}=\dfrac{a}{2}$.

16. Combine as indicated:

$$45-\frac{90-b}{2} \qquad\qquad 64-\frac{256-3a}{4}$$

$$3-\frac{18-5a}{6} \qquad\qquad 14-\frac{70-2x}{5}$$

17. What is the sum of $\angle 1$, $\angle 2$, $\angle 3$, and $\angle 4$ if $\angle 1 = a°$, $\angle 2 = a°$, $\angle 3 = 90 - a°$, and $\angle 4 = 90 - a°$? If $\angle 1 + \angle 2 = \angle A$ and $\angle 3 + \angle 4 = \angle B$, are $\angle A$ and $\angle B$ supplementary?

18. Combine as indicated:

$$2a + 2a + (180 - 2a) + (180 - 2a)$$

$$3b + 180 - 3b + 3b + 180 - 3b$$

19. Show by combining that $\dfrac{b}{2}-\dfrac{b-a}{2}=\dfrac{a}{2}$.

20. Combine as indicated:

$$\frac{x}{3}-\frac{x-y}{3} \qquad\qquad \frac{2a}{3}-\frac{2a-3}{3}$$

$$\frac{c}{4}-\frac{c-d}{4} \qquad\qquad \frac{3x}{4}-\frac{3x-5y}{4}$$

21. Show by adding that $\dfrac{a}{2} + \dfrac{360 - a}{2} = 180$.

22. Combine as indicated:

$$\dfrac{a}{2} + \dfrac{18 - a}{2} \qquad\qquad \dfrac{2b}{3} + \dfrac{21 - 2b}{3}$$

$$\dfrac{4x}{5} + \dfrac{20 - 4x}{5} \qquad\qquad \dfrac{3b}{4} + \dfrac{36 - 3b}{4}$$

23. Write each expression as one fraction:

    a $\dfrac{a}{2} + \dfrac{b}{2}$ b $\dfrac{a}{2} - \dfrac{b}{2}$ c $\dfrac{a}{3} - \dfrac{b}{3}$

    d $\dfrac{2a}{3} - \dfrac{5b}{3}$ e $\dfrac{3m}{7} - \dfrac{2n}{7}$

24. If $x + \dfrac{b}{2} = \dfrac{a}{2}$, how do you get $x = \dfrac{a}{2} - \dfrac{b}{2}$?

25. Solve for x without clearing of fractions:

$$x + \dfrac{b}{3} = \dfrac{a}{3} \qquad\qquad x - \dfrac{2a}{5} = \dfrac{b}{5}$$

$$x - \dfrac{3b}{4} = \dfrac{5a}{4} \qquad\qquad x + \dfrac{b}{4} = \dfrac{a}{4}$$

■ Using Algebra in Proofs

EXAMPLE 1: Prove that the bisectors of two successive angles of a parallelogram are perpendicular to each other.

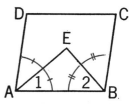

Given $\square ABCD$. AE bisects $\angle A$ and BE bisects $\angle B$.

To prove that $AE \perp BE$.

The *plan* is to show that $\angle E = 90°$, no matter how many degrees there are in the other angles.

You have learned that a letter may represent all possible numbers. If, therefore, you let $\angle A = a°$ and then find that $\angle E = 90°$, the proof is general.

Before you attempt the algebraic proof try two or three special cases to make sure you understand the relationships.

If $\angle A = 70°$, then $\angle B = 110°$. Why? (Figure on page 232.)
$\angle 1 = 35°$ and $\angle 2 = 55°$. $\angle 1 + \angle 2 = 90°$.
This leaves 90° for $\angle E$.

Now try $\angle A = 60°$ and also 65°.   Each time you will end
with $\angle E = 90°$.

Proof. Let $\angle A = a°$.

STATEMENTS	REASONS
1. $\angle B = 180° - a°$.	1. The successive angles of a parallelogram are supplementary.
2. $\angle 1 = \dfrac{a°}{2}$, $\angle 2 = \dfrac{180° - a°}{2}$.	2. $\angle A$ and $\angle B$ are bisected.
3. $\angle 1 + \angle 2 = \dfrac{a°}{2} + \dfrac{180° - a°}{2}$ $= \dfrac{180°}{2} = 90°$.	3. Adding the values of $\angle 1$ and $\angle 2$.
4. $\angle E = 90°$.	4. The sum of the angles of a triangle is 180°.
5. $AE \perp BE$.	5. Why?

EXAMPLE 2: **Given** this figure, in which $AC = BC$, $AD = AC$, and
BCD and EAB are straight lines.

To prove   that $\angle EAD = 3\angle B$.
First try special cases. Note that $\angle 2$
is an exterior angle of $\triangle ACB$ and that
$\angle EAD$ is an exterior angle of $\triangle ABD$.

Proof. Let $\angle B = a°$.

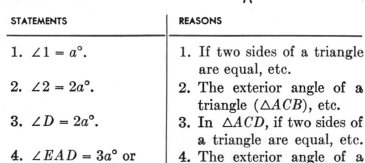

STATEMENTS	REASONS
1. $\angle 1 = a°$.	1. If two sides of a triangle are equal, etc.
2. $\angle 2 = 2a°$.	2. The exterior angle of a triangle ($\triangle ACB$), etc.
3. $\angle D = 2a°$.	3. In $\triangle ACD$, if two sides of a triangle are equal, etc.
4. $\angle EAD = 3a°$ or $3\angle B$.	4. The exterior angle of a triangle ($\triangle ABD$), etc.

The use of algebraic symbols makes the two preceding proofs easy, but you should know that the symbols are not necessary. One *numerical* example with *analysis* of your method constitutes a proof. Note the following proof of Example 1.

If $\angle A$ is assumed to be 40°, $\angle B$ must be 140°, and if $\angle A$ is 63°, $\angle B$ must be 117°, because $\angle A + \angle B$ will always be 180°, no matter what value $\angle A$ has. So the sum of the halves of these angles ($\angle 1 + \angle 2$) will always be 90° regardless of the size of $\angle A$. This leaves 90° for $\angle E$.

EXERCISES

First show that the following statements are true for some numerical value. Then give a proof by means of algebra or show that your method will hold for whatever numerical value you choose.

1. The exterior angle at the vertex of an isosceles triangle is equal to twice one of the base angles. (If $\angle A = 70°$, is $\angle BCD = 140°$? Let $\angle A = a°$ and then show that $\angle BCD = 2a°$.)

2. The bisectors of two supplementary adjacent angles are perpendicular to each other. (If $\angle ACD = 140°$, is $\angle SCR = 90°$? Then let $\angle ACD = a°$ and evaluate $\angle SCR$.)

3. If the bisectors of two adjacent angles are perpendicular to each other, the angles are supplementary.

Let $\angle 1 = 70°$, then $\angle 2 = 70°$; and if $\angle FBE = 90°$, then $\angle 3 = 20°$ and $\angle 4 = \_?\_$. $\angle 1 + \angle 2 + \angle 3 + \angle 4 = \_?\_$ and so ABD is a straight line.

Now let $\angle 1 = a°$, then $\angle 2 = a°$, $\angle 3$ will equal $\_?\_$ and $\angle 4 = \_?\_$. So ABD is a straight line.

4. In $\triangle ABC$, $AC = BC$. If $EC \perp BC$ and $DC \perp AC$, then $\angle DCE = 2\angle A$. (ACE and BCD are not necessarily straight lines.)

First try numerical values. If $\angle A = 70°$, is $\angle DCE = 140°$? Then let $\angle A = a°$ and find that $\angle DCE = 2a°$.

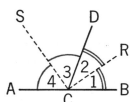

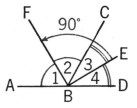

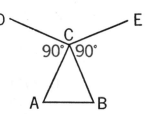

■ Central Angles and Their Intercepted Arcs

The picture below shows a protractor for measuring angles from 0° to 360°. Note that the scale is on the circle; it is the arc that is divided into 360°, and yet this same scale is used to measure the central angles. There are 360 arc degrees around a circle and 360 angle degrees about the center.

A 10° arc has a 10° angle at the center. A 60° arc has a central angle of 60°. When you use a protractor to measure an angle, you really measure the arc intercepted (cut off) by the angle. The relationship between the measure of an arc and the measure of the corresponding central angle is the basic relationship of this chapter.

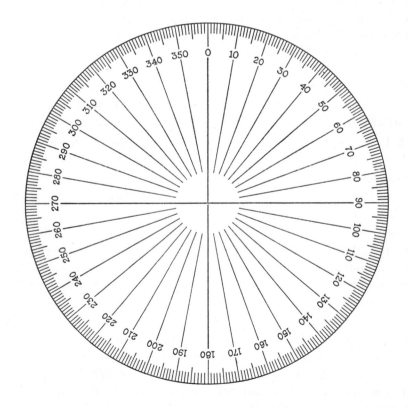

Postulate   A central angle has the same number of degrees as its intercepted arc.

1. In the figure, O is the center of the circle; AB and CD are perpendicular to each other. How many degrees are there in each central angle? How many degrees are there in each arc? Then the postulate on page 235 is true for this special case.

2. In the figure, the six arcs are equal and O is the center of the circle. How many degrees are there in each arc? The postulate says that the angles at the center are also 60° each. Can you see why it is so in this special case?

Before you study Theorem 34

△ An **inscribed angle** is an angle whose vertex is on a circle and whose sides are chords of the circle. In the figure ∠ABC is an inscribed angle and arc AC is the arc intercepted by it.

Theorem 34 states: *An inscribed angle has half as many degrees as the intercepted arc.* You wish to prove, for example: If arc $AC = 50°$, ∠$ABC = 25°$.

You will consider this theorem in three steps or cases, because the center of the circle may lie **a** on one side of the angle, **b** within the angle, or **c** outside the angle.

CASE I: Suppose the center O lies on one side of the angle and that the intercepted arc AC is 80°. You can show that ∠$B = 40°$.

Arc $AC = 80°$, so ∠$AOC = 80°$. (Post., page 235.)
Note that ∠AOC is an exterior angle of $\triangle BOC$.
∠B + ∠$C = 80°$. Why?
Since $OC = OB$, ∠B = ∠C and ∠B = _?_°.

Would all these steps be the same and all the relationships the same no matter what number of degrees you take for arc AC?

Since this is so, you have shown that Case I of Theorem 34 is true; that is, it can be deduced from previously accepted statements. You can use Case I to help you with the other cases.

CASE II: Suppose the center O lies within the angle. You can draw the diameter BD and use Case I to help you find the relationship between arc AC and ∠ABC.

If you let arc AC equal 80° and arc $DC = 30°$, you can show that ∠$B = 40°$.

Arc $AC = 80°$ and arc $DC = 30°$, so arc $AD = 50°$.
∠$2 = \frac{1}{2}$ of 30° or 15°, and ∠$1 = \frac{1}{2}$ of 50° or 25° by Case I.

Hence $\angle ABC$, which is $\angle 1 + \angle 2$, equals $40°$.

Would all these steps and all the relationships be the same no matter how many degrees you take for arcs AC and DC?

You have shown that Case II of Theorem 34 is true.

CASE III: Suppose the center O lies outside the angle. Let arc $AC = 40°$ and arc $AD = 70°$. Use Case I to show that $\angle ABC = 20°$.

The proof of Theorem 34 by means of algebra follows.

THEOREM 34 | *An inscribed angle has half as many degrees as the intercepted arc.*

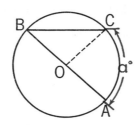

CASE I: *The center is on one side of the angle.*

Given $\odot O$ with inscribed angle ABC and intercepted arc AC. AB is a diameter.

To prove that $\angle ABC = \frac{1}{2}$ arc AC.

Proof. Draw radius OC. Let arc $AC = a°$.

STATEMENTS	REASONS
1. $\angle AOC = a°$.	1. Postulate, page 235.
2. $OB = OC$.	2. Radii of the same circle are equal.
3. $\angle B = \angle C$. Let $\angle B$ and $\angle C = x°$.	3. Theorem 1.
4. Then $2x = a$.	4. Cor. 8, page 165.
5. Then $x = \dfrac{a}{2}$.	5. Solving for x.
6. $\angle B = \dfrac{a°}{2}$, or $\dfrac{1}{2} \overset{\frown}{AC}$.	6. Substituting $\angle B$ for x.

THEOREM 34

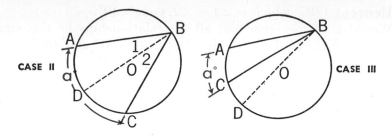

CASE II: *The center lies within the angle.*

  Given   ⊙O with inscribed angle ABC and intercepted arc ADC. O lies within the angle.

To prove   that $\angle ABC = \frac{1}{2}$ arc AC.

Outline of proof. Draw the diameter BOD. Let arc $AC = a°$.

  1. Let arc $AD = b°$. Then arc $DC = a° - b°$.

  2. $\angle 1 = \dfrac{b°}{2}$ and $\angle 2 = \dfrac{a° - b°}{2}$. (Case I)

  3. $\angle ABC = \angle 1 + \angle 2 = \dfrac{b°}{2} + \dfrac{a° - b°}{2} = \dfrac{a°}{2}$.

CASE III: *The center lies outside the angle.*

  Given   ⊙O with inscribed angle ABC and intercepted arc AC. O lies outside the angle.

To prove   that $\angle ABC = \frac{1}{2}$ arc AC.

Outline of proof. Draw the diameter BOD. Let arc $AC = a°$.

  1. Let arc $ACD = b°$. Then arc $CD = b° - a°$.

  2. $\angle ABD = \dfrac{b°}{2}$ and $\angle CBD = \dfrac{b° - a°}{2}$. (Case I)

  3. $\angle ABC = \angle ABD - \angle CBD = \dfrac{b°}{2} - \dfrac{b° - a°}{2}$

$$= \dfrac{b° - b° + a°}{2} = \dfrac{a°}{2}.$$

  Since these three cases comprise all the possible positions of an inscribed angle with respect to the center of the circle, the theorem has been proved in general.

  This theorem is also stated: *An inscribed angle is measured by one half its intercepted arc.*

  Either algebraic symbols, or a special case and analysis, as on pages 236 and 237, is adequate for a proof of Theorem 34.

EXERCISES

These exercises will not only give you practice with applications of Theorem 34 but will prepare you for some of the theorems still to come in this chapter.

1. Name the central angles and the inscribed angles in the figures on this page. With each angle name the intercepted arc.

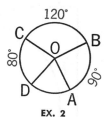

EX. 2

2. O is the center of the circle. Arc $AB = 90°$, arc $BC = 120°$, and arc $CD = 80°$. How many degrees are there in each of the angles? Draw a larger figure and write your answers in the proper place on the figure.

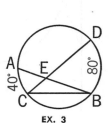

EX. 3

3. Find first the number of degrees in $\angle B$ and $\angle C$ and then the number of degrees in $\angle AEC$. Note that E is *not* the center of the circle.

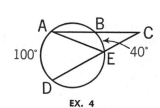

EX. 4

4. Find first the number of degrees in $\angle AED$ and in $\angle A$. Then find the number of degrees in $\angle C$.

EX. 5

5. AOB is a diameter. How many degrees are there in $\angle C$? in $\angle D$? in $\angle E$?

6. DOB is a diameter. BC is a tangent. Arc $AB = 80°$. Find the number of degrees in arc BD, arc AD, $\angle DBA$, $\angle DBC$, and $\angle ABC$ in the order given.

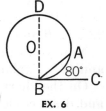

EX. 6

USING INSCRIBED ANGLES

■ The Three-Point Problem in Navigation — *Optional*

The map is part of a navigator's chart showing lighthouses at A, B, and C. The lighthouses can be seen from a ship. The ship's position is located on the chart by plotting circles.

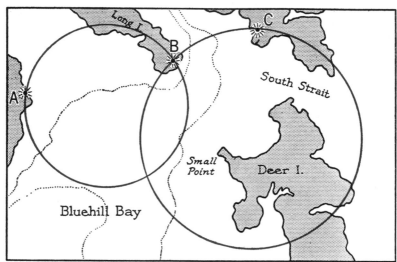

In the diagram one circle is drawn through A and B and another through B and C in such a way that an intersection of these two circles gives the position. The analysis will show a method of finding the centers and radii of these circles.

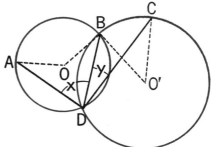

A, B, and C, in the diagram, are the lighthouses and D is the ship's position (unknown). $\angle ADB$ and $\angle CDB$ ($\angle x$ and $\angle y$) can be measured by the observer. Suppose $\angle x = 68°$ and $\angle y = 24°$. Then arc $AB = 136°$ and arc $BC = 48°$. (Why?) That makes $\angle O = 136°$ and $\angle O' = 48°$. (Why?) Now $\triangle ABO$ and $\triangle BCO'$ are isosceles. (Why?) So $\angle BAO = \angle ABO$ and $\angle BCO' = \angle CBO'$. (Why?) $\angle A$ and $\angle B$ in $\triangle ABO$ are each $22°$. $\angle B$ and $\angle C$ in $\triangle BCO' = 66°$.

Now you can draw $\triangle ABO$ and $\triangle BCO'$ on the chart and find O and O'. Explain how this can be done.

On the chart use O and O' as centers and AO and BO' as radii and draw circles. The intersection at D is the ship's position.

■ Angles Inscribed in an Arc

An angle is *inscribed in an arc* if the vertex is on the arc and its sides meet the extremities of the arc. In Figure 1 ∠*ABC* is inscribed in arc *ABC*. The vertex *B* is on the arc *ABC* and the sides *AB* and *BC* go to points *A* and *C*. Note that the angle is inscribed in major arc *ABC* but it intercepts and is measured by ½ minor arc *AC*.

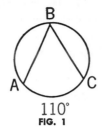

FIG. 1

1. In ∠*ABC*, Figure 1, there are _?_ degrees. In arc *ABC* there are _?_ degrees.

2. In Figure 2 how many angles are inscribed in arc *DEF*? Name the angles. How many degrees are there in ∠*G*? in ∠*E*? in ∠*H*? in ∠*K*?

3. Would these angles be equal no matter how many degrees there were in arc *DF* just so long as they were all inscribed in arc *DEF*?

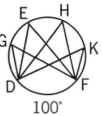

FIG. 2

COROLLARY 1 **Inscribed angles which intercept the same arc are equal.** This may also be stated: **Angles inscribed in the same arc are equal.**

4. Arc *ABC* in Figure 3 is a semicircle. ∠*ABC* is inscribed in this semicircle. It is measured by ½ arc *AEC*. Angle *ABC* is a _?_ angle.

FIG. 3

COROLLARY 2 **An angle inscribed in a semicircle is a right angle.**

5. In Figure 4 is shown an interesting way to construct a line perpendicular to *AB* at *A*. Using any convenient point *C* as center and *CA* as radius, draw an arc *EAD* as shown. Draw a straight line from *S* through *C* until it meets the arc at *T*. Then draw *TA* which is perpendicular to *AB*. Why?

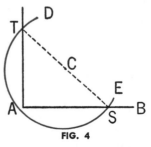

FIG. 4

6. Can you think of a way, using Corollary 2, to construct a right triangle whose hypotenuse is 2 in. long? (Draw the hypotenuse first.)

1. In the three figures below name inscribed angles that are equal because they intercept the same arc.

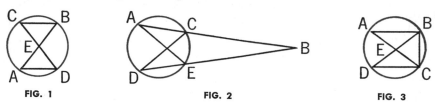

FIG. 1   FIG. 2   FIG. 3

2. In Figure 1, AB and CD are two chords intersecting at E. Prove that three angles of $\triangle CEB$ are equal to three angles of $\triangle AED$.

3. ACB and DEB in Figure 2 are straight lines. AE and CD are chords. Prove that three angles of $\triangle AEB$ are equal to three angles of $\triangle DCB$.

4. Prove that three angles of $\triangle DEC$ in Figure 3 are equal to three angles of $\triangle AEB$.

■ Angle Formed by a Tangent and a Chord

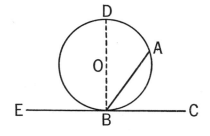

The line EBC is tangent to circle O. AB is a chord meeting the tangent at the point of contact. $\angle ABC$ is therefore **an angle formed by a tangent and a chord meeting it at the point of contact.** The angle intercepts the arc AB.

If arc AB is 100°, you can show that $\angle ABC$ is 50°.

Draw the diameter BOD. Then arc $BAD = 180°$ and arc $AD = 80°$. $\angle DBA = \underline{\ ?\ }°$. (Theorem 34) $\angle DBC = 90°$. (Why?) So $\angle ABC = 50°$. What is the relationship between $\angle ABC$ and its intercepted arc AB?

Go through these same steps with arc AB equal to 80° and 150°.

Would these steps and relationships be the same no matter what arc AB is?

By means of these special cases and the analysis you have shown that Theorem 35, which follows, is true in general. The proof with algebraic symbols follows on page 243.

THEOREM 35	*An angle formed by a tangent and a chord meeting it at the point of contact has half as many degrees as the intercepted arc.*

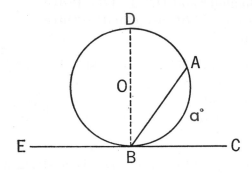

Given $\odot O$ and $\angle ABC$ formed by tangent EBC and chord AB.

To prove that $\angle ABC = \frac{1}{2}$ arc AB.

Proof. Draw diameter BD. Let arc $AB = a°$.

STATEMENTS	REASONS
1. Arc $BAD = 180°$.	1. Why?
2. Arc $AD = 180° - a°$.	2. Why?
3. $\angle DBA = \dfrac{180° - a°}{2}$.	3. Theorem 34.
4. $\angle DBC = 90°$.	4. Why?
5. $\angle ABC = 90° - \dfrac{180° - a°}{2}$ $\quad = \dfrac{a°}{2}$ or $\dfrac{1}{2}\ \widehat{AB}$.	5. Subtracting from the value of $\angle DBC$ the value of $\angle DBA$.

EXERCISES

1. If arc AB in the figure above equals 80°, how many degrees are there in $\angle ABC$? (Use Theorem 35.)

2. Show that $\angle ABE$ in the figure above equals $\frac{1}{2}$ arc ADB.

3. Prove: If a tangent and a chord are parallel and the chords of the intercepted arcs are drawn, the chords will make equal angles with the tangent.

4. AB is a diameter extended to C and $DC \perp AC$. EBD is a straight line. How many degrees are there in each angle of the figure if arc $AE = 70°$?

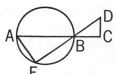

5. AB is a diameter and $DE \perp AB$. How many degrees are there in each angle of the figure if arc $BC = 65°$?

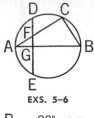

EXS. 5–6

6. AB is a diameter and $DE \perp AB$. Prove that three angles of $\triangle ABC$ are equal to three angles of $\triangle AFG$.

7. AB is a tangent. If arc $BC = 80°$ and $\angle A = 25°$, how many degrees are there in $\angle ABD$ and $\angle D$? Are three angles of $\triangle BAD$ equal to three angles of $\triangle BAC$?

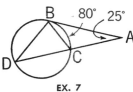

EX. 7

8. BDE bisects $\angle ABC$ and ADC is a straight line. How many degrees are there in each angle of the figure if arc $AE = 80°$ and arc $BC = 130°$?

EX. 8

9. Chord AB is parallel to diameter CD. Arc $AB = 85°$. Find the number of degrees in $\angle 1$, $\angle 2$, and arc AC.

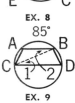

EX. 9

EXTRA

10. AB and CD are parallel tangents. BD is a tangent. O is the center of the circle. If $\angle ABD$ is $74°$, how many degrees are there in $\angle O$?

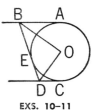

EXS. 10–11

11. Do Ex. 10, changing $\angle ABD$ to $80°$.

12. $AC = BC$, $EFD \perp AB$, and $\angle A = 44°$. Find the number of degrees in $\angle E$ and $\angle CFE$. Does FC equal CE?

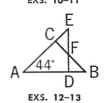

EXS. 12–13

13. Do Ex. 12, changing $\angle A$ to $50°$.

14. AB is a diameter. FDE and BEC are tangents. $\angle C$ is $30°$. Find the number of degrees in $\angle CDE$. What kind of triangle is $\triangle DEC$?

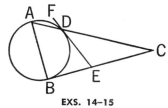

EXS. 14–15

15. Do Ex. 14, changing $\angle C$ to $40°$.

ALGEBRA IN PROOFS

■ Square Through Four Points—*Optional*

Four points A, B, C, and D are arranged relatively as shown.

Can you construct a square so that each side will contain one of the points?

The exercise is done for you below.

Given points A, B, C, and D as above.

Required to construct a square so that each side of the square will pass through one of the points.

Construction. Draw $\odot O$ and $\odot O'$ with AB and CD, respectively, as diameters.

Find P, the mid-point of the lower arc AB, and Q, the mid-point of the upper arc, CD.

Draw PQ and extend it to meet $\odot O$ at E and $\odot O'$ at F.

Draw EB, EA, FC, and FD and extend them to form the quadrilateral $EGFH$.

$EGFH$ is the required square.

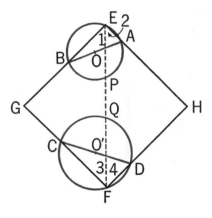

Outline of proof.

$\angle E$ and $\angle F$ are right angles. Why?

$\angle 1$, $\angle 2$, $\angle 3$, and $\angle 4$ are $45°$. They each intercept an arc of $90°$.

In $\triangle EFG$, $\angle 1$ and $\angle 3$ are each $45°$, hence $\angle G$ is a right angle. (Why?) Similarly, $\angle H$ is a right angle.

$\triangle EFG \cong \triangle EFH$. Prove it.

Hence $EH = HF = FG = GE$.

$EGFH$ is a square.

Since the opposite sides of $EGFH$ are equal, it is a parallelogram. Since two adjacent sides are equal, it is a rhombus. Then one right angle is sufficient to make it a square.

The points may be placed so that this exercise is more difficult. Are there any positions of the points which make the construction impossible?

■ Angle Formed by Two Chords

Use the figure for Theorem 36 below.

1. What arc is intercepted by $\angle AEB$? What arc is intercepted by its vertical angle?

2. If arc $AB = 80°$ and arc CD equals $100°$, can you find out how many degrees there are in $\angle AEB$?

3. Note that $\angle AEB$ is an exterior angle of $\triangle BEC$. Then find the number of degrees in $\angle C$, $\angle B$, and $\angle AEB$ in that order.

4. Do you see that in this case $\angle AEB$ has half as many degrees as the sum of the two intercepted arcs?

Your method would be exactly the same no matter how many degrees there are in the two arcs. The proof with algebraic symbols follows.

THEOREM 36

> An angle formed by two chords intersecting within a circle has half as many degrees as the sum of the two arcs intercepted by it and by the vertical angle.

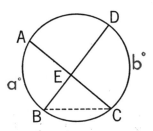

Given a circle with two chords intersecting at E.

To prove that $\angle AEB = \frac{1}{2}(\text{arc } AB + \text{arc } DC)$.

Outline of proof. Draw BC. Let arc $AB = a°$ and arc $DC = b°$.

1. Then $\angle B = \dfrac{b°}{2}$ and $\angle C = \dfrac{a°}{2}$. (Why?)

2. $\angle AEB = \angle B + \angle C$. (Why?)

3. Hence $\angle AEB = \dfrac{a°}{2} + \dfrac{b°}{2} = \dfrac{a° + b°}{2}$, or $\dfrac{1}{2}(\widehat{AB} + \widehat{DC})$.

■ Angle Formed by Two Secants

△ *A **secant** is a line that intersects a circle at two points.* In the figure for Theorem 37, AB and CB are secants.

To prove Theorem 37 numerically combined with analysis, let arc $AC = 100°$ and arc $DE = 60°$. Show that $\angle B = \frac{1}{2}(100° - 60°)$ or 20°. Note that $\angle AEC$ is an exterior angle of $\triangle ABE$ and then find the number of degrees in $\angle AEC$, $\angle A$, and $\angle B$ in that order. Your steps and relationships are the same no matter how many degrees there are in the arcs.

THEOREM 37 *An angle formed by two secants intersecting outside a circle has half as many degrees as the difference between the two intercepted arcs.*

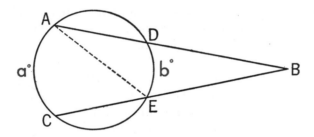

Given   a circle with secants BDA and BEC.

To prove   that $\angle B = \frac{1}{2}(\text{arc } AC - \text{arc } DE)$.

Outline of proof.   Draw AE.   Let arc $AC = a°$ and arc $DE = b°$.

1. $\angle A = \dfrac{b°}{2}$ and $\angle AEC = \dfrac{a°}{2}$.

2. $\angle AEC = \angle A + \angle B$.   (Why?)

3. Let $\angle B = x°$.   Then $\dfrac{a}{2} = \dfrac{b}{2} + x$, $x = \dfrac{a}{2} - \dfrac{b}{2} = \dfrac{a-b}{2}$.

4. Hence $\angle B = \dfrac{a° - b°}{2}$, or $\dfrac{1}{2}(\widehat{AC} - \widehat{DE})$.

COROLLARY   **The angle formed by a secant and a tangent or two tangents meeting outside the circle has half as many degrees as the difference between the intercepted arcs.**

EXERCISES

1. Use Theorem 36 to get the answers to the following:

a Arc $AC = 50°$, arc $DB = 80°$, $\angle AEC =$ _?_ °

b Arc $AC = 40°$, arc $BD = 80°$, $\angle AEC =$ _?_ °

c Arc $AC = 60°$, arc $BD = 100°$, $\angle AED =$ _?_ °

2. Use Theorem 37 to get the answers to the following:

a If arc $AC = 80°$ and arc $DE = 50°$, $\angle B =$ _?_ °

b If arc $AC = 94°$ and arc $DE = 57°$, $\angle B =$ _?_ °

c If $\angle B = 20°$ and arc $AC = 100°$, how many degrees are there in arc DE? (Let arc $DE = x°$ and write an equation.)

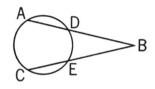

3. Prove: The angle between a tangent and a chord drawn to the point of contact is one half of the angle between the radii drawn to the extremities of the chord.

4. AB and AC are tangents. Arc $BC = 110°$. How many degrees are there in $\angle A$? (Use the corollary to Theorem 37 or draw the chord BC and use Theorem 35.)

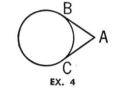

EX. 4

5. Triangle ABC is drawn within a circle so that all three vertices are on the circle, $\angle A = 50°$ and $\angle B = 60°$. How many degrees are there in the smaller arc AB?

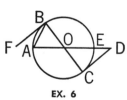

6. AOE and BOC are diameters, CD and FB are tangents, and $AOED$ is a straight line. $\angle FBA = 15°$. Find the number of degrees in $\angle D$.

EX. 6

7. BA and BC are tangents and AD is a diameter. $\angle DAC = 20°$. How many degrees are there in $\angle B$?

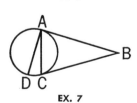

EX. 7

8. How many degrees are there in $\angle B$ of Ex. 7 if $\angle DAC = 30°$?

ALGEBRA IN PROOFS

Parallel lines intercept equal arcs on a circle.

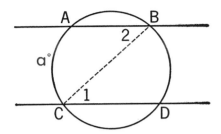

Given a circle and parallel lines AB and CD.
To prove that arc AC = arc BD.
Outline of proof. Draw BC.

1. Let arc $AC = a°$, then $\angle 2 = \dfrac{a°}{2}$.

2. Since $AB \parallel CD$, $\angle 1 = \angle 2$ and $\angle 1 = \dfrac{a°}{2}$. (Why?)

3. Hence arc $BD = a°$ and arc AC = arc BD. (Why?)

You may prove this theorem by taking a special numerical case and noting that the procedure would be the same for any number.

Are all arcs of the same number of degrees equal in length? In the figure are three concentric circles. If $\angle AOB = 80°$, how many degrees are there in each of the arcs EF, CD, and AB? Are the arcs of equal length?

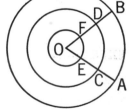

In the theorem above we have proved that arc AC and arc BD have the same number of degrees. Since they are in the same circle, they are of the same length.

The theorem is true and the proof is essentially the same whether the two parallel lines are two secants as in the figure, or a secant and a tangent, or two tangents.

EXERCISES

1. In the figure for Theorem 38 prove that arc CAB = arc DBA if $AB \parallel CD$.

2. Prove. If a tangent and a chord are parallel and the chords of the intercepted arcs are drawn, an isosceles triangle is formed.

The opposite angles of an inscribed quadrilateral are supplementary.

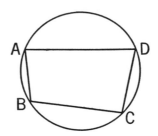

Given a circle with inscribed quadrilateral $ABCD$.

To prove that $\angle A$ is supplementary to $\angle C$ and $\angle B$ is supplementary to $\angle D$.

Outline of proof.

    1. Let arc $DCB = a°$, then arc $DAB = 360° - a°$.

    2. Then $\angle A = \dfrac{a°}{2}$ and $\angle C = \dfrac{360° - a°}{2}$. (Why?)

    3. $\angle A + \angle C = \dfrac{a°}{2} + \dfrac{360° - a°}{2} = \dfrac{360°}{2} = 180°$.

    4. Hence $\angle A$ and $\angle C$ are supplementary. (Why?)

In the same way it can be proved that $\angle B$ is supplementary to $\angle D$.

If you wish, try a special numerical case and note that it can be made general.

EXERCISES

1. If arc $AB = 90°$, arc $BC = 110°$, and arc $CD = 70°$, how many degrees are there in each angle of the inscribed quadrilateral in the figure above?

2. In the figure at the right, BA and BC are secants. Prove that three angles of $\triangle ABC$ are equal to three angles of $\triangle EBD$. (Note the inscribed quadrilateral.)

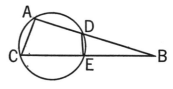

3. Prove: If two triangles are inscribed in equal circles and have three angles of one equal to three angles of the other, they are congruent.

■ Can You Find the Errors?

1. When you have an exercise to prove, an accurate drawing is very often useful. Inaccurate drawings may present a false appearance that, in turn, leads to false reasoning.

Using the diagram at the right, it would seem that there may be two lines perpendicular to a given line from a given point.

Two circles O and O' intersect at C and F. $AO'C$ and COB are diameters and the line AB intersects the circles at D and E as shown.

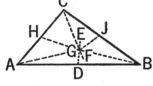

$\angle AEC$ and $\angle CDB$ are both right angles. Why?

Hence $CD \perp AB$ and $CE \perp AB$. This seems to contradict the postulate that from a point outside a line only one perpendicular to the line can be drawn.

If you draw an accurate figure, you will see what the fallacy is. (A fallacy is an error in reasoning.)

2. An inaccurate drawing will help you to show erroneously that all triangles are isosceles.

The triangle ABC is any triangle. In this figure BC is obviously longer than AC. Yet, with this figure you apparently can prove that the triangle is isosceles.

Draw CF the bisector of $\angle C$ and DE the perpendicular bisector of AB. Let these lines intersect at G.

Draw $GH \perp AC$ and $GJ \perp CB$. Draw lines AG, BG, and CG.

You can now prove that $\triangle CHG \cong \triangle CJG$ and so $CH = CJ$.

You can prove that $\triangle AGH \cong \triangle BGJ$ and so $HA = JB$.

Adding, you have $CA = CB$ and the triangle is isosceles.

Of course, all triangles are **not** isosceles. You can see what the trouble is by drawing an accurate figure.

3. What is wrong with this one?

Any line through the vertex of an isosceles triangle and meeting the base, bisects the base.

Outline of proof.

$AC = BC$. (Given.) $\angle A = \angle B$. (Why?)
$CD = CD$. $\triangle ADC \cong \triangle BDC$. (s.s.a. = s.s.a.)
So $AD = BD$. (C.p.c.t.e.)

■ Attacking the Proof
of an Exercise

There are two questions you should ask yourself when given an exercise to prove. One of them is, "How can I prove that the conclusion is correct?" The other is, "How can I use the hypothesis?" The answer to the first question leads from the conclusion back toward the hypothesis. The answer to the second leads from hypothesis to conclusion. With these questions in mind we offer another illustration of a method of attacking an exercise that involves a proof.

Prove: If two circles are tangent to each other externally and a line through the point of contact intersects the circles in A and B, tangents to the circles at these two points of intersection are parallel.

Given two circles tangent at P, AB drawn through P, and tangents DAE and FBG.

To prove that $DE \parallel FG$.

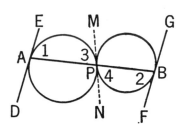

The first question is, "How can I prove that $DE \parallel FG$?" The answer is, "I can prove that $DE \parallel FG$ if I can prove that the alternate interior angles, $\angle 1$ and $\angle 2$, are equal."

The next step of the analysis would be, "How can I prove that $\angle 1 = \angle 2$?" Since the answer to this question does not come readily, it is wise to turn to the other question, "How can I use the hypothesis?"

You are given that the two circles are tangent to each other. This means that they are tangent to the same line at the same point. To use this part of the hypothesis you should draw this line, the common internal tangent, MN.

The rest of the hypothesis is that DE and FG are tangents. To use this information you will ask yourself, "What theorems do I know concerning tangents?" and you will choose one that applies to this figure. It is Theorem 35. By this theorem you see that $\angle 1$ and $\angle 3$ are both equal to one half the arc AP; hence they are equal. Similarly $\angle 2 = \angle 4$. Now you readily see that $\angle 3 = \angle 4$, and then you know that $\angle 1 = \angle 2$.

■ Finding Errors in a Proof

The following proofs, taken from students' papers, show false reasoning. Find the error in each proof.

Prove: Parallel chords drawn to the ends of a diameter are equal.

Given a diameter AB and parallel chords CB and DA. O is the center of the circle.

To prove that $CB = DA$.

First attempted proof. Draw CD.

STUDENT'S STATEMENTS	STUDENT'S REASONS
1. $AO = OB$.	1. Equal radii.
2. $CO = OD$.	2. Same as 1.
3. $\angle 1 = \angle 2$.	3. Vertical angles.
4. $\triangle COB \cong \triangle AOD$.	4. $s.a.s. = s.a.s.$
5. $CB = DA$.	5. $C.p.c.t.e.$

Second attempted proof. Draw CO and DO.
Then follows the same proof as above.

Third attempted proof. Draw CO and DO.

STUDENT'S STATEMENTS	STUDENT'S REASONS
1. $AO = OB$.	1. Radii of the same circle.
2. $\angle A = \angle B$.	2. Alternate interior angles of parallel lines.
3. $\angle C = \angle D$.	3. Same as 2.
4. $\triangle COB \cong \triangle AOD$.	4. $a.a.s. = a.a.s.$
5. $CB = DA$.	5. $C.p.c.t.e.$

Note that in the first and second proofs part of the hypothesis was not used. When an alleged proof is given and part of the hypothesis is not used, one of two things is true. Either there is a fallacy in the proof, or the statement to be proved is still true even if that part of the hypothesis is omitted.

The errors in the first and second proofs are easily seen if the chords are drawn non-parallel.

EXERCISES — Optional

Prove these exercises by means of algebra. Let a convenient arc or angle be a° and evaluate whatever arcs or angles you need to complete the proof.

1. *BDE* bisects ∠*ABC* and *ADC* is a straight line. Prove that three angles of △*ABD* are equal to three angles of △*EBC*.

2. *BDE* bisects ∠*ABC* and *ADC* is a straight line. Prove that three angles of △*EDC* are equal to three angles of △*EBC*.

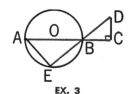

EXS. 1–2

3. *AB* is a diameter extended to *C* and *DC* ⊥ *AC*. *EBD* is a straight line. Prove that three angles of △*AEB* are equal to three angles of △*BDC*.

EX. 3

4. *BE* is a diameter and *BD* ⊥ *AC* in triangle *ABC*. How many degrees are there in each angle of the figure if arc *BC* = $a°$ and arc *AE* = $b°$?

5. *BE* is a diameter and *BD* ⊥ *AC* in △*ABC*. Prove that three angles of △*ABD* are equal to three angles of △*BEC*.

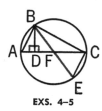

EXS. 4–5

6. Prove: If a triangle is inscribed in a circle and a tangent is drawn at one of the vertices, each angle formed between the tangent and the sides of the triangle will equal one of the remote interior angles of the triangle.

7. Prove: If two chords drawn to the same point on a circle make equal angles with the tangent at that point, they are equal.

8. *AB* is tangent to both circles at *C*. *FCG* and *DCE* are straight lines. Prove that *FD* ∥ *EG*.

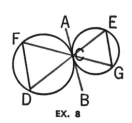

EX. 8

254

ALGEBRA IN PROOFS

Using Equations in Geometric Exercises — *Optional*

If you are given the number of degrees in arc AC and the number of degrees in arc BD and are asked to find the number of degrees in $\angle AEC$, you have a problem to which a theorem applies directly. But if you are given the angle and one arc and are asked to find the other arc, the theorem applies indirectly. In all such cases it is advisable to represent the unknown by a letter, form an equation, and solve it.

1. If arc $AC = 102°$ and $\angle AEC = 87°$, how many degrees are there in arc BD?

Let arc $BD = x°$. Then $87 = \dfrac{x + 102}{2}$. (Why?)

Solving the equation, $174 = x + 102$
$$x = 174 - 102 = 72$$
Arc $BD = 72°$

CHECK: $\dfrac{72 + 102}{2} = \dfrac{174}{2} = 87$

2. How many degrees must there be in the vertex angle of an isosceles triangle in order that the exterior angle at the base shall be three times the vertex angle?

Let $\angle C = x°$. Then $\angle A = \dfrac{180° - x°}{2}$. (Why?)

$\angle CBD = x° + \dfrac{180° - x°}{2}$. (Why?)

Forming the equation, $x + \dfrac{180 - x}{2} = 3x$

Solving the equation, $2x + 180 - x = 6x$
$$180 = 5x$$
$$x = 36$$
$\angle C$ must be $36°$.

CHECK: $36 + \dfrac{180 - 36}{2} = 3 \times 36 = 108$

Note that the degree sign is omitted from the equations. In an equation you deal with numbers only.

1. AB and CD are chords intersecting at E. Find the number of degrees in arc BD in each of the following cases:

EX. 1

a $\angle 1 = 80°$, arc $AC = 100°$.

b $\angle 1 = 67°$, arc $AC = 98°$.

c $\angle 1 = 46\frac{1}{2}°$, arc $AC = 62\frac{3}{4}°$.

d $\angle 1 = a°$, arc $AC = b°$.

e $\angle 1 = 3a°$, arc $AC = a°$.

f $\angle 2 = a°$, arc $AC = b°$.

g $\angle 1 = 180° - a°$, arc $AC = \dfrac{a°}{2}$.

2. AB and CB are secants. Find the number of degrees in arc AC in each of the following cases:

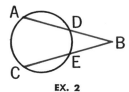

EX. 2

a $\angle B = 30°$, arc $DE = 40°$.

b $\angle B = 37°$, arc $DE = 64°$.

c $\angle B = a°$, arc $DE = b°$.

d $\angle B = \dfrac{a°}{3}$, arc $DE = b°$.

e $\angle B = \dfrac{3a°}{4}$, arc $DE = a°$.

f $\angle B = 90° - a°$, arc $DE = 90° + a°$.

3. How many degrees must there be in the vertex angle of an isosceles triangle in order that it shall be twice one of the base angles? (Let one base angle be $x°$. Then the vertex angle is $2x°$. Make an equation.)

4. Each base angle of an isosceles triangle is three fourths of the vertex angle. How many degrees are there in each angle?

5. The exterior angle at the base of an isosceles triangle is five times the vertex angle. How many degrees are there in each angle of the triangle?

6. $AB = CB$, AD bisects $\angle A$, and CD bisects $\angle C$. If $\angle D = 2\angle B$, how many degrees are there in $\angle B$? (Let $\angle B = x°$, evaluate $\angle D$ in terms of x, and form an equation.)

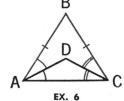

EX. 6

1. AB is a diameter of a circle. On the same side of AB, chords AC and DB are drawn and extended to meet in E. If arcs AC and DB are respectively one fourth and one twelfth of the circle, how many degrees are there in angle E?

2. Two circles are internally tangent at A. AB and AC are chords of the larger circle that intersect the smaller circle in D and E respectively. If DE is a diameter of the smaller circle, then BC will be a diameter of the larger circle.

3. AD is a straight line passing through the centers of two intersecting circles. AD meets the circles in points A, B, C, and D in order from left to right. EF is a common external tangent. EF is also lettered from left to right. Prove that EA is parallel to FB.

4. Through two points A and B on the diameter of a circle and equidistant from the center O, two parallel chords are drawn intersecting the circle on the same side of the diameter at C and D. Prove that CD is perpendicular to AC and BD.

5. Two unequal chords, AB and AC, neither of them a diameter, are drawn from a point A on a circle. On AB and AC as diameters circles are drawn intersecting each other in A and D. Prove that B, D, and C lie in a straight line.

6. The vertex of a 35° angle is outside a circle. The sides of the angle intercept on the circle two arcs whose sum is 120°. How many degrees are in each of the intercepted arcs?

7. A right triangle ABC with the right angle at C is inscribed in a circle. A tangent to the circle is drawn at B. The bisector of angle A meets BC in D and the tangent in E. Prove that triangle DBE is isosceles.

8. Triangle ABC is inscribed in a circle. From D, any other point on the circumference, DE, DF, and DG are drawn perpendicular to BC, AB, and AC respectively. DE, DF, and DG meet the circle at H, K, and L respectively, as shown in the figure. Prove that AH, LB, and KC are parallel.

1. If the acute angles of a right triangle are bisected and the bisectors continued until they meet, how many degrees are there in the angle formed? Prove your answer.

2. $DC = EC$, $AD = EB$, and $ADEB$ is a straight line. Prove that $AC = BC$.

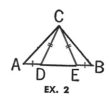

EX. 2

3. Prove: If the equal sides of an isosceles triangle are continued beyond the base and the exterior angles are bisected, another isosceles triangle is formed.

4. $\angle C$ is a right angle and $CD \perp AB$. Prove that $\angle 1 = \angle B$ and $\angle 2 = \angle A$.

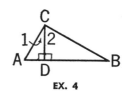

EX. 4

5. Prove: A line through the vertex of an angle and perpendicular to the bisector of the angle makes equal angles with the sides of the given angle.

6. Prove: The perpendiculars to the sides of any circumscribed polygon at the points of contact meet at a common point. (What point is it?)

7. Can the sum of the angles of a polygon be 700°?

8. How many sides has a regular polygon each of whose angles is ten times its adjacent exterior angle?

9. How many sides has a polygon if the sum of its angles is 900°? 1080°? 1440°?

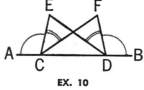

EX. 10

10. $\angle ACE = \angle BDF$, $\angle ECF = \angle FDE$, and $ACDB$ is a straight line. Prove that $\triangle CDE \cong \triangle DCF$.

11. $AB \parallel CD \parallel EF$. Prove that $\angle 1 + \angle 2 = \angle BDF$.

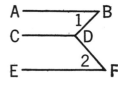

EX. 11

12. Prove: Two lines are parallel if any two points of one are equally distant from the other.

13. If $\angle AEB = 80°$ and arc $AB = 100°$, how many degrees are there in arc CD?

14. How many degrees are there in $\angle AEB$ if arc $AB = a°$ and arc $CD = \dfrac{a°}{2}$?

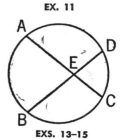

EXS. 13–15

15. How many degrees are there in $\angle AED$ if arc $AB = 2a°$ and arc $CD = \dfrac{3a°}{4}$?

■ Arcs and Angles in Spheres — *Optional*

Latitude and longitude is a matter of the relationship between central angles and arcs.

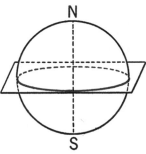

The equator is a great circle made by the intersection of a plane and the sphere. The plane is perpendicular to the axis NS drawn from the north pole to the south pole. The equator is 0° latitude. Approximately one minute of arc of a great circle of the earth is a nautical mile. (The U.S. nautical mile for many years has been 6,080.20 ft. The International nautical mile adopted by the Department of Defense in 1954 is 6076.10333 ft.)

The circles of latitude are made by planes parallel to the plane of the equator. In the figure is shown the circle at B of latitude 30° North. It is 30° because the angle at the center is 30°. Since $\angle O$ is 30°, arc AB is 30° and the circle of latitude through B is latitude 30° N.

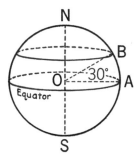

The 0° meridian showing longitude passes through Greenwich in England near London. Longitude is measured in degrees east and west of this zero meridian. In the figure at the bottom of the page the zero meridian is NAS. The meridian NBS is the 70° West meridian, so called because the angle at the center is 70° and the direction is west; so arc AB is 70° W.

Draw a figure like this one and show the 110° West meridian.

It is interesting to note that spherical angles are measured in degrees and are related to plane angles. A spherical angle is an angle made by the arcs of two great circles. In the figure BNA is a spherical angle of 70° because $\overset{\frown}{AB}$ and $\angle O$ are 70°.

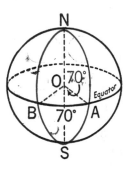

I. Vocabulary

1. Illustrate and explain the following terms:

Central angle

Intercepted arc

Inscribed angle

Inscribed quadrilateral

Angle inscribed in an arc

Angle formed by two chords intersecting within the circle

Angle formed by a tangent and a chord meeting it at the point of contact

Angle formed by two secants meeting outside the circle

Angle formed by a tangent and a secant meeting outside the circle

Angle formed by two tangents meeting outside the circle

II. Postulate

2. What is the relation between the number of degrees in a central angle and the number of degrees in the intercepted arc?

III. Theorems

3. State the relation between the number of degrees in the angle and the number of degrees in the intercepted arc or arcs:

a An inscribed angle

b An angle formed by two chords intersecting within the circle

c An angle formed by a tangent and a chord

d An angle formed by two secants, a secant and a tangent, or two tangents

4. What is the theorem concerning parallel lines and the intercepted arcs?

5. Complete: The opposite angles of an inscribed quadrilateral are _?_.

TEST 1

Which of these statements are True *and which are* False?

1. If $AB = BC$ and ABD is a straight line, $\angle DBC = 2a°$.

2. If AB and CD extended meet at a point, $\angle EFD = 180° - a°$.

3. The length of a degree of arc which is $\frac{1}{360}$ of a circle is always the same.

4. If $\angle A = 80°$ in quadrilateral $ABCD$, $\angle C = 100°$.

5. O is the center of the circle and AOB is a straight line. $\angle COB = 145°$.

6. If $\angle AEC = 80°$, then arc $AC = 80°$.

7. If $A, B, D,$ and E are on the circle, $\angle ABE = \angle ADE$.

8. If arc ABC exceeds $180°$, $\angle ABC$ is less than $90°$.

9. If $\angle A = 55°$ and $\angle B = 45°$, then arc $AB = 160°$.

10. O is the center of the circle. Then $\angle AOB$ is twice $\angle ACB$.

11. $ABCD$ is an inscribed quadrilateral. If $\angle A$ is $90°$, then $\angle B$ is $90°$.

12. If ABC is a tangent, then $\angle DBC = \frac{1}{2}$ arc BE.

13. If arc $AD = 148°$ and arc $BC = 80°$, $\angle CEA = 66°$.

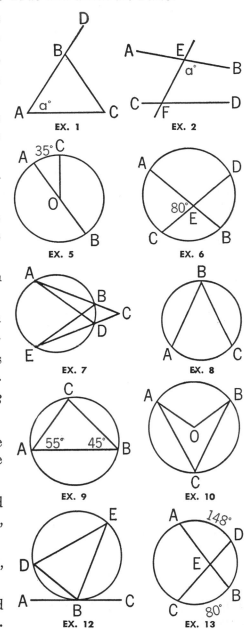

EX. 1   EX. 2

EX. 5   EX. 6

EX. 7   EX. 8

EX. 9   EX. 10

EX. 12   EX. 13

TEST 2

Be ready to give reasons for your answers.

1. If $\angle ABC = 90°$, arc $ADC = \underline{\ ?\ }°$.

2. If the circumference of a circle is 540 miles, a central angle of 1° will intercept an arc of $\underline{\ ?\ }$ miles.

3. In the figure AB is a tangent and BCD is a secant. If arc $AD = 120°$ and arc $AC = 85°$, $\angle B = \underline{\ ?\ }°$.

4. All the vertices of a regular pentagon $ABCDE$ lie on a circle with its center at O. $\angle AOC = \underline{\ ?\ }°$ and arc $ABC = \underline{\ ?\ }°$.

5. O is the center of both circles and $AO = 2CO$. If $\angle AOB = 70°$, then arc $CD = \underline{\ ?\ }°$ and arc $AB = \underline{\ ?\ }°$.

6. $OD \perp AB$ and O is the center of the circle. If $\angle COD = 110°$, then $\angle CDB = \underline{\ ?\ }°$.

7. $ABCD$ is an inscribed quadrilateral and $AB \parallel CD$. If $\angle D = 90°$, arc $BCD = \underline{\ ?\ }°$.

8. AB is a tangent and ACD is a secant. If arc $BC = 88°$ and $\angle A = 25°$, then $\angle BCA = \underline{\ ?\ }°$ and $\angle ABD = \underline{\ ?\ }°$.

9. AC and BD are common tangents. If arc $AKB = 300°$ and $DC = 3$ in., $BC = \underline{\ ?\ }$ in.

10. CD is a diameter perpendicular to AB. If $\angle A = 82°$ and arc $AE = 60°$, $\angle AED = \underline{\ ?\ }°$.

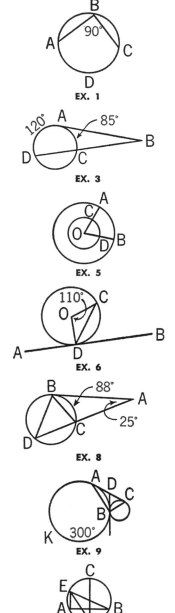

EX. 1

EX. 3

EX. 5

EX. 6

EX. 8

EX. 9

EX. 10

262

ALGEBRA IN PROOFS

You ARE already familiar, in an intuitive way, with the idea behind the word *locus* even though the word itself is unfamiliar. You know, for example, that if a point moves on level ground so that it is always 10 feet from the base of a pole, it will trace a circle.

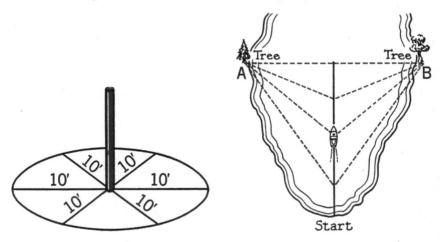

If you wish to run a boat across a lake in a straight line, you can do it approximately by watching two trees on the shore, one on each side of the boat. If you keep the same distance from one tree as from the other, you will travel in a straight line.

While attending a barbecue, you take part in a *scavenger hunt*. You are told that a prize is hidden at a point 30 feet from the fireplace. Would you be able to walk immediately to the point where the prize is hidden or would there be a number of places that satisfy the condition? Make a drawing to explain your answer.

A MOVING POINT 263

■ Meaning of Locus

Locus (plural, *loci*, pronounced lō′sī) is the Latin word for *place*. The exercises below will help you to understand the meaning of this word as it is used in geometry and acquaint you with some of the language used in connection with it.

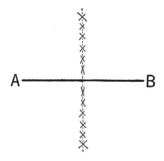

1. In the figure at the right you see 8 points, each $\frac{3}{4}''$ from O. Are these all the points that are $\frac{3}{4}''$ from O? Reproduce this figure and put in several more points that are $\frac{3}{4}''$ from O. How many points do you think there are $\frac{3}{4}''$ from O? Where are all these points?

The answer to the last question is: All the points $\frac{3}{4}''$ from O form a circle with the center O and a radius of $\frac{3}{4}''$. (It is assumed, of course, that all these points are in one plane.)

The circle is the *place* where all the points satisfying the condition ($\frac{3}{4}''$ from O) are found. And you may be sure that any point on the circle (the converse of the preceding statement) is $\frac{3}{4}''$ from O. We say:

The *locus* of a point (moving so that it is always) $\frac{3}{4}''$ from a given point O is a circle with center O and a radius of $\frac{3}{4}''$.

Note that the locus **is** the circle. We do **not** say, "The locus is *on* the circle."

2. Complete: The locus of a point (moving so that it is always) 3″ from a point O is _?_.

3. Complete: The locus of a point at a given distance d from a given point O is _?_.

4. In the figure at the right you see AB and several points, each point as far from A as from B. Are these the only points that are equidistant from A and B? How many such points are there? Where do all these points appear to lie with respect to the line AB?

Complete: The locus of a point (moving so that it is always) equally distant from two points is _?_.

5. Draw a line AB of indefinite length. Locate five points on each side of AB and 1 inch from it. (Remember that each 1-inch distance should be measured on a line perpendicular to AB.) Where do all the points 1 inch from AB appear to lie? Complete: The locus of a point at a given distance d from a given line AB is a pair of lines . . .

EXERCISES

In Exs. 1–7 first decide what condition has to be fulfilled. Make a drawing and locate five or more points that satisfy the condition. Decide what the locus is and then complete the sentence.

EXAMPLE: The locus of the center of a car wheel moving along a straight level track is *a line parallel to the track at a distance equal to the radius of the wheel.*

1. A cow is hitched to a post by a rope that is free to turn on the post and is 20 ft. long. The boundary of the surface over which she may graze is . . .

2. The locus of the center of a circle that has a radius r and passes through a point A is . . .

3. The locus of the middle point of a radius of circle O is . . . (Each radius has only one middle point, but there are an infinite number of radii.)

4. The locus of the middle point of a chord of given length in circle O is . . .

5. The locus of a point outside a circle of radius 2 in. and $\frac{1}{2}$ in. from the circle is . . .

6. The locus of the vertex of an isosceles triangle with a fixed base is . . . (How many such triangles are there?)

EXTRA

7. The locus of a point within an angle and at a distance of 4 cm. from the vertex is . . .

8. A dog is tied to a square corner of a building 30 × 15 ft. by a rope 18 ft. long. Make a drawing of the boundary of the surface over which the dog may roam.

9. A circle of radius 2 cm. moves around the outside of a rectangle 6 × 8 cm. so that it just touches the rectangle. Make a drawing of the locus of the center of the circle.

■ Discovering More Difficult Loci

Discovering a locus is like plotting a graph in algebra. In making a graph you have the two co-ordinate axes (the X-axis and the Y-axis) *fixed in position*. You start with these fixed lines. Then you plot, with respect to the axes, a sufficient number of points to determine the character or shape of the graph.

Likewise in geometry, to discover a locus which you cannot see intuitively, you start with a fixed line or lines. The first step is to decide from the given conditions what lines (or line) are *fixed in position*. Next decide what is *variable*. Then locate one point that satisfies the condition, then another and another, until you have a sufficient number of points to suggest what the locus is. The points should be located close together so that the trend of the locus may be seen.

EXAMPLE 1: What is the locus of the middle point of a chord drawn to a given point on a given circle?

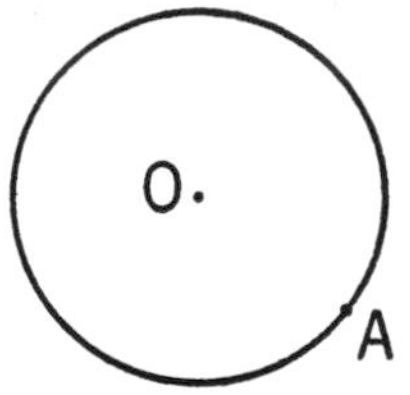

a Decide what is *fixed in position*. You have a given circle and a point A on it (Fig. 1).

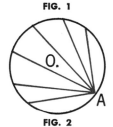

FIG. 1

b Decide what is *variable*. There are many chords that can be drawn to this point A (Fig. 2). You may think of this chord as moving from one position to another. You wish to find the locus of the middle point of this movable chord.

FIG. 2

c Now that you have analyzed the statement, you are ready to find the locus. Draw ⊙O and place point A on it. Draw one chord to A and indicate its middle point (Fig. 3).

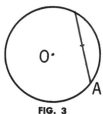

d Draw another chord to A, varying its position slightly from that of the first chord and locate the middle point on this new chord (Fig. 4, page 267).

FIG. 3

e Continue to draw chords which are not far apart and locate the middle point of each. You should begin to see what the locus is (Fig. 5).

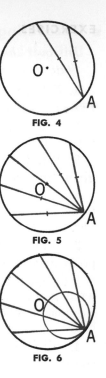

FIG. 4

f Complete your work by considering special positions of the chord. Consider, for example, the *longest chord*. It is the diameter and its middle point is the center of the circle. There is no *shortest chord* but a chord can be drawn as short as you wish. The middle point of this chord is very close to A. Now you see what the locus is (Fig. 6).

FIG. 5

The apparent locus is as follows: The locus of the middle point of a chord drawn to a point A on a circle O is another circle with OA as diameter.

Note that the locus has been defined in terms of what was given. We cannot say that the locus is a line through the plotted points. (We use the word *apparent* because we have not proved that the locus is correct.)

FIG. 6

EXAMPLE 2: Plot the locus of points such that $y = x^2 - 2x - 3$.

In this case the co-ordinate axes (the X-axis and the Y-axis) are the fixed lines. The position of the point varies in such a way that its co-ordinates always satisfy the equation. To plot the locus (or graph, as it is usually called in algebra), you must make a table of corresponding values of x and y.

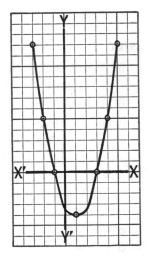

x	-3	-2	-1	0	1	2	3	4	5
y	12	?	?	-3	?	?	?	?	12

Make a table of values, using integral values of x from -3 to $+5$. Plot the points and draw the graph.

Note: In Example 2 we have said *locus of points*. In other exercises we have said *locus of a point*. The two phrases have the same meaning and use.

Discover the locus in the way indicated on the preceding pages. State the apparent locus without proof.

1. What is the locus of the center of a circle that passes through two given points?

The two points are fixed. You can draw several circles through these two points. The circles will vary in position and in size.

2. What is the locus of the center of a circle that is tangent to a given line at a given point?

The line and a point on it are fixed in position. You can draw one circle tangent to the line at the point. You can then draw another and another, and so on. The circles will vary in size.

3. What is the locus of the extremities of lines meeting at a given point and bisected by a line not through the point?

A is a fixed point and *BC* is a fixed line. Draw *AD* so that it is bisected at *E*. Draw several other lines from *A* in such a way that they will be bisected by *BC*.

4. What is the locus of the vertex of the right angle of a right triangle with a fixed hypotenuse?

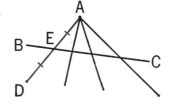

The hypotenuse *AB* is fixed. The other two sides of the triangle are variable. One side must pass through *A*, the other through *B*, and the two sides must make a right angle at *C*. Draw these lines close enough together so that you can see what the locus of *C* is.

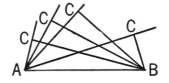

5. What is the locus of the center of a circle that has a radius *r* and is tangent externally to a given circle?

6. What is the locus of a point that is equally distant from the sides of an angle?

7. On a graph chart, what is the locus of points where $x = 0$? where $y = 0$? where $x = 3$? where $y = 4$? where $x = -2$? where $y = -1$?

8. Plot the locus of points that satisfy each of the following equations:

a $y = 2x$	b $y = -3x$	c $y = x$
d $y = 2x + 3$	e $y = 3x - 4$	f $y = 2x - 5$
g $y = x^2$	h $y = x^2 + 3$	i $y = x^2 + 2x - 2$

■ Plotting a Cycloid — *Optional*

An interesting curve used in engineering design and in the construction of machines is the *cycloid*.

△ *A* **cycloid** *is the locus of a point on a circle which rolls along a straight line.*

Figure 1 shows some positions of the point P as the circle rolls along the line AB. You can see from this drawing that the locus is not a straight line. By careful plotting of points you will discover that the locus is not a circle. It is a cycloid (Fig. 2).

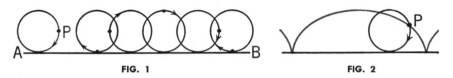

FIG. 1   FIG. 2

Below is shown a draftsman's construction of a cycloid.

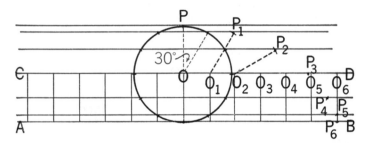

a AB is equal to the circumference of the circle O (3.14 times the diameter). The circle is drawn tangent to AB at its mid-point.

b The line CD is drawn parallel to AB through O. This is the locus of the center of the circle as the circle rolls along AB.

c The circle is divided into 12 equal parts (30° central angles). At these points of division, lines are drawn parallel to AB.

d AB is also divided into 12 equal parts and, at the points of division, lines are drawn perpendicular to AB.

e As the center of the circle moves from O to O_1, P will move to P_1. P_1 is found by using O_1 as center and OP as radius.

f As the center of the circle moves from O_1 to O_2, P_1 will move to P_2. P_2 is found by using O_2 as center and OP as radius.

g Points P_3, P_4, P_5, and P_6 are found in a similar manner.

The other half can be plotted by working backward from P.

■ Television, a Moving Point — *Optional*

You have been working with locus as the path of a moving point. Do you know that the picture you see on your television screen is "painted" by a single spot of light which moves with seemingly incredible speed? The spot begins at the upper left of the picture tube and moves straight across to the right side; it then goes back to the left side just under the place where it began and moves to the right again. The spot of light makes over 500 lines before it ends at the lower right of the tube. It completes all these trips in $\frac{1}{30}$ of a second! You do not see this spot moving because the eye retains what it sees for only about $\frac{1}{16}$ of a second. The picture is a blend of several complete trips. You see a picture because the spot grows bright and dim as it moves in perfect synchronization with the camera in the stadium or at the studio.

Press Association Inc.

Note how the lines of dots of different shades form the picture

■ Fundamental Locus Theorems

You have been working with *locus* as the path of a moving point. With this concept you have been able to state some loci intuitively and have discovered others by plotting points. Before you can prove deductively that these loci are correct you will need a more precise definition.

△ *In a plane a locus is a geometric figure such that —*
1. *any point that satisfies a given condition is on it, and*
2. *any point on it satisfies the given condition.*

Note: The definition has two parts. In order that a geometric figure be established as a locus, you must prove both parts.

| LOCUS THEOREM 1 | *The locus of a point at a given distance from a given point is a circle with the point as center and the given distance as radius.* |

This means that if ⊙O has a radius d, then:
a any point A at a distance d from O is on the circle, and
b any point B on the circle is at a distance d from O.
These statements are obvious from the definition of a circle. No formal proof is required.

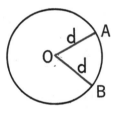

| LOCUS THEOREM 2 | *The locus of a point at a given distance from a given line is a pair of lines, one on each side of the given line, parallel to the given line at the given distance from it.* |

This means that if CD and EF are parallel to the given line AB and each is a distance d from AB, then:
a any point G which is a distance d from AB is on one of the parallels, and
b any point H on one of the parallels is at a distance d from AB.
The proof of this theorem is obvious since parallel lines are at all points the same distance apart. Formal proof is not required.

LOCUS THEOREM 3	*The locus of a point equally distant from two parallel lines is a line parallel to them and midway between them.*

This means that if AB and CD are parallel and EF is parallel to them and midway between them, then

    a any point G that is equally distant from AB and CD is on EF, and

    b any point H on EF is equally distant from AB and CD.

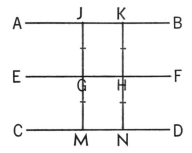

The proof of this theorem depends upon the same statement as Locus Theorem 2. Formal proof is not required.

LOCUS THEOREM 4	*The locus of a point equally distant from two given points is the perpendicular bisector of the line segment joining the two points.*

Tell what this theorem means. The proof is on the next page.

LOCUS THEOREM 5	*The locus of a point equally distant from the sides of an angle is the bisector of the angle.*

Tell what this theorem means. The proof is on page 274.

LOCUS THEOREM 6	*The locus of the vertex of the right angle of a right triangle with a fixed hypotenuse is a circle whose diameter is the hypotenuse.*

What does this theorem mean? The proof is on page 275.

The locus of a point equally distant from two given points is the perpendicular bisector of the line segment joining the two points.

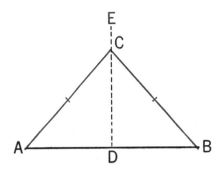

a *Any point equally distant from two points is on the perpendicular bisector of the line between the two points.*

Given AB with C so located that $CA = CB$.
To prove   that C is on the perpendicular bisector of AB.
Proof.   Through C draw $ED \perp AB$.

STATEMENTS	REASONS
1. $CA = CB$.	1. Given.
2. $CD = CD$.	2. Identity.
3. ADC and BDC are right angles.	3. Why?
4. $\triangle ADC \cong \triangle BDC$.	4. Why?
5. $AD = DB$.	5. $C.p.c.t.e.$

Since C is on ED (by construction) and ED is the perpendicular bisector of AB, C is on the perpendicular bisector of AB.

b *Any point on the perpendicular bisector of the line joining two points is equally distant from the two points.*

Proof.   This has already been established (Theorem 5).
Since you have proved **a**, and its converse, **b**, you have proved Locus Theorem 4.

COROLLARY   **The perpendicular bisector of a chord passes through the center of the circle.**

The locus of a point equally distant from the sides of an angle is the bisector of the angle.

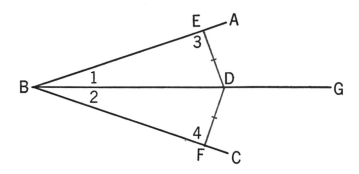

a *Any point equally distant from the sides of an angle is on the bisector of the angle.*

Given   ∠*ABC* and *D* so located that the perpendiculars *DE* and *DF* are equal.

To prove   that *D* is on the bisector of ∠*ABC*.

Proof.   Draw *BG* through *D*.

STATEMENTS	REASONS
1. *DE* ⊥ *AB*, *DF* ⊥ *BC*.	1. Given.
2. ∠3 and ∠4 are rt. angles.	2. Why?
3. *DE* = *DF*.	3. Given.
4. *BD* = *BD*.	4. Identity.
5. △*BED* ≅ △*BFD*.	5. Why?
6. ∠1 = ∠2.	6. *C.p.c.t.e.*

Since *D* is on *BG* (by construction) and *BG* bisects ∠*ABC*, *D* is on the bisector of ∠*ABC*.

b *Any point on the bisector of an angle is equally distant from the sides of the angle.*

Given   ∠*ABC* with bisector *BG* and point *D* on *BG*.   *DF* ⊥ *BC* and *DE* ⊥ *AB*.

To prove   that *DE* = *DF*.

Proof.   Part b has already been established.   It is the same as Theorem 8 although the wording is different.

Since a and b have been proved, Locus Theorem 5 has been established.

> *The locus of the vertex of the right angle of a right triangle with fixed hypotenuse is a circle with the hypotenuse as diameter.*

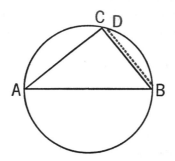

a *If a circle is drawn upon the hypotenuse of a right triangle as diameter, the vertex of the right angle is on the circle.*

Given   right triangle ABC with hypotenuse AB and a circle with AB as diameter.

To prove   that C is on the circle.

Proof. AC or AC extended must meet the circle at some point we shall call D.   Draw DB.

Outline of proof.

    1. Then $\angle ADB$ is a right angle.   It is inscribed in a semicircle.

    2. $BD \perp AC$.   (Why?)

    3. $BC \perp AC$.   (Given.)

    4. Hence BD and BC are the same line (Postulate 6, page 89); and C and D are the same point.   (Postulate 2, page 89.)

Since D is on the circle (by construction), C is on the circle.

b *If any point on a circle is joined with the extremities of a diameter, a right triangle is formed and the point is the vertex of the right angle.*

Proof.   This has already been proved, since an angle inscribed in a semicircle is a right angle.

Since **a** and **b** have been proved, Locus Theorem 6 has been established.

EXERCISES

1. Find a point on a given line that is equally distant from two points not on the line. (Draw the line that contains all the points equidistant from the two given points. The point where this line intersects the given line is the required point.) Are there any positions of the given points with respect to the given line such that no solution is possible?

2. Find a point equally distant from three points not in a straight line. Explain why the given points must not be in a straight line.

3. PQ intersects the sides of $\angle ABC$. Find a point on PQ equally distant from the sides of $\angle ABC$. (Draw the line that contains all the points that are equally distant from the sides of $\angle ABC$.)

4. DE is the perpendicular bisector of AC, and FG is the perpendicular bisector of BC. Prove that O, the point of intersection of DE and FG, is equally distant from A and B. Is O on the perpendicular bisector of AB?

EX. 4

5. In $\triangle ABC$, AD bisects $\angle A$ and BE bisects $\angle B$. Is O, the intersection of AD and BE, on the bisector of $\angle C$?

6. What is the locus of the center of a circle that has a given radius and that is tangent to a given line?

7. What is the locus of the center of a circle that is tangent internally to a larger circle at a given point?

EXTRA

8. What is the locus of the middle point of a chord drawn through a given point within a circle?

9. Draw the locus of the middle point of chords which, extended, pass through a given point outside the circle.

10. What is the locus of the vertex C of $\triangle ABC$ having a given size and shape and altitude CD, if A is on one of two parallel lines, B on the other, and AB is perpendicular to the parallels?

11. A straight line of given length moves so as to remain constantly parallel to one side of an angle while one end is in contact with the other side. Draw the locus of the unattached end of the moving line.

12. Draw the locus of the intersection of the diagonals of $\square ABCD$, in which AB is fixed and BC is of given length.

■ A Linkage — *Optional*

Below is shown a certain **linkage.** It is a device to make point A move along a straight line. Other linkages cause points to move in a circle, a figure eight, and many other curves.

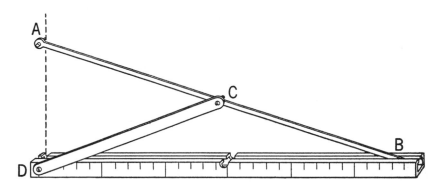

The linkage in the illustration is made of two links AB and DC. AB is twice the length of CD. C is the mid-point of AB.

Point D is fixed, but link DC is pivoted at D and C. Part DB is grooved so that B can move along the straight line BD.

When end B of link AB is moved to the left, point A will move upward and trace a straight line DA (extended).

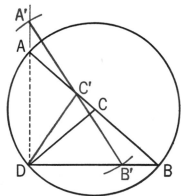

The following is a proof that A traces a straight line:

A circle with C as center and CD as radius will pass through B, D, and A. $AC = CB = DC$.

AB will always be the diameter of the circle. (C is always the center and arc ADB is always a semicircle.)

(This will be true no matter how the linkage is moved, as shown in red. $A'C' = C'B' = DC'$)

$\angle ADB$ is a right angle. (An angle inscribed in a semicircle . . .)

$AD \perp DB$. (The sides of a right angle are perpendicular.)

Since DB is a fixed line, AD is fixed in direction. (At a point in a line only one perpendicular can be drawn.)

You should find it interesting to make a drawing of this linkage and plot the locus of A. As C moves it traces the arc of a circle.

■ Intersection of Loci

When a point must satisfy each of two conditions, its position or positions can be found by the intersection of two loci. Any point on one locus satisfies one condition; any point on the other locus satisfies the other condition. Hence the points of intersection of the two loci must satisfy both conditions.

EXAMPLE 1: Find all the points that are a distance d from a given point A and also a distance d' from another given point B.

The locus of points at a distance d from A is a circle with A as center and d as radius (Locus Theorem 1). The locus of points at a distance d' from B is a circle with B as center and d' as radius. The required points are the points of intersection of the two circles (in the figure, C and D).

There are many possibilities in connection with this exercise.

If you assume that $d' > d$, how many points are there if $AB < d' - d$? if $AB = d' - d$? if $AB > d' - d$ but $< d' + d$? if $AB = d' + d$? if $AB > d' + d$?

EXAMPLE 2: Find all the points whose co-ordinates satisfy the following pair of equations: $3x + 2y = 0$, $2x + 3y = -5$.

First make a table of corresponding values of x and y that satisfy each equation. Then draw the graph of each equation.

$3x + 2y = 0$

x	y
-2	3
2	-3
4	-6

$2x + 3y = -5$

x	y
-1	-1
2	-3
5	-5

The locus of points whose co-ordinates satisfy one equation is one straight line. The locus of points whose co-ordinates satisfy the other equation is another straight line. Hence the co-ordinates of the point of intersection $(2, -3)$ satisfy both equations. There is only one point that satisfies them.

1. A and B are 2 in. apart. Find all points 3 in. from A and 2 in. from B.

2. A is 1 in. from CD. Find all points 3 in. from A and 2 in. from CD.

3. C is 1 in. from A and 2 in. from B. A and B are $1\frac{1}{2}$ in. apart. Find all points equally distant from A and B and $1\frac{1}{2}$ in. from C.

4. Angle BAC is 45°, D is within the angle $\frac{1}{2}$ in. from BA on a perpendicular drawn to BA at a point 2 in. from A. Find all points equally distant from AB and AC and 1 in. from D.

5. In $\triangle ABC$, $AB = 1\frac{1}{2}$, $BC = 2$, and $AC = 3$ units. Find all points equally distant from A and C and also equally distant from AB and BC.

6. In $\triangle ABC$, $AB = 3$, $AC = 4$, and $BC = 5$ units. Find all points 2 units from AB and equally distant from B and C.

EXTRA

7. Find all the points at a given distance from a given point and also equally distant from the sides of a given angle. Discuss the possibilities.

8. Find, by graphing, the co-ordinates of all the points that satisfy each of the following pairs of equations. Check your answers by substituting in the equations.

a $y = 3x$
    $y = -x$

b $2x + y = -1$
    $x + y = 1$

c $2x - 3y = 5$
    $3x - 2y = 0$

d $y = x^2 + 2x - 4$
    $y = 2x$

9. Prove that the intersection of the perpendicular bisectors of two sides of a triangle is equally distant from the extremities of the third side. Does the perpendicular bisector of the third side pass through this point of intersection? Give a reason for your answer.

10. Prove that the intersection of the bisectors of two angles of a triangle is equally distant from the sides of the third angle. Can you show that the bisector of the third angle passes through this point of intersection?

11. Construct an isosceles triangle having given the base and an altitude upon one arm.

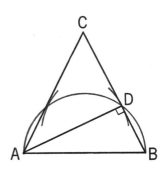

As you see from the figure, $\angle ADB$ must be a right angle.

The locus of vertex D is a semicircle on AB as a diameter. Construct this semicircle.

Then, to find point D in the triangle, use A as center and the given altitude as radius.

12. You are given a line BC and a point A that is 1 inch from line BC. If you find the locus of a point that is always as far from A as from BC, you will have a curve called a parabola.

Find the locus by plotting points.

Find one point halfway between A and BC. That will be the turning point of the parabola.

Then find two points each $\frac{5}{8}$ in. from A and from BC.

Find two points each $\frac{3}{4}$ in. from A and from BC.

Find two points each $\frac{7}{8}$ in. from A and from BC.

Continue this process until you find several more points.

Draw a smooth curve through the points.

13. Point A is 2 inches from line BC. AD is a line from A perpendicular to BC with D on BC. Plot the locus of a point that is always one half as far from A as from BC.

Find one point by dividing AD into three equal parts.

Find two points that are $\frac{3}{4}$ in. from A and $1\frac{1}{2}$ in. from BC.

Find two points that are 1 in. from A and 2 in. from BC.

Continue this process until you find a point on the extension of DA that is 2 in. from A and 4 in. from BC.

Draw a smooth curve through the points. The curve you draw is called an ellipse.

14. Plot the locus of a point that is always twice as far from a point A as from a line BC (A not on BC). Follow the procedure of Exercises 12 and 13. There are two parts to the locus. It is called a hyperbola.

15. Plot the locus of a point the sum of whose distances from two given points is always equal to a given line.

▪ Plotting a Location — *Optional*

When a ship is near land the navigator can use landmarks or anchored buoys to help guide his ship through waters which may contain dangerous rocks or shoals. Such navigation is known as *piloting* and is the oldest form of navigation. Certain fixed landmarks were available to the earliest sailors, who had no instruments for long-distance navigation.

A navigator has charts which show him how to navigate relative to the landmarks. What he needs to know most of all is the location of his ship. You have seen how he can find his location (page 240) with three lighthouses visible on shore. Here is a method for finding the location of a ship, using only two known points on shore.

Figure 1 is a diagram in which point A is a radio tower and point B is a possible (unknown) position of the ship. AN and BN' are north-south lines. The navigator's chart shows A. The problem is to plot the ship's position on the chart.

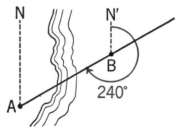

FIG. 1

The navigator *sights* A from the ship and finds the angle $N'BA$ to be 240° ($\angle N'BA$ is measured in a clockwise direction from north as shown by the arrow). The remaining angle at B is then 120° and $\angle A = 60°$. Explain. The navigator can now draw a line on his chart making an angle of 60° with the known line AN.

This gives him the line through A and B. His ship must be on the line AB but as yet he does not know whether his ship is between A and B or beyond B.

To find his location he sights another point C just as he did point A. From this procedure he gets a second line CD on which the ship must be located. Since the ship is somewhere on the line AB and also on the line CD, he knows that the ship is actually at the point E, the intersection of these two loci (Fig. 2).

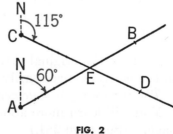

FIG. 2

■ The Inverse of a Statement — *Optional*

You have learned about converse statements and how to form them. You know that if a statement is true, its converse (or converses) may not be true. Every statement that can be put into the if-then form has at least one converse. It may have many converses. Similarly every such statement has at least one inverse and may have many inverses.

Consider the following statements:

1. *If a point is equally distant from the sides of an angle, it is on the bisector of the angle.*

2. *If a point is on the bisector of an angle, it is equally distant from the sides of the angle.*

These are converse statements. Each statement is the converse of the other.

Now consider the next two statements:

3. *If a point is not equally distant from the sides of an angle, it is not on the bisector of the angle.*

4. *If a point is not on the bisector of an angle, it is not equally distant from the sides of the angle.*

Statements 1 and 3 are inverses; statements 2 and 4 are inverses. You see how the inverse of a statement is formed. The inverse of a statement having one conclusion is formed by negating one of the conditions and also the conclusion. A statement having two (or more) conclusions may be written as two (or more) statements, then the inverse of each statement can be formed.

You should note that statement 4 is the inverse of the converse (or the converse of the inverse) of statement 1. Explain.

Here is another illustration to help you see the relationships:

STATEMENT: When it is raining, this road is slippery.

CONVERSE: When this road is slippery, it is raining.

INVERSE: When it is not raining, this road is not slippery.

INVERSE OF THE CONVERSE: When this road is not slippery, it is not raining.

Suppose the original statement is always true of a certain road. Is the converse necessarily true? Is the inverse necessarily true? *The inverses of a statement are not necessarily true.*

You will learn more about the *inverse of the converse* on another page. (See page 284.)

EXERCISES

Read the following statements and then answer the questions:

1. If a creature is a horse, then it is an animal.
   a Is this statement true?
   b Is the converse true?
   c Is the inverse true?
   d Is the inverse of the converse true?

2. A person who steals is not honest.
   Answer the same questions as in Ex. 1. (How do you negate a negative conclusion?)

3. People who eat a good deal of candy become overweight.
   Can you explain why this statement is not necessarily true? Note that the inverse of the converse is also not necessarily true.

4. If a point is equally distant from two parallel lines, then it is on the line parallel to and halfway between the given lines.
   Answer the questions in Ex. 1. (Note that what you say about the given statement is also your answer for the inverse of the converse.)

5. If a line segment is bisected, it is divided into two equal parts.
   The statement and its converse are true because this is a definition. Are the inverse and the inverse of the converse true?

6. If a line segment joins the mid-points of two sides of a triangle, then it is parallel to the third side and equal to one half of the third side.
   a How many conclusions does this statement have?
   b How many inverses does this statement have? State them in the form given on page 124.
   c Are the inverses true?

7. If $x = 7$, then $4x = 28$.
   a Is this statement true?
   b Is the converse true?
   c Is the inverse true?
   d Is the inverse of the converse true?

8. All equal angles are right angles.
   Answer the questions in Ex. 7.

Note that your answer to the question on the given statement is also your answer for the inverse of the converse.

INVERSE OF A STATEMENT   **283**

■ The Contrapositive—*Optional*

The *contrapositive* is another name for the *inverse of the converse.*

You have seen from the exercises on the preceding page that the contrapositive and the original statement always contain the same degree of truth. If one is entirely true, the other is entirely true. If one is only partially true or entirely false, so also is the other. The contrapositive of a statement is formed by first writing the converse and then writing the inverse of the converse. It may be formed directly from the given statement by negating one of the conditions in the hypothesis and also the conclusion, and interchanging them. (If the statement has more than one conclusion, make a separate statement for each conclusion as you did in dealing with the inverse.)

<u>Postulate</u> If a statement is true, its contrapositive is true, and vice versa.

This postulate we shall call the *contrapositive principle.*

■ Using the Contrapositive Principle—*Optional*

Suppose you wish to prove: If two sides of a triangle are not equal, then the angles opposite those sides are not equal. You can proceed as follows:

Given AC not equal to BC.
To prove that $\angle A$ is not equal to $\angle B$.
Proof.

STATEMENTS	REASONS
1. The contrapositive of this proposition is: If $\angle A = \angle B$, then $AC = BC$.	1. Definition of contrapositive.
2. If $\angle A = \angle B$, then $AC = BC$.	2. Theorem 2.
3. AC is not equal to BC.	3. Given.
4. $\angle A$ is not equal to $\angle B$.	4. If the contrapositive is true (statement 2), then the statement is true.

State the contrapositive of each of the following theorems and use the contrapositive principle to prove that your statements are true:

1. If two sides of a triangle are equal, the angles opposite those sides are equal.

2. If two lines are cut by a transversal so that the alternate interior angles are equal, the lines are parallel.

3. If two parallel lines are cut by a transversal, the corresponding angles are equal.

4. In the same circle or in equal circles, chords equally distant from the center are equal.

■ Application to Proof of Loci — *Optional*

If a statement and its converse are true, the inverse of each is true. In proving the locus theorems, we proved in each case a statement and its converse. The statement of a locus theorem is therefore a short way of saying the following four things:

   a *Any point that satisfies the condition is on the locus.*

   b *Any point on the locus satisfies the condition.* (Converse)

   c *Any point that does not satisfy the condition is not on the locus.* (Inverse)

   d *Any point that is not on the locus does not satisfy the condition.* (Contrapositive)

We might prove one of these statements and its inverse, instead of its converse. In either case all four will be true.

Often, instead of proving statements **a** and **b**, statement **b** and statement **d**, which is the contrapositive of statement **a**, are proved.

1. Write the four statements above as applied to each of the six locus theorems.

2. Write the four statements above as applied to the graph of an equation. The first statement is: Any point whose co-ordinates satisfy an equation is on the graph of the equation.

3. If you proved the following two statements, would you prove Locus Theorem 4? Give a reason for your answer.

   a Any point on the perpendicular bisector of a line joining two points is equally distant from the two points.

   b Any point not on the perpendicular bisector of a line joining two points is not equally distant from the two points.

Note: For a minimum course, the *proofs* of Theorems 40–43 may be omitted.

THEOREM
40
| *The perpendicular bisectors of the sides of a triangle meet at a point which is equally distant from the vertices of the triangle.*

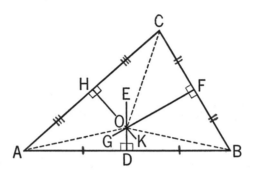

Given △*ABC* with *DE*, *FG*, and *HK* perpendicular bisectors of *AB*, *BC*, and *CA*, respectively.

To prove that *DE*, *FG*, and *HK* meet at a point *O* and that *OA* = *OB* = *OC*.

Outline of proof.

1. *HK* will meet *DE* at some point *O*. (If they do not meet, they will be parallel and *AB* and *AC* will either be parallel or coincide. This is impossible, since *AB* and *AC* are the sides of a triangle.)
2. *OA* = *OC*, *OA* = *OB*. (Locus Theorem 4.)
3. *OC* = *OB*. (Why?)
4. *O* is on *FG*. (Locus Theorem 4.)
5. *OA* = *OB* = *OC*. (Steps 2 and 3.)

Construction   Circumscribing a circle about a triangle.
   Problem

Given   △*ABC*.

Required   to circumscribe a circle about △*ABC*.

Analysis.   You must find a point *O* equally distant from *A*, *B*, and *C* to use as a center. This can be done by means of Theorem 40.

The construction and proof are left for you.

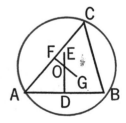

THEOREM	*The bisectors of the angles of a triangle meet at*
41	*a point that is equidistant from the sides of the*
	triangle.

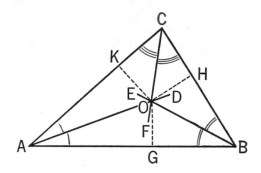

Given $\triangle ABC$ with AD, BE, and CF bisectors of $\angle A$, $\angle B$, and $\angle C$, respectively.

To prove   that AD, BE, and CF meet at a point O and that O is equally distant from AB, BC, and CA.

Outline of proof.

AD and BE will meet at some point O.   (If they do not meet, they will be parallel and $\angle OAB + \angle OBA$ will equal 180°. $\angle OAB + \angle OBA$ cannot equal 180°, for they are halves of two angles of a triangle.)

The rest of the proof is left for you.

Construction   Inscribing a circle in a triangle.
   Problem

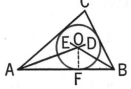

Given $\triangle ABC$.

Required   to inscribe a circle in $\triangle ABC$.

Analysis.   We must find a point equally distant from the three sides of the triangle. This can be done by means of Theorem 41.

Construction.   Construct AD and BE, the bisectors of $\angle A$ and $\angle B$, respectively.   They will meet at some point O.   (Theorem 41.)   Construct $OF \perp AB$.   Using O as center and OF as radius, draw a circle.   This circle will be tangent to AB, BC, and CA.

Proof.   The proof is left for you.

The altitudes of a triangle meet at a point.

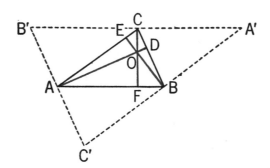

Given   △ABC with altitudes AD, BE, and CF.

To prove   that AD, BE, and CF meet at a point.

The *plan* is to show that the three altitudes are the perpendicular bisectors of the sides of the larger triangle formed by drawing lines through the vertices of △ABC parallel to the opposite sides.

Proof.   The proof is left for you.   (To show that $B'C = CA'$, prove that $ABCB'$ and $ABA'C$ are parallelograms.   To finish the proof, use Theorem 40.)

△ *The point of intersection of the altitudes of a triangle is called the **orthocenter** of the triangle; the point of intersection of the perpendicular bisectors of the sides is called the **circumcenter;** and the point of intersection of the bisectors of the angles is called the **incenter.***

EXERCISES — *Optional*

1. Is the orthocenter of a triangle always within the triangle? Could it be the same point as the circumcenter?

2. Is the orthocenter the same point as the incenter in an isosceles triangle?   in an equilateral triangle?

3. Is it possible for the three medians of a triangle to coincide with the three corresponding altitudes and the three corresponding angle bisectors of the triangle?   Illustrate.

4. Is it possible for a line to be both a median and an altitude of a triangle, but not an angle bisector of the triangle?

Δ **A median of a triangle** *is a line drawn from any vertex to the mid-point of the opposite side.*

THEOREM 43

The medians of a triangle meet at a point which is two thirds of the distance from each vertex to the mid-point of the opposite side.

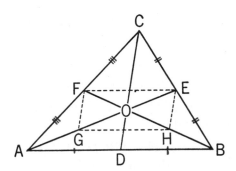

Given △ABC, with the medians AE and BF intersecting at O.

To prove that the median from C passes through point O and that $AO = \frac{2}{3}AE$, $BO = \frac{2}{3}BF$, and $CO = \frac{2}{3}CD$.

The *plan* is to take G and H as the mid-points of AO and BO respectively and show (1) that $EFGH$ is a parallelogram, (2) that AE and BF are trisected, and (3) that CD passes through O.

Outline of proof.

Show that (1) GH is $\parallel$ to AB and equal to $\frac{1}{2}AB$, EF is $\parallel$ to AB and equal to $\frac{1}{2}AB$, and $EFGH$ is a $\square$; (2) $OE = OG = AG$, making $AO = \frac{2}{3}AE$; and (3) $OF = OH = BH$, thus making $BO = \frac{2}{3}BF$.

If CD does not intersect BF at O, but at some other point as O', then you can prove that $BO' = \frac{2}{3}BF$. This makes $BO' = BO$; so O' coincides with O.

MENTAL EXERCISES

Write answers only:

1. In the figure above, if $AE = 6$ in., how long are AO and OE?
2. If $AO = 8$ in., how long is AE?
3. If $BF = 7$ in., how long are BO and OF?
4. If $OF = 3$ in., how long is BO?
5. If $AE = 2\frac{1}{2}$ in., how long are AO and OE?

EXERCISES

1. The location of a water shut-off is stated as 20 ft. from a point A in a northerly direction and 25 ft. from a point B in a northwesterly direction. B is 15 ft. east of A. Make a drawing to show the location of the shut-off.

2. What is the locus of the middle points of the radii of a given circle?

3. What is the locus of the middle points of parallel chords in a circle?

4. Make a drawing to show the locus of the center of a circle that rolls around an equilateral triangle.

5. What is the locus of points from which tangents to two tangent circles are equal?

6. In a certain rectangle $ABCD$, AB is 2 units and BC is 1 unit. The line EC is drawn from E, the middle point of AB. Make a drawing to show the locus of the middle points of lines parallel to EC and terminated by the sides of the rectangle.

7. Construct a circle which shall be tangent to a given line at a given point and which shall pass through a given point not on the line.

EXTRA

8. Plot the locus of the vertex C of $\triangle ABC$ with fixed base AB and a given perimeter.

9. With a given radius construct a circle that shall be tangent externally to a given circle and pass through a point not on the circle.

10. What is the locus of the end point of a line which is of given length and tangent to a circle?

11. What is the locus of the vertex of an angle of given size whose sides are tangent to a given circle?

12. What is the locus of the mid-points of secants drawn to a given circle from a given external point?

13. Secants are drawn to a circle from an external point. What is the locus of the mid-points of the external segments of the secants?

■ One Circle through Three Points

The construction problem on page 286 shows that one circle can be drawn through three points not in a straight line. There is only one such circle. Its center must be equally distant from all three points.

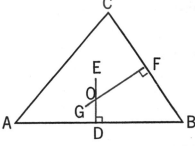

DE the perpendicular bisector of *AB* contains all the points equally distant from *A* and *B*.

FG the perpendicular bisector of *BC* contains all the points equally distant from *B* and *C*.

Since *DE* and *FG* can intersect at only one point, *O* is the only point equally distant from *A*, *B*, and *C*.

Why can no circle be drawn through three points that are in a straight line?

EXERCISES

1. Draw an acute triangle and circumscribe a circle about it. Do the same for a right triangle; an obtuse triangle.

2. Construct an equilateral triangle and circumscribe a circle about it.

3. Does the center of a circle circumscribed about a triangle fall within the triangle? When will it fall within the triangle? when on one side? when outside the triangle?

4. Does the center of a circle inscribed in a triangle fall within the triangle?

5. Under what conditions will the center of circles circumscribed about and inscribed in the same triangle be the same point?

6. How many triangles may be inscribed in a circle?

7. Can a circle be drawn through any four points?

8. Can a circle be drawn through the four vertices of a rectangle? a square? a rhombus? any parallelogram?

9. Inscribe a circle in a given square.

10. Circumscribe a circle about a given square.

11. Find the center of a given arc.

■ Determining a Figure—*Optional*

To determine a figure, it is necessary to give enough conditions to fix exactly the size, shape, and location of the figure.

EXAMPLE 1: A line segment is determined by the position of its two end points.

EXAMPLE 2: A circle is determined by any three points not in a straight line. You have seen that through any three such points a circle can be constructed. On the preceding page you saw that there can be only one circle.

EXERCISES

Answer the following questions without giving proofs:

1. How else may a circle be determined than by giving three points through which it must pass?

2. Does the position of the center of a circle determine the circle? What else is necessary?

3. Is a circle determined by the position of a chord? of a diameter?

4. Is a circle determined by a given fixed chord and a radius of given length? If the radius were less than half the chord, would your answer be the same?

5. Do the positions of the three vertices of a triangle determine the triangle?

6. Do the position of one vertex and the lengths and directions of the two sides meeting at that vertex determine a triangle?

7. Do the position and length of one side of a triangle and the directions of the other two sides determine the triangle?

8. Do the position and length of the base of a triangle and the lengths of the other two sides determine the triangle?

9. Is a square determined by the position of a side? of a diagonal?

10. Do the positions of three vertices of a parallelogram determine the parallelogram?

11. State as many ways as you can of determining a parallelogram, a square, and an equilateral triangle.

1. All possible lines are drawn from a given point outside a circle to points on the circle. Find the locus of the middle points of these lines.

2. In two triangles that have the same base and an angle opposite the base of the same size, prove that the angles, whose vertices are the centers of the inscribed circles and that are subtended by the base, are equal.

3. One end of a straight-line segment of given length always touches a given circle and is always parallel to a given line. Find the locus of the other end.

4. Two circles O and O' are always tangent externally to each other. Circles O and O' are also tangent to a given line AB at the fixed points A and B respectively on the line. Find the locus of the points of contact of these circles.

5. Find the locus of the intersection of the bisectors of the base angles of parallelograms that have a fixed line as base.

6. Two fixed equal circles are tangent externally. What is the locus of the centers of all circles tangent to both given circles?

7. If a square is moved along a given line by revolving it successively about its vertices, what is the locus of one vertex?

8. Prove: If the opposite angles of a quadrilateral are supplementary, a circle may be circumscribed about it. (SUGGESTION. Draw a circle through three of its points and prove by the indirect method that the circle will pass through the fourth point.)

9. At point A in line BC all possible circles are drawn tangent to line BC. From C tangents are drawn to these circles. What is the locus of the points of contact of these tangents?

10. AB is a diameter of circle O. From any point C on the circle a line is drawn perpendicular to AB intersecting AB in D. OE is marked off on OC equal to CD. Find the locus of point E as C takes all possible positions.

11. Prove: The sum of the diameters of the two circles circumscribed about and inscribed in a right triangle equals the sum of the two sides of the right angle.

12. The vertex angle of an isosceles triangle is 120°. The perpendicular bisectors of the equal sides AB and AC meet BC at D and E respectively. Prove that BD equals DE equals EC.

13. Two fixed equal circles intersect. What is the locus of the centers of all circles that are tangent to both circles?

14. The medians of two sides of a triangle are equal. Prove that the triangle is isosceles.

15. All possible chords are drawn from a fixed point on a circle. Each chord is extended its own length. Find the locus of the extremities of these lines.

SUPPLEMENTARY EXERCISES

1. Is an equilateral triangle isosceles? Is an isosceles triangle equilateral?

2. Are adjacent angles always supplementary? Are supplementary angles always adjacent? Illustrate.

3. Can two circles that are tangent to each other have a common chord? Illustrate.

4. In a given circle is the chord of an arc of 60° twice as long as the chord of an arc of 30°? Give a reason for your answer.

5. Three of the angles of a quadrilateral are 100°, 80°, and 60°. How many degrees are there in the fourth angle?

6. An angle APB is inscribed in a circle whose diameter is AB. How many degrees are there in $\angle APB$?

7. An angle APB is inscribed in a circle. If arc APB contains 80°, how many degrees are there in $\angle APB$?

8. If arc AT contains 100°, how many degrees has the acute angle PTA formed by chord AT and tangent PT?

9. Two chords AB and CD intersect at P. Find the number of degrees in $\angle APC$ if arc $CB = 60°$, arc $BD = 80°$, and arc $AD = 130°$.

10. How many sides has a polygon if the sum of its angles is 1440°?

11. Prove: If the angle at the vertex of an isosceles triangle is 36°, the bisector of one base angle divides the figure into two isosceles triangles.

12. Construct an isosceles triangle, having given the base and a base angle.

13. Prove: If the perpendiculars drawn from the center of a circle to two chords are equal, the arcs of these chords are equal.

14. AB is tangent to a circle at A, BD is tangent at C, and DE is tangent at E. Prove that $AB + DE = BD$.

15. Prove: The line connecting the middle points of the nonparallel sides of a trapezoid bisects the diagonals.

16. Prove: Lines joining the middle points of two opposite sides of a parallelogram with the ends of a diagonal trisect the other diagonal.

17. Prove: If lines are drawn from any point within a triangle perpendicular to two sides of the triangle, the angle formed by the two perpendiculars is the supplement of the angle formed by the two sides of the triangle.

18. Prove: An equilateral polygon inscribed in a circle is also equiangular. (Draw the radii to each vertex of the polygon, let one of the central angles thus formed be $a°$, and evaluate the angles of the polygon.)

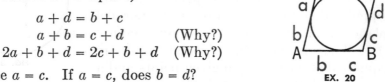

19. Prove: If AE bisects $\angle A$ of $\triangle ABC$ and BE bisects the exterior angle CBD, then $\angle E = \frac{1}{2}\angle C$. (Let $\angle A = a°$ and $\angle C = b°$.)

EX. 19

20. Prove: A circumscribed parallelogram is a rhombus. (SUGGESTION: Why are the segments lettered alike equal?)

$$a + d = b + c$$
$$a + b = c + d \qquad \text{(Why?)}$$
$$2a + b + d = 2c + b + d \quad \text{(Why?)}$$

Hence $a = c$. If $a = c$, does $b = d$?

EX. 20

21. Prove: The middle point of the hypotenuse of a right triangle is equally distant from all three vertices of the triangle.

22. Prove: The bisectors of the base angles of an isosceles triangle meet on the perpendicular bisector of the base.

23. In $\triangle ABC$, D and E are the mid-points of AC and BC, respectively. AE and BD are extended their own lengths to F and G. Prove that F, C, and G are in a straight line. (SUGGESTION: Prove that GC and FC are parallel to the same line.)

■ Loci in Three Dimensions — *Optional*

1. Complete: The locus of points in three dimensions (in space) at a given distance from a given point is a . . .

2. Complete: The locus of points in space at a given distance d from a given plane is a pair of planes, one on each side of the given plane and . . .

3. Complete: The locus of points equally distant from two given points (A and B) is a plane . . . (See Fig. 1.)

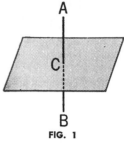
FIG. 1

4. You know that the locus of points in a plane at a distance d from a given line AB is a pair of lines (CD and EF) parallel to the given line. Think of this figure as revolving about AB as an axis and you will be able to state the locus of points in space at a given distance from a given line. What is the nature of this locus? (Fig. 2)

5. What is the locus of points equally distant from two parallel planes?

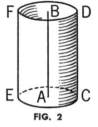
FIG. 2

The locus of points that satisfy two conditions is the intersection of two loci, each locus satisfying one of the conditions. Thus the locus of points which lie in a given plane and which are a given distance m from a given point P is the intersection of the given plane and the sphere whose radius is m and whose center is the given point. (See Fig. 3.)

6. What is the locus of points that are equally distant from two given parallel planes and a distance d from a given point?

7. What is the locus of points that are equally distant from two given points and a distance d from a given point?

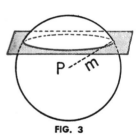
FIG. 3

Chapter Summary

I. Locus by intuition or other informal methods

1. What is the locus of the vertices of all isosceles triangles on the same base?

2. What is the locus of the middle points of lines drawn parallel to the base of a triangle and terminated by the other two sides?

II. Discovering loci by plotting points

3. $AB \perp BC$. DE is a line of given length located so that D is always on AB and E is always on BC. Discover the locus of the middle point of DE by plotting points.

III. Locus theorems

Complete the statements in Exs. 4–9:

4. The locus of a point at a given distance from a given point is __?__.

5. The locus of a point at a given distance from a given line is __?__.

6. The locus of a point equally distant from two parallel lines is __?__.

7. The locus of a point equally distant from two points is __?__.

8. The locus of a point equally distant from the sides of an angle is __?__.

9. The locus of the vertex of the right angle of a right triangle with a fixed hypotenuse is __?__.

10. Prove that the locus of a point equally distant from two points is the perpendicular bisector of the line joining the two points.

IV. Other theorems

11. State the theorems concerning —
a The perpendicular bisector of the sides of a triangle.
b The bisectors of the angles of a triangle.
c The altitudes of a triangle.
d The medians of a triangle.

V. Constructions

12. Describe how you would —
a Circumscribe a circle about a triangle
b Inscribe a circle in a triangle

VI. Intersection of loci

13. A, B, and C are the vertices of an equilateral triangle. Find a point that is equally distant from A and C and equally distant from the sides of $\angle C$. Is there a point equally distant from A and C and equally distant from the sides of $\angle B$?

Complete the sentences in Exs. 1–10:

1. The locus of a point 5 inches from a point *A* is _?_.

2. The locus of a point equally distant from the sides of a 30° angle is _?_.

3. The locus of a point equally distant from *A* and *B* when *AB* = 5 inches is _?_.

4. *AB* is the hypotenuse of right triangle *ABC*. The locus of *C* is _?_.

5. The locus in a circle of the mid-points of all chords parallel to a given line is _?_.

6. The locus of the center of a circle that is tangent to both sides of an angle is _?_.

7. The locus of the center of a circle that passes through two given points *A* and *B* is _?_.

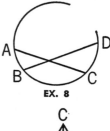

EX. 8

8. The center of this arc is at the intersection of the _?_ of *AC* and *BD*.

9. $\triangle ABC$ is equilateral and *CD*, *AE*, and *BF* are altitudes. If *CD* = 6 in., then *CO* = _?_ in.

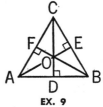

EX. 9

10. The intersection of the bisectors of the angles of a triangle is the center of the _?_ circle.

11. *AC* of $\triangle ABC$ is fixed in position. $\angle B$ is always 60° but *B* varies in position although it always remains above *AC*. Find the locus of *B* by plotting points. Let your drawing show what the locus is.

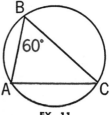

EX. 11

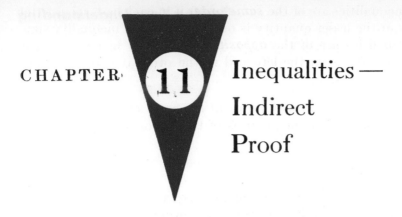

CHAPTER **11** Inequalities — Indirect Proof

A LITTLE girl has learned to put on her shoes but, as yet, is unable to tell which shoe goes on which foot. With a pair of her shoes in front of her, she holds out her right foot, points to the shoe for her left foot, and questions her mother, "This one?" Her mother answers, "No, not that one." Does the girl then know, indirectly, that the other shoe is the shoe for her right foot?

Consider this situation: Mr. Everett Mitchell returned to his office Thursday afternoon after closing time and found a note that his secretary had left on his desk. The note merely stated, "Mr. Brown will see you at 9:30 tomorrow morning."

Among Mr. Mitchell's acquaintances there were four Browns — Jim, George, Fred, and Bill — but the note contained no first name.

Mr. Mitchell thought this way: Jim and his wife are in Europe for a month's tour. Fred told me this morning that he was catching the noon train to spend the week end with his mother. Bill is now serving on a jury and has to report at court at 9:30 each morning. That leaves George, who is trying to land the Farquar account. Therefore, the note must refer to George Brown.

Much of the reasoning you do every day is of this type. It is *indirect*, not direct. In this chapter you will learn how to use the **indirect method of proof**. At the same time, you will learn about **unequal quantities** and **relationships of inequality**.

Symbols of inequality. The symbol for *is greater than* is >, and for *is less than* is <. $a > b$ means a is greater than b. The symbol for *is not equal to* is ≠.

Two inequalities are of the *same order* if in each case the greater quantity or the lesser quantity is on the left of the inequality sign. Two inequalities are of the *opposite order* when in one case the greater quantity is on the left and in the other it is on the right of the inequality sign.

$a > b$ and $c > d$ are inequalities of the same order.
$a > b$ and $c < d$ are inequalities of the opposite order.

AXIOMS OF INEQUALITY

| 1 | If equal quantities are added to unequal quantities, the sums are unequal quantities in the same order. |

| 2 | If unequal quantities are added to unequal quantities of the same order, the sums are unequal in the same order. |

| 3 | If equal quantities are subtracted from unequal quantities, the remainders are unequal in the same order. |

| 4 | If unequal quantities are subtracted from equal quantities, the remainders are unequal in the opposite order. |

| 5 | If unequal quantities are multiplied by positive equal quantities, the products are unequal in the same order. As a special case of this axiom we have: **Doubles of unequals are unequal in the same order.** |

| 6 | If unequal quantities are divided by positive equal quantities, the quotients are unequal in the same order. As a special case of this axiom we have: **Halves of unequals are unequal in the same order.** |

| 7 | If three quantities are so related that the first is greater than the second and the second is greater than the third, then the first is greater than the third. |

| 8 | The whole is greater than any of its parts. |

COROLLARY Supplements or complements of unequal angles are unequal in the opposite order.

■ Choosing the Correct Axiom

Answer the questions and choose the correct axiom as an authority. In case it is not possible to answer the question, give the answer as Not known.

1. John has more money than Frank and Frank has more than Fred. How do John's and Fred's amounts compare?

2. John has more than Mary and Frank has more than Ann. How do John's and Frank's amounts together compare with Mary's and Ann's? How do John's and Mary's together compare with Frank's and Ann's?

3. John and Mary have equal amounts of money. John spends more than Mary. How do their amounts then compare?

4. John has more than Mary. They spend equal amounts. How do their amounts then compare?

5. John has less than Fred. Each doubles his amount. How do their amounts then compare?

6. John has less than Fred. Each loses half of his amount. How do the amounts then compare?

7. John has three times as much money as Mary and Frank has three times as much as Ann, and furthermore Mary has more than Ann. How do John's and Frank's amounts compare?

8. John has one third as much as Mary and Frank has one third as much as Ann. How do John's and Frank's amounts compare?

9. John has more than Frank. Then each earns $5. How do the amounts then compare?

10. John, Frank, and Mary together have $18. Does Frank have more or less than $18?

11. Mary has less than Ann. Then they each spend $2. How do the amounts then compare?

12. Mary and Ann have equal amounts. Mary spends a dollars and Ann b dollars. If $a > b$, how do the amounts then compare?

EXERCISES

Copy the following exercises and supply the symbol >, <, *or* = *if the relationship can be determined. Otherwise replace the question mark in the blank space. If you do not see what the relationship is, substitute numbers for the given letters. Choose the correct axiom as your authority.*

1. If $a = 2b$, $c = 2d$, and $b > d$, then $a \underline{\ ?\ } c$.

2. If $a > b$ and $b > c$, then $a \underline{\ ?\ } c$.

3. If $c = a + b$, then $c \underline{\ ?\ } b$.

4. If $a > b$ and $c = d$, then $a - c \underline{\ ?\ } b - d$.

5. If $a = b$ and $c < d$, then $a + b \underline{\ ?\ } c + d$.

6. If $a = b$ and $c < d$, then $a - c \underline{\ ?\ } b - d$.

7. If $a > b$ and $c = b$, then $a \underline{\ ?\ } c$.

8. If $a > b$ and $c > d$, then $a + c \underline{\ ?\ } b + d$.

9. If $a = \frac{1}{2}b$ and $c = \frac{1}{2}d$, then $a \underline{\ ?\ } c$.

10. If $a + b = c + d$ and $b < d$, then $a \underline{\ ?\ } c$.

11. If $a > b$ and $c = d$, then $a + c \underline{\ ?\ } b + d$.

Exercises 12–21 refer to the diagram at the right.

12. If $\angle 1 = \angle 2$ and $\angle 3 = \angle 4$, then $\angle D \underline{\ ?\ } \angle B$.

13. If $\angle 1 = \angle 2$ and $\angle 3 > \angle 4$, then $\angle D \underline{\ ?\ } \angle B$.

14. If $\angle 1 > \angle 2$ and $\angle 3 > \angle 4$, then $\angle D \underline{\ ?\ } \angle B$.

15. If $\angle 1 + \angle 3 = \angle D$, then $\angle D \underline{\ ?\ } \angle 3$.

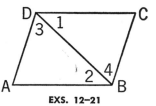

EXS. 12–21

16. If $\angle B = \angle 2 + \angle 4$ and $\angle 3 = \angle 4$, then $\angle B \underline{\ ?\ } \angle 2 + \angle 3$.

17. If $\angle D = 2\angle 3$, $\angle B = 2\angle 4$, and $\angle 3 < \angle 4$, then $\angle D \underline{\ ?\ } \angle B$.

18. If $\angle 1 = \angle 3$ and $\angle 2 = \angle 4$, then $\angle D \underline{\ ?\ } \angle B$.

19. If $\angle 1 > \angle 3$ and $\angle 2 > \angle 4$, then $\angle D \underline{\ ?\ } \angle B$.

20. If $\angle D = \angle B$ and $\angle 1 = \angle 2$, then $\angle 3 \underline{\ ?\ } \angle 4$.

21. If $\angle D > \angle B$ and $\angle 1 = \angle 2$, then $\angle 3 \underline{\ ?\ } \angle 4$.

Choose the correct axiom as an authority for your answer to each of the following exercises:

22. $AB \perp CD$, $\angle 2 > \angle 1$. Compare $\angle 3$ and $\angle 4$.

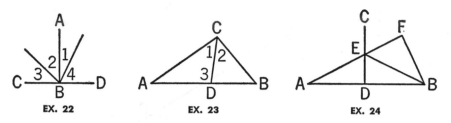

EX. 22   EX. 23   EX. 24

23. $\angle 3 > \angle 2$ and CD bisects $\angle C$. Compare $\angle 3$ and $\angle 1$.

24. $FE + EB > FB$, and CD is the perpendicular bisector of AB. Compare $FE + EA$ with FB.

■ Inequality of Angles

You have proved that if one side of a triangle is extended, the exterior angle is equal to the sum of the two remote interior angles; that is, $\angle CBD = \angle A + \angle C$. Since this is so, $\angle CBD$ in this figure is greater than either $\angle A$ or $\angle C$. Why?

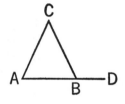

The relationship illustrated here is true in general.

COROLLARY **If one side of a triangle is extended, the exterior angle is greater than either of the remote interior angles.**

This corollary is useful in proving angles unequal.

1. ADB is a straight line. Which angle is an exterior angle of $\triangle BCD$? State two inequalities. Which angle is an exterior angle of $\triangle ADC$? State two inequalities. Prove that if CD bisects $\angle C$, $\angle 3 > \angle 1$.

2. In $\triangle ABC$, CD is so drawn that $CD = AC$. Prove that $\angle A > \angle B$.

THEOREM 44

If two sides of a triangle are unequal, the angles opposite those sides are unequal in the same order.

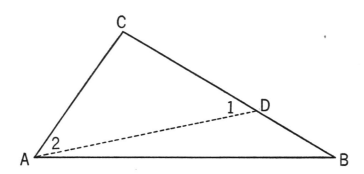

Given $\triangle ABC$, in which $BC > AC$.

To prove that $\angle A > \angle B$.

Proof. Mark off $CD = AC$. Draw AD.

STATEMENTS	REASONS
1. $\angle A > \angle 2$.	1. Axiom 8, page 300.
2. $AC = CD$.	2. Construction.
3. $\angle 2 = \angle 1$.	3. Why?
4. $\angle A > \angle 1$.	4. Axiom 1, page 84.
5. $\angle 1 > \angle B$.	5. Cor., page 303.
6. $\angle A > \angle B$.	6. Axiom 7, page 300.

It is often helpful when one line or angle is given greater than another to mark off the smaller on the larger as was done above.

EXERCISES

1. The sides of a triangle are 7 inches, 10 inches, and 11 inches. Which angle of the triangle is the largest? Which angle is the smallest?

2. Prove: In a scalene triangle no two angles are equal.

3. In quadrilateral $ABCD$, $AB > BC$ and $AD > DC$. Prove that $\angle C > \angle A$.

4. Prove: In a parallelogram which is not a rhombus, the diagonals do not bisect the angles.

■ Indirect Proof

You are familiar with indirect proof in an informal way. Suppose a friend told you that John broke his leg a week ago and yet you had seen John walking normally only an hour before. You would say, "That cannot be. I saw him walking only an hour ago." If your friend believed you, he would be convinced that he was wrong about the time.

This would not be a direct proof. For a direct proof you would have to investigate the facts and find out the date that John broke his leg. You did not do this, but instead you brought to bear facts that you know about broken bones. You know that in a week a broken leg will not mend enough for normal walking. You proved your point indirectly.

Indirect proofs of this kind depend upon the fact that two *contradictory* statements cannot both be true at the same time. Two lines are either equal or they are not equal. If the first is true, the second must be false, and vice versa. If you can prove that one of only two possibilities is false, then you know that the other is true.

Postulate 1   If a statement is true, then its contradictory is false.

Postulate 2   If a statement is false, then its contradictory is true.

If a proposition is given, the contradictory statement is made by keeping the same hypothesis and negating the conclusion. There is only one contradictory statement, but there may be more than one case to consider in connection with it.

Proposition: If two lines are perpendicular to the same line all in the same plane, they are parallel.
Contradictory proposition: If two lines are perpendicular to the same line all in the same plane, they are *not* parallel.

Each proposition is the contradiction of the other. The first contradicts the second just as the second contradicts the first. To contradict a negative statement, omit the *not*.

To prove a proposition true indirectly, prove the contradictory proposition false.

■ Contradictory Propositions

1. Give the statement that contradicts each of the following:

a If two sides of a triangle are equal, the angles opposite those sides are equal.

b If two sides of a triangle are unequal, the angles opposite those sides are unequal.

2. How would you prove indirectly that $AB = CD$? (Answer: Prove that the statement, $AB \neq CD$, is false.)

3. How would you prove indirectly that $AB \parallel CD$?

4. How would you prove indirectly that $\angle A > \angle C$? (Answer: By proving that the statement, $\angle A$ is not greater than $\angle C$, is false.)

5. How would you prove indirectly that only one perpendicular can be drawn from a point to a line? (Answer: By proving that the statement, Two perpendiculars can be drawn from a point to a line, is false. Note that the *two* contradicts the *only one*.)

6. How would you prove indirectly that a triangle may have only one obtuse angle?

Proving a statement false. How did you prove in the illustration on page 305 that the statement, "John broke his leg a week ago," was false? First, you assumed for the moment that it was true. You said in effect, "Suppose he did break his leg last week." Then you thought what the case would be if this were true. You thought, "If he did break his leg last week, he would not be walking now." This conclusion was contrary to a known fact; you had seen him walking only an hour before. Hence you knew that the original statement was false.

Here is another illustration. Police officers suspect that a man is pretending deafness in order to avoid questioning. They wish to find out whether or not he is deaf. In fact, they wish to prove that the statement, "He is deaf," is false. To do this they assume that he is deaf. They know that if he is deaf, he will not be startled by a noise. They make a sudden noise behind him and he jumps. They know then that he is not deaf.

To prove that a statement is false, assume that it is true and see what would result. If you arrive at a conclusion contrary to some known fact, you know that the statement is false.

■ Reduction to an Absurdity

If the reasoning of the police officers were written out, it would be like this:

Suppose he is deaf. (Assuming the truth of the statement they wish to prove false.)

Then he cannot hear.

If he cannot hear, he will not be disturbed by a sudden noise behind him. (This is a conclusion contrary to a known fact; he was startled by a sudden noise behind him.)

Hence he is not deaf.

Note that if the man had *not* been outwardly disturbed by the noise nothing would have been proved. It might only have shown the possession of strong nerves or the knowledge that such a test would be attempted. Proof occurs only when there is a conclusion *contrary* to some known fact.

This method of proving a statement false is known as *reduction to an absurdity*.

■ Summary of the Indirect Method

To show by indirect proof that a statement is true, prove that the contradictory statement is false. To prove that the contradictory statement is false, assume that it is true and draw conclusions from the assumption until you reach a statement contrary to some known fact. Then you will know that the contradictory statement is false and the original statement is true.

You will be surprised at the frequency of this kind of proof in everyday reasoning. The following example will indicate to you how commonplace it is.

A man and his wife were driving along the state road soon after having a picnic with their friends, the Packers. A car which looked like the Packers' passed them. "There goes the Packers' car," the wife said. "No," said the husband. "They were ahead of us from the start." (Note how the statement, "There goes the Packers' car," was reduced to an absurdity. It is a known fact that a car cannot be passing and be ahead at the same time.)

Bring to class examples of indirect reasoning.

■ An Indirect Proof

Prove indirectly: *If two angles of a triangle are unequal, the sides opposite these angles are unequal.*

Given △ABC in which ∠A ≠ ∠B.

To prove that BC ≠ AC.

Proof. Assume that BC = AC (the contradictory conclusion).

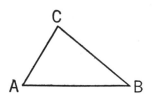

STATEMENTS	REASONS
1. Then ∠A = ∠B.	1. Theorem 1.
2. This is contrary to the hypothesis that ∠A ≠ ∠B.	2. Given.
3. Hence the assumption is false and BC ≠ AC.	3. If a statement is false, its contradictory is true.

Note that you assumed that BC = AC and showed that the assumption leads to a false conclusion. The assumption is therefore false and its contradictory is true.

EXERCISES

Prove the following exercises by indirect proof:

1. If two straight lines are cut by a transversal so that the alternate interior angles are not equal, the lines are not parallel.

2. If two straight lines are cut by a transversal so that the corresponding angles are not equal, the lines are not parallel.

3. If two nonparallel lines are cut by a transversal, the alternate interior angles are not equal.

4. In the same circle or in equal circles, unequal arcs have unequal chords.

5. In the same circle or in equal circles, unequal chords are unequally distant from the center.

6. Any point unequally distant from the extremities of a line does not lie on the perpendicular bisector of the line.

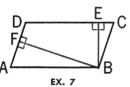

EX. 7

7. $ABCD$ is a parallelogram, BE ⊥ DC, and BF ⊥ AD. If AB ≠ BC, then BE ≠ BF.

If two angles of a triangle are unequal, the sides opposite those angles are unequal in the same order.

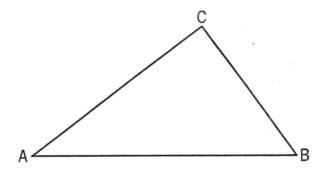

Given △ABC in which ∠B > ∠A.
To prove that AC > BC.
Plan. The proof is indirect.
Outline of proof. Suppose that AC is not greater than BC.

Then there are two cases to consider: **a** $AC = BC$ and **b** $AC < BC$.
Suppose **a** $AC = BC$.
Then ∠B = ∠A. Why?
This is contrary to the hypothesis that ∠B > ∠A.
Hence the assumption that $AC = BC$ is false.
Suppose **b** $AC < BC$.
Then ∠B < ∠A. (Theorem 44.)
This is contrary to the hypothesis that ∠B > ∠A.
Hence the assumption that $AC < BC$ is false.

Since the statements, "$AC = BC$" and "$AC < BC$," are both false, then the assumption that AC is not greater than BC is false and the statement that $AC > BC$ is true.

EXERCISES

1. Two angles of a triangle are 80° and 60°. Opposite what angle of the triangle is the shortest side?

2. Show that the hypotenuse of a right triangle is the longest side.

3. What side of an obtuse triangle is the longest?

4. In $\triangle ABC$, $AC > BC$, AO bisects $\angle A$, and BO bisects $\angle B$. Prove that $AO > BO$.

5. Prove: Any point on the equal sides of an isosceles triangle except the point where they meet is unequally distant from the vertices of the equal angles.

6. If the diagonals of a parallelogram are not equal, the figure is not a rectangle. (Indirect proof.)

7. Prove: If, in quadrilateral $ABCD$, $AB = BC$, $AD = DC$, and $AD > AB$, then $\angle ABC > \angle ADC$.

8. Prove: If a line is drawn from the vertex C of an isosceles triangle ABC to any point D on the base, then $CD < CA$.

EXTRA

9. Prove: Of two oblique lines drawn from any point on a perpendicular to a line and cutting off unequal distances from the foot of the perpendicular, the one cutting off the greater distance is the greater.

10. Of two oblique lines drawn from any point on a perpendicular to a line, the greater cuts off the greater distance from the foot of the perpendicular. (Indirect proof. You may use Ex. 9 in your proof.)

EX. 9

11. In $\odot O$, $AB > BC$, $OD \perp AB$, and $OE \perp BC$. Prove that $OE > OD$. (Is $BD > BE$?)

12. In $\odot O$, $OD \perp AB$, $OE \perp BC$, $OD < OE$. Prove that $AB > BC$.

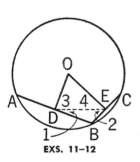

EXS. 11–12

13. Prove: If two straight lines are cut by a transversal so that the sum of the interior angles on one side of the transversal is less than 180°, the lines will meet on that side of the transversal.

14. In this figure made by three intersecting straight lines, prove that $\angle 1 + \angle 2 > 180°$.

(SUGGESTION: $\angle 2 = \angle 4 + \angle 5$, and $\angle 1 = \angle 4 + \angle 3$.)

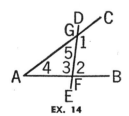

EX. 14

■ Inequality of Lines

The basic statement used in proving the inequality of lines is the following postulate:

A straight line is the shortest line that can be drawn between two points.

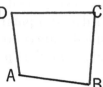

Consider two routes between A and B. According to this postulate, the route by the broken line $ADCB$ is longer than the straight-line route AB; that is, $AD + DC + CB > AB$.

COROLLARY **The sum of two sides of a triangle is greater than the third side.**

1. In $\triangle ABC$, $AB + BC > AC$. Why? Draw a triangle and write two other inequalities.

2. Prove: The difference between any two sides of a triangle is less than the third side. (If $AB + BC > AC$, then $AB > AC - BC$ or $AC - BC < AB$. Why?)

3. CD is the perpendicular bisector of AB, E is not on CD. Prove that $EA > EB$. (SUGGESTION: $EF + FB > EB$. Why? Substitute FA for FB.)

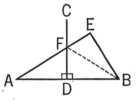

The postulate, *A perpendicular is the shortest line from a point to a line*, may also be used to prove lines unequal.

EXERCISES

1. Is it possible to form a triangle whose sides are 2 in., 3 in., and 3 in.? 2 in., 3 in., and 4 in.? 2 in., 3 in., and 5 in.? 4 in., 2 in., and 1 in.?

2. Prove: If the alternate vertices A, C, and E of a regular hexagon $ABCDEF$ are joined, the perimeter of the triangle so formed is less than the perimeter of the hexagon. (SUGGESTION: Write three appropriate inequalities and add them.)

3. Prove: Each arm of an isosceles triangle is longer than half the base.

■ An Interesting Construction

Two towns A and B are situated on the same side of a river. The near bank of the river is straight from M to N, as shown in the diagram below. A bridge is to be built across the river somewhere between A and B. The problem is to build the entrance to the bridge at a point on the near bank so that the sum of the straight-line distances from A to the bridge and from B to the bridge shall be as small as possible.

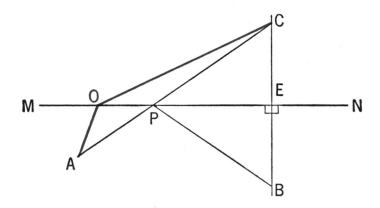

Construct $BC \perp MN$ and make $CE = EB$.
Draw AC which will intersect MN at P.
P is the place for the bridge.

Outline of proof. Let O represent any other point than P on MN.

1. $AO + OC > AC$. Why?

2. PE is the perpendicular bisector of BC.

3. So $PB = PC$. Theorem 5.

4. $AO + OC > AP + PC$. Why?

5. So $AO + OC > AP + PB$. Substitution of PB for PC.

You have shown that if the bridge is at any other point than P, the sum of the distances to it from A and B will be greater than if the bridge is at P. Therefore, the sum of the distances AP and PB is as small as possible.

<table>
<tr><td>THEOREM
46</td><td>*If two sides of one triangle are equal to two sides of another triangle and the included angle of the first is greater than the included angle of the second, then the third side of the first is greater than the third side of the second.*</td></tr>
</table>

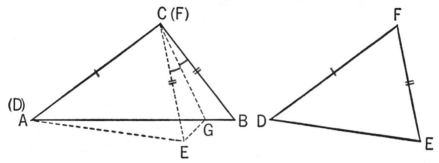

Given △*ABC* and △*DEF* in which *AC* = *DF*, *BC* = *EF*, and ∠*C* > ∠*F*.

To prove that *AB* > *DE*.

Outline of proof.

1. Place △*DEF* on △*ABC* so that *DF* coincides with its equal *AC* and *E* lies on the same side of *AC* as *B*.
2. *FE* will fall within ∠*ACB*, since ∠*C* > ∠*F*.
3. Bisect ∠*ECB* by *CG* meeting *AB* at *G*.
4. Prove that △*ECG* ≅ △*BCG*.
5. *AG* + *GE* > *DE*. Why?
6. *GB* = *GE*. Hence *AG* + *GB* or *AB* > *DE*. Why?

EXERCISES

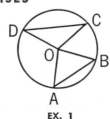

EX. 1

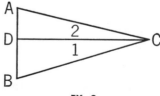

EX. 2

1. *O* is the center of the circle and ∠*DOC* > ∠*AOB*. Prove that *DC* > *AB*.

2. *AC* = *BC* and ∠1 > ∠2. Prove that *AD* < *DB*.

THEOREM 47	*If two triangles have two sides of one equal to two sides of the other and the third side of the first is greater than the third side of the second, then the angle opposite the third side of the first is greater than the angle opposite the third side of the second.*

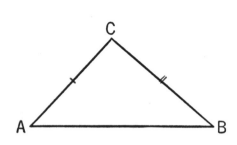
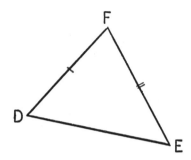

Given $\triangle ABC$ and $\triangle DEF$ in which $AC = DF$, $BC = EF$, and $AB > DE$.

To prove that $\angle C > \angle F$.

Plan. The proof is indirect.

Proof. The proof is left for you. You may use the proof of Theorem 45 as a guide.

EXERCISES

1. O is the center of the circle and $DC > AB$. Prove that $\angle COD > \angle AOB$. (See the figure for Ex. 1, page 313.)

2. $AC = BC$ and $BD > AD$. Prove that $\angle 1 > \angle 2$. (See the figure for Ex. 2, page 313.)

The next two statements are corollaries to Postulates 6 and 7 on page 207. They are needed here because they are used in proving optional Theorems 48 and 49.

COROLLARY 1   In the same circle or in equal circles, the larger of two central angles has the longer arc.

COROLLARY 2   In the same circle or in equal circles, the longer of two minor arcs has the larger central angle.

Note: Theorems 48, 49, 50, and 51 are *Optional.*

THEOREM 48 | *In the same circle or in equal circles, the longer of two minor arcs has the longer chord.*

THEOREM 49 | *In the same circle or in equal circles, the longer of two chords has the longer minor arc.*

Prove this theorem both directly and indirectly.

THEOREM 50 | *In the same circle or in equal circles, unequal chords are unequally distant from the center, the longer chord being the nearer.*

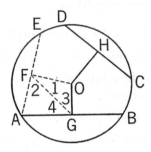

Given ⊙O in which $AB > CD$, $OG \perp AB$, and $OH \perp CD$.
To prove that $OH > OG$.
Outline of proof.

From A construct chord $AE = CD$, make $OF \perp AE$,
and draw FG.
$AB > CD$, $AE = CD$, hence $AB > AE$.
$OF \perp AE$, $OG \perp AB$, hence $AF = \frac{1}{2}AE$, $AG = \frac{1}{2}AB$,
and $AG > AF$.
$\angle AFO$ and $\angle AGO$ are right angles and equal.
$\angle 2 > \angle 4$, $\angle 3 > \angle 1$, hence $OF > OG$.
$OH \perp CD$, $OH = OF$, hence $OH > OG$.

The proper form and the reasons are left for you.

THEOREM 51	*In the same circle or in equal circles, chords un-equally distant from the center are unequal, the nearer being the longer.*

For a direct proof use the same figure as for Theorem 50. This theorem may be proved indirectly also.

■ Proof by Coincidence — *Optional*

Another type of indirect proof is *proof by coincidence.* In Theorem 12 we did not prove directly that $CD \perp FE$. Instead we proved that CD coincided with XY, which we knew to be perpendicular to FE. A similar type of proof was used for Theorem 33.

By this method you prove that a line fulfills the required conditions by showing that it coincides with a line which you already know fulfills those conditions.

Propositions you may use to prove that lines coincide are:

1. Between two points only one straight line can be drawn.

2. From a point outside a line or a point on a line only one perpendicular can be drawn.

3. An angle has only one bisector.

4. Through a point outside a line only one line can be drawn parallel to a given line.

Prove: *If two chords are parallel, the line connecting their middle points passes through the center of the circle.*

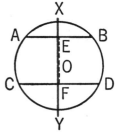

Through O, the center, draw a line XY $\perp AB$. It will pass through E. (Why?) It will be perpendicular to CD. (Why?) It will pass through F. (Why?) You now have two lines EF and XY both passing through E and F. Hence XY and EF must be the same line. (Why?)

Since you know that XY passes through O, you now know that EF passes through O.

Prove the following exercises by the method discussed on the preceding page:

1. If a line is perpendicular to a tangent at the point of tangency, it passes through the center of the circle. (This is Postulate 3, page 214. Prove that a line from the center to the point of tangency is the same line as the given perpendicular.)

2. A line perpendicular to a tangent from the center of the circle passes through the point of tangency. (This is Postulate 4, page 214.)

3. The bisector of one angle of a rhombus passes through the vertex of the opposite angle.

4. Any point equally distant from the extremities of a line lies on the perpendicular bisector of the line. (Draw a line from the point perpendicular to the line and prove that it is the perpendicular bisector.)

5. The perpendicular bisector of a chord passes through the center of the circle.

6. The bisector of the angle between two tangents passes through the center of the circle.

7. Any point equally distant from the sides of an angle lies on the bisector of the angle.

8. In an equilateral triangle, the median, the altitude, the internal segment of the angle bisector, and the internal segment of the perpendicular bisector of a side are identical.

9. In parallelogram $ABCD$, O is the point of intersection of the diagonals, E and F are the middle points of AD and BC respectively. Prove that EO and OF lie in the same straight line. (Show that they are parallel to the same line through the same point.)

10. In a trapezoid the middle points of the diagonals and the middle points of the nonparallel sides lie in a straight line.

■ Dependent Postulates — *Optional*

A postulate has already been defined as a geometric proposition accepted without deductive reasoning (see page 74). We have assumed a considerable number of postulates in this book. However, the postulates we have assumed are not all independent of one another. By this we mean that some of them could be proved by means of the others. The ideal, of course, is to have as small a set of postulates as possible and to have each postulate independent. We cannot meet this ideal here; its fulfillment must be left to college courses in the foundations of geometry.

To make sure that we have as few postulates as is possible, it would be necessary to investigate each one to see if that postulate could be proved by using any of the others. Furthermore, it would be desirable to search for even more simple postulates. This is a task for mathematicians, and through their efforts great advances have been made in the foundations of geometry in the last hundred years. Although most of the superstructure of the geometry we are studying was built up more than 2000 years ago, satisfactory work on the foundations (postulates and definitions) is comparatively recent.

Below and on the next page you will prove two dependent postulates.

1. **Two lines perpendicular to a third line all in the same plane are parallel.** (See page 140.)

Given CD and $EF \perp AB$.
To prove that $CD \parallel EF$.
Outline of proof.

Suppose that CD and EF are not parallel (the contradictory statement). Then they would meet at some point G if sufficiently extended. We should then have GCD and GEF both perpendicular to AB from one point G. This is contrary to the postulate, "From a point outside a line only one perpendicular can be drawn to the line." Hence the assumption that CD and EF are not parallel is false and the statement that CD is parallel to EF is true.

Note that by "proof" we mean that we have deduced this postulate from one of the other postulates. We were convinced of its truth before. What we have done is to fit it into the system more securely.

You will now prove the postulate upon which the proof in Ex. 1 depends.

2. **From a point outside a line only one perpendicular can be drawn to the line.** (See page 89.)

Given $CD \perp AB$ from C.

To prove   that CD is the only perpendicular that can be drawn from C to AB.

Outline of proof.

Suppose that CE is some other perpendicular from C to AB. Extend CD to F so that $DF = CD$. Draw EF.

Since $CD = DF$, $DE = DE$,   and $\angle CDE = \angle FDE$, $\triangle CDE \cong \triangle FDE$ (*s.a.s.* = *s.a.s.*), and $\angle 1 = \angle 2$.

If CE were perpendicular to AB, then $\angle 1$ would be a right angle and its equal $\angle 2$ would be a right angle.

That would make $\angle CEF$ an angle of 180° and CEF a straight line. We should then have two straight lines CDF and CEF between the two points C and F.

This is contrary to the postulate, "Between two points only one straight line can be drawn." Hence the assumption that $CE \perp AB$ is false and the statement that CD is the only perpendicular from C to AB is true.

These two propositions may now be taken from the list of postulates and placed in the list of theorems.

The postulate in Ex. 2 depends, as you have seen, upon another postulate. We might investigate to see if that postulate could be proved by the use of any other. You can readily see, however, that this process cannot be continued forever. We should finally reach a stage where the remaining postulates are independent. We cannot prove all postulates.

The parallel postulate, "Through a point outside a line only one line can be drawn parallel to a given line," caused a long controversy among mathematicians from the time of Euclid. For centuries they thought that it might be proved by means of the other postulates. Occasionally, supposed proofs were offered, but all of them contained fallacies. Only in the last century was it proved that the parallel postulate is independent of all other postulates assumed by Euclid.

■ Proof by Contrapositive — *Optional*

Here again the contrapositive is used in a proof (see page 284). *A line that passes through the center of a circle and does not bisect a given chord is not perpendicular to the chord.*

Given   Circle O with chord AB
              DE passes through O
              DE does not bisect AB
To prove DE is not $\perp AB$
Proof.

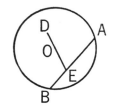

STATEMENTS	REASONS
1. A contrapositive of this proposition is: If DE passes through O and $\quad DE \perp AB$ then DE bisects AB	1. Definition of contrapositive
2. If DE passes through O and $\quad DE \perp AB$ then DE bisects AB	2. A line through the center of a circle perpendicular to a chord bisects the chord.
3. DE passes through O and does not bisect AB	3. Given.
4. DE is not $\perp AB$	4. The contrapositive principle.

EXERCISES

Prove by means of the contrapositive principle:

1. If a line is not parallel to one of two parallel lines, then it is not parallel to the other.

2. If two unequal oblique line segments are drawn to a line from a point in the perpendicular to the line, then they cut off unequal segments from the foot of the perpendicular.

3. If one pair of opposite sides of a quadrilateral are equal and the other pair are not equal, then the equal sides are not parallel.

4. If two sides of a quadrilateral are parallel and one pair of opposite angles are not equal, the remaining sides are not parallel.

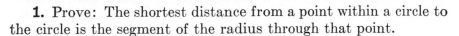

1. Prove: The shortest distance from a point within a circle to the circle is the segment of the radius through that point.

2. In triangle ABC the bisector of angle C meets AB at D. Prove that AC is greater than AD and that BC is greater than BD.

3. If D is any point inside triangle ABC, then $AB + BC > AD + DC$. (SUGGESTION. Extend AD to E on BC. Prove $AB + BC > AE + EC$.)

4. Prove that the line from the vertex B of triangle ABC to the middle point of the opposite side is less than half the sum of AB and BC.

5. Prove: The sum of the diagonals of a quadrilateral is less than its perimeter and greater than one half its perimeter.

6. CD is a diameter of a circle. AB is an intersecting diameter of a larger concentric circle. Prove that $\angle CAD < \angle ACB$.

7. The medians from A and B of triangle ABC are extended their own length to E and F. Prove that ECF is a straight line. Use the indirect method.

8. Point D is inside a right angle ABC. DE and DF are drawn so that AB and BC are perpendicular bisectors of DE and DF, respectively. Prove that E, B, and F are in a straight line. Use the indirect method.

9. AB and AC are two equal lines drawn from point A inside a circle to points B and C on the circle. A point D is taken on arc BC so that arc BD is greater than arc DC. Prove that angle BAD is greater than angle DAC.

10. Prove: If the side AB of the square $ABCD$ is extended to some point E, then ED is greater than AC.

11. AC is greater than AB in $\triangle ABC$. Prove that any line from A to a point on BC between B and C is less than AC.

12. AB is greater than AC in triangle ABC. The median AD and the bisector AE of angle BAC are drawn from A to D and E on BC. Prove that angle CAD is greater than angle CAE. (SUGGESTION. Extend AD its own length to F. Draw FC. Show that angle CAD is greater than angle DAB and therefore more than one half of angle BAC.)

PROBLEMS FOR PACEMAKERS

1. Describe briefly the indirect method of proof that involves contradictory propositions.

2. If a proposition is given, how is the contradictory proposition formed?

In Exs. 3–5, fill in the blanks and write the axiom that applies.

3. If $\angle D = \angle B$ and $\angle 1 > \angle 2$, then $\angle 3 \underline{\ ?\ } \angle 4$.

4. If $\angle D > \angle B$ and $\angle 1 = \angle 2$, then $\angle 3 \underline{\ ?\ } \angle 4$.

5. If $\angle 3 = \frac{1}{2}\angle D$, $\angle 4 = \frac{1}{2}\angle B$, and $\angle D < \angle B$, then $\angle 3 \underline{\ ?\ } \angle 4$.

6. By what methods can you prove that two angles are unequal?

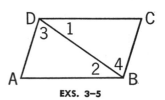

EXS. 3–5

7. By what methods can you prove that two lines are unequal?

8. In the figure, $AB \perp CD$, $BD > BC$, $BE = BC$. Give a reason for each of the following statements:

   a $AD > AB$ **b** $\angle 4 > \angle 2$
   c $\angle 2 > \angle D$ **d** $\angle 4 > \angle D$
   e $AD > AE$ **f** $AC = AE$
       g $AD > AC$

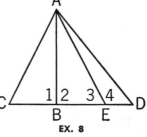

9. In $\triangle ABC$, $BC > AC$ and E is the midpoint of side AB. Is $\angle CEA$ obtuse or acute? Why?

EX. 8

10. In $\triangle ABC$, $\angle B$ is obtuse and M is the midpoint of BC. Prove that $AC > AM$.

11. Prove by the indirect method:

If a line from any vertex of a triangle to the middle point of the opposite side is not perpendicular to that side, the other two sides are unequal.

12. Prove by the indirect method:

If two lines are parallel to the same line, they are parallel to each other.

13. The sides of $\triangle ABC$ are respectively 5, 6, and **7** inches. Give the angles in order of size.

14. Prove: If the vertex angle of an isosceles triangle is more than 60°, the base is the longest side.

15. Prove: If the exterior angle at the base of an isosceles triangle is less than 120°, the base is the shortest side.

16. Prove: If the angles of a parallelogram are not right angles, the diagonals are not equal.

17. Prove: If a line from one vertex of a triangle to the middle point of the opposite side is not perpendicular to it, the other two sides are not equal.

18. Prove: The perimeter of any pentagon is greater than the sum of the two diagonals drawn from any one vertex.

19. Prove: If a point is taken within a triangle, the sum of the lines drawn to it from the vertices is greater than half the perimeter.

20. Prove: In a parallelogram the diagonal drawn between the vertices of the two smaller angles is longer than the other diagonal.

21. Quadrilateral $ABCD$, in which $AD \perp AB$ and $DC \perp CB$, is inscribed in a circle, and arc $AB >$ arc BC. Prove that $DC > AD$.

22. In $\triangle ABC$, in which $AC > BC$, a line is drawn from the vertex C to the middle point D of AB. Any point E is taken on CD. AE and BE are drawn. Prove that $AE > BE$.

■ An Inequality in Three Dimensions — *Optional*

The sum of any two face angles of a trihedral angle is greater than the third face angle.

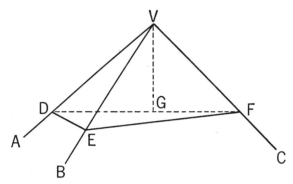

The angle V–ABC is called a trihedral angle because there are *three* face angles AVB, BVC, and AVC meeting at the common vertex V. This proposition means that in the trihedral angle V–ABC, $\angle AVB + \angle BVC > \angle AVC$. ($\angle AVC$ is the greatest face angle.)

Outline of proof.

Take convenient points D and F on VA and VC respectively. Draw DF.

In the face AVC make $\angle DVG = \angle DVB$, G is on DF. Make $VE = VG$. Draw DE and EF.

In ⧍DVE and DVG —
> $VE = VG, VD = VD$, and $\angle DVG = \angle DVE$. Why?
> Hence $\triangle DVE \cong \triangle DVG$. *s.a.s.* = *s.a.s.*
> Now $DE + EF > DF$. Why?
> So, since $DE = DG$, (*C.p.c.t.e.*)
> $EF > GF$. Axiom 3, page 300.

In ⧍EVF and FVG —
> $VE = VG, VF = VF$, and $EF > GF$.
> Hence $\angle EVF > \angle FVG$. (Theorem 47)
> But $\angle DVE = \angle DVG$. *C.p.c.t.e.*
> So $\angle DVE + \angle EVF > \angle DVG + \angle FVG$
> or $\angle DVE + \angle EVF > \angle DVF$. Axiom 2, page 300.
> Since $\angle DVE$ is the same as $\angle AVB$, $\angle EVF$ is the same as $\angle BVC$, and $\angle DVF$ is the same as $\angle AVC$.
> Then $\angle AVB + \angle BVC > \angle AVC$.

I. Axioms

1. State the axiom that applies.

a If $BC > AC$ and $AC > AB$, then $BC > AB$.

b If $CD > BE$ and $AE = BD$, then $BC > AB$.

c If $CD + DB = CB$, then $CB > BD$.

d If $AE = BD$ and $CB > AB$, then $CD > BE$.

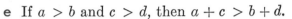

EX. 1 (a–d)

e If $a > b$ and $c > d$, then $a + c > b + d$.

f If $a = b$ and $c > d$, then $a - c < b - d$.

g If $a = 3b$, $c = 3d$, and $b > d$, then $a > c$.

h If $a = \frac{1}{3}b$, $c = \frac{1}{3}d$, and $b > d$, then $a > c$.

II. Indirect proof

2. What is the contradictory statement to "If two angles of a triangle are equal, the sides opposite those angles are equal"?

3. If you were asked to prove indirectly that AB is not parallel to CD, what would be your procedure?

4. Explain what *reducing to an absurdity* means.

III. Theorems

5. In $\triangle ABC$, $\angle A = 80°$, $\angle B = 40°$, and $\angle C = 60°$. Which side of this triangle is the longest? Why?

6. In $\triangle DEF$, $DE > EF$ and $EF > FD$. Which angle of this triangle is the largest? Why?

7. Complete: If two sides of one triangle are equal to two sides of another and the angle between the two sides of the first is greater . . .

8. State a converse of Ex. 7, the one that is proved in this chapter.

State the reason for each exercise. If more than one reason is required, state the final one.

1. If ∠2 > ∠3, then *GB* > *AG*.

2. If ∠2 = ∠3 and ∠1 > ∠4, then ∠*A* > ∠*B*.

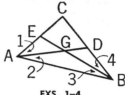

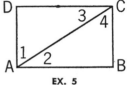

3. *AE* = *EC* and *BD* = *DC*, but *AC* < *BC*; therefore *AE* < *BD*.

EXS. 1–4

4. If *AC* = *BC* and *BD* > *AE*, then *CD* < *CE*.

5. If *ABCD* is a rectangle and ∠1 > ∠3, then ∠2 < ∠4.

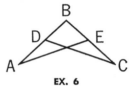

EX. 5

6. In the figure, ∠*ADC* > ∠*C*.

7. In △*ABC*, *AB* is extended to *D*. If ∠*CBD* = 120°, ∠*C* < 120°.

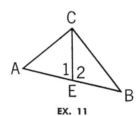

EX. 6

8. In △*ABC*, *BC* = 10 in., *AC* = 8 in., and ∠*B* = 25°; so ∠*A* > 25°.

9. In a rhombus *ABCD*, ∠*ABC* > ∠*BCD*, then *AC* > *BD*.

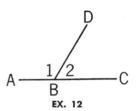

EX. 11

10. If *a* > *b*, then *a* − *n* > *b* − *n*.

11. If *E* is the midpoint of *AB* and *BC* > *AC*, then ∠2 > ∠1.

12. If ∠1 = 120° and ∠2 = 59°, *ABC* cannot be a straight line. If it were a straight line, ...

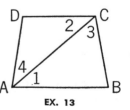

EX. 12

13. If *AB* ∥ *CD* and ∠*D* > ∠*B*, then ∠3 > ∠4.

EXTRA

14. If a chord *AB* 6″ long is 2″ from the center of a circle, then another chord 5″ long will be more than 2″ from the center.

EX. 13

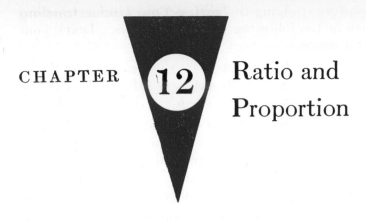

CHAPTER **12** Ratio and Proportion

FINDING THE ratio of one number to another is a means of comparing those two numbers by division. The ratio of 4 to 5, for instance, is $\frac{4}{5}$, or, expressed as a decimal, it is .8. You should realize that ratio always involves numbers. You do not find the ratio of one thing to another. You find the ratio of measures of those things and measures involve numbers. You do not find the ratio of one rock to another. But you may find the ratio of the weights of the two rocks. If the first rock weighs 24 pounds and the second weighs 36 pounds, the ratio of the weight of the first to the weight of the second is 24 to 36 or $\frac{24}{36}$, which reduces to $\frac{2}{3}$.

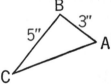

For brevity, you may say that the ratio of AB to BC, in the triangle at the right, is 3 to 5, but what you really mean is that the ratio of the number of inches in AB to the number of inches in BC is 3 to 5.

◼ Ratio

Δ *The **ratio** of one number to another number is their quotient — the first number divided by the second.*

A ratio is a fraction, and all the rules governing fractions may be used in working with ratios.

The ratio of 3 to 4 is $\frac{3}{4}$, sometimes written 3 : 4. The ratio of 8 to 2 is $\frac{8}{2}$ or 4. The ratio of a to b is $\frac{a}{b}$ or $a : b$.

For practice before studying the next section, write as fractions the ratio of each of the following pairs of numbers. Leave your answers in lowest terms.

a 2 to 3 **b** 8 to 24 **c** $4x$ to $5x$

d $10x^2$ to $4x$ **e** x to $20 - x$ **f** $a - b$ to $a^2 - b^2$

g $a + b$ to $a^2 - b^2$ **h** $a - b$ to $a - b$ **i** $a - b$ to $b - a$

Quantities to be measured must be of the same kind. You do not find the ratio of a line to an angle. The measures of quantities to be compared by ratio must be expressed in the same units. The ratio of 4 feet to 20 inches is obviously not 4 to 20 but 48 to 20. Each distance is expressed as a number of inches.

Give the ratio of each of these pairs of measures:

a \$90 to \$270 **b** 5 in. to 11 in.

c 5 ft. to 3 yd. **d** 800 lb. to 2 tons

e $(20 - y)$ in. to y in. **f** $3a$ ft. to $5a$ ft.

Draw a line AB 6 inches long and place a point C on it so that $AC = 2$ in. Find the numerical values of the following ratios:

a $AC : CB$ **b** $AC : AB$ **c** $CB : AB$

d $CB : AC$ **e** $AB : CB$ **f** $AB : AC$

EXERCISES

1. What is the ratio of one line 8 in. long to another line 15 in. long? of one 7 in. to another 21 in.?

2. If a line AB is 21 in. long and C is placed on it so that AC is 7 in., what is the ratio of the shorter segment to the longer segment? of each segment to the whole line?

3. If a line 24 in. long is divided by a point 6 in. from one end, what is the ratio of the longer segment to the shorter segment?

4. Draw a line segment a. Then construct lines of length $2a$ and $3a$. What is the ratio of $2a$ to $3a$?

5. In the accompanying figure, $AB = 5a$ and $AC = 5b$. With these given facts can you find the numerical value of the ratio $AB : AC$? Give a reason for your answer.

6. What is the numerical value of the ratio $AD : DB$? of the ratio $AE : EC$?

Note that both ratios are equal numerically to $\frac{3}{2}$.

EXS. 5–6

7. Find the lengths of two lines whose sum is 21 units and whose ratio is 3 : 4.

SUGGESTION: Instead of using ratios you can use the equation $3x + 4x = 21$.

8. Find the lengths of two lines whose difference is 15 units and whose ratio is 3 : 8.

9. Draw two lines, one 4.3 cm. and the other 2.5 cm. Express their ratio as a single number to the nearest tenth.

10. Draw a large triangle ABC and bisect $\angle B$ by a line BD (D is on AC). Measure AB, BC, AD, and DC to the nearest tenth of a centimeter. Express the ratios $AB : BC$ and $AD : DC$ as numbers to the nearest tenth. Are the ratios equal?

■ Ratio in Lettering — *Optional*

Did you ever notice how carefully the lettering on an engineer's drawing is done? One reason for this is that certain ratios are adhered to in the making of the letters. For example, in one system the ratio of the width to the height of A is $\frac{1}{1}$. The ratio of the height of the crossbar to the height of the letter is $\frac{1}{2}$. And the ratio of the length of the crossbar to the length of the base is $\frac{2}{3}$.

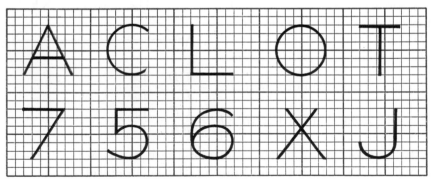

What letters or numerals shown here are drawn with the ratio of width to height equal to $\frac{1}{1}$?

Give the ratio of the width to the height of the others.

What is the ratio of the height of the curve in number 5 to its total height?

What is the ratio of the top width to the bottom width of X?

■ Line Parallel to One Side of a Triangle

A line parallel to one side of a triangle divides the other two sides in such a way that the ratios of the corresponding segments are equal. You will not prove this statement deductively. You will accept it as a postulate after two illustrations.

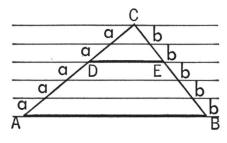

EXAMPLE 1: On paper ruled with equally spaced parallel lines draw $\triangle ABC$ as shown. You know that the segments marked a are equal and the segments marked b are equal. Explain.

$$DC = 2a \quad \text{and} \quad AD = 3a \quad \text{so} \quad \frac{DC}{AD} = \frac{2a}{3a} = \frac{2}{3}$$

$$EC = 2b \quad \text{and} \quad BE = 3b \quad \text{so} \quad \frac{EC}{BE} = \frac{2b}{3b} = \frac{2}{3}$$

Hence $\dfrac{DC}{AD} = \dfrac{EC}{BE}$ (Why?), and the statement at the top of the page is, in this case, true.

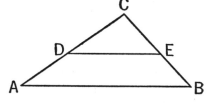

EXAMPLE 2: Triangle ABC is any triangle with $DE \parallel AB$. If you measure, you will find that $CD = 1.8$ cm., $DA = 1.5$ cm., $CE = 1.4$ cm., and $EB = 1.2$ cm.

$$\text{The ratio of } CD \text{ to } DA = \frac{CD}{DA} = \frac{1.8}{1.5}$$

$$\text{The ratio of } CE \text{ to } EB = \frac{CE}{EB} = \frac{1.4}{1.2}$$

By division you find that both of these ratios are 1.2, to the nearest tenth, which is the limit of the accuracy of our original measurements on the triangle. Hence, in this case also, the two ratios are equal.

Postulate A line parallel to one side of a triangle and intersecting the other two sides divides them into segments which, taken in the same order, have the same ratio.

This postulate *does not mean* that $AD = BE$ or that $DC = EC$. They will not be equal unless $AC = BC$. If you know the length of three of these segments, you can find the fourth.

This is a corollary to the postulate on the preceding page.

COROLLARY   **Three parallel lines cut off on any two transversals segments which, taken in the same order, have the same ratio.**

Given $AB \parallel CD \parallel EF$.
To prove   that $MN : NP = QR : RS$.
The *plan* is to draw $MX \parallel JK$ and use the postulate on page 330.
Outline of proof.

You know that $\dfrac{MN}{NP} = \dfrac{MT}{TX}$. (Why?)

You can prove that $QR = MT$ and $RS = TX$. (Opposite sides of parallelograms.) Hence $\dfrac{MN}{NP} = \dfrac{QR}{RS}$.

You should draw a figure much larger than this one using ruled paper, and show by measurement that the ratios of the corresponding segments are equal.

EXERCISES

1. Solve the following equations for x:

a $\dfrac{2}{5} = \dfrac{7}{x}$ b $\dfrac{3}{x} = \dfrac{5}{7}$ c $\dfrac{a}{b} = \dfrac{c}{x}$

d $\dfrac{2}{7} = \dfrac{5}{x}$ e $\dfrac{3}{5} = \dfrac{x}{7}$ f $\dfrac{3-x}{3+x} = \dfrac{2}{3}$

In the figure at the right $DE \parallel AB$:

2. If $DC = \frac{1}{2}AD$, does $CE = \frac{1}{2}BE$?

3. If $AD = DC$, does $BE = EC$?

4. If $\dfrac{DC}{AD} = \dfrac{2}{3}$ and $\dfrac{EC}{BE} = \dfrac{2}{3}$, does $\dfrac{DC}{AD} = \dfrac{EC}{BE}$?

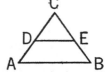

5. If $AD = 2DC$, does $BE = 2CE$?

6. If $DC = 1''$, $AD = 2''$, and $EC = 1\frac{1}{2}''$, then $BE = \underline{\ ?\ }$.

7. Draw a line segment and with ruler and compass divide it into two segments that are in the ratio $2 : 3$.

Before you begin Theorem 52

1. Construct a figure like this in which $AC = 2''$, $BC = 3''$, and $AB = 2\frac{1}{2}''$. Bisect $\angle C$ by a line CD.

We shall show that in this case the ratio $\dfrac{AD}{DB}$ equals the ratio $\dfrac{AC}{CB}$.

Bisect AD and call each of the parts a. Then you will find that DB equals $3a$.

$AD = 2a$, $DB = 3a$. $\quad \dfrac{AD}{DB} = \dfrac{2a}{3a} = \dfrac{2}{3}.$

$AC = 2''$, $CB = 3''$. $\quad \dfrac{AC}{CB} = \dfrac{2}{3}.$

Hence $\dfrac{AD}{DB} = \dfrac{AC}{CB}$ because both are equal to $\dfrac{2}{3}$.

In this specific case you see that the bisector of $\angle C$ divides AB into segments which have the same ratio as the other two sides. In Theorem 52 you prove deductively that this relationship holds in every triangle. The rest of this page will help prepare you for that proof.

2. Refer to the statement of Theorem 52 (on next page), but do not read the plan. Draw a triangle ABC and bisect $\angle C$ by a line CD. What is given? What is to be proved?

You have already learned a method of showing that the ratio of two lines is equal to the ratio of two other lines. (Postulate, page 330.) In order to use the postulate you must fulfill its conditions; you must have a triangle with a line parallel to one side.

In the figure you have drawn, construct a line through A parallel to CD and continue it until it meets the extension of BC at E. Do you see a triangle in which there is a line parallel to one side?

In the figure $\dfrac{AD}{DB} = \dfrac{EC}{CB}.$ Why? How do these two ratios differ from the two you wish to prove equal? Can you prove that $AC = EC$? Say to yourself, "I can prove that $AC = EC$ if I can prove . . ." Also ask the question, "How can I use the hypothesis and construction?"

Can you prove the theorem?

THEOREM **52** | *The bisector of an angle of a triangle divides the opposite side into segments which have the same ratio as the other two sides.*

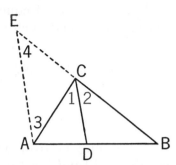

Given $\triangle ABC$, in which CD bisects $\angle C$.

To prove   that $\dfrac{AD}{DB} = \dfrac{AC}{CB}$.

The *plan* is to draw through A a line parallel to CD and continue it until it meets the extension of BC at E, to show that $\dfrac{AD}{DB} = \dfrac{EC}{CB}$ and that $AC = EC$, and then to substitute AC for EC.

Outline of proof.   The statements without reasons are —

$EA \parallel CD$, $\dfrac{AD}{DB} = \dfrac{EC}{CB}$, $\angle 3 = \angle 1$, $\angle 4 = \angle 2$, CD bisects $\angle C$, $\angle 1 = \angle 2$, so $\angle 3 = \angle 4$ and $EC = AC$.

Hence $\dfrac{AD}{DB} = \dfrac{AC}{CB}$.

EXERCISES

The following exercises refer to $\triangle ABC$ in which CD bisects $\angle C$.

1. If $AC = 3$ cm., $CB = 4$ cm., and $AD = 2$ cm., $DB = \underline{\ ?\ }$.

2. If $AC = 5$ in., $CB = 9$ in., and $AD = 3$ in., how long is DB?

3. If $AC = 3$ in., $CB = 6$ in., and $AB = 7$ in., how long are AD and DB?   (Let $AD = x$, then $DB = 7 - x$.)

EXTRA

4. If $AC = 16$ cm., $CB = 20$ cm., and $AB = 24$ cm., how long are AD and DB?

5. If $AC = a$, $CB = b$, and $AD = c$, how long is DB?

6. If $AC = a$, $CB = b$, and $AB = c$, how long are AD and DB?

■ Proportion

Equations of the type $\dfrac{a}{b} = \dfrac{c}{d}$ or $a : b = c : d$, with which you have dealt in the preceding pages, are frequent in mathematics and warrant special study. Note that such equations state that two ratios are equal.

△ *An equation which states that two ratios are equal is called a **proportion**.*

The equations $\dfrac{3}{4} = \dfrac{6}{8}$ (or $3 : 4 = 6 : 8$) and $\dfrac{a}{b} = \dfrac{c}{d}$ (or $a : b = c : d$) are proportions. A proportion may be read in either of two ways: "*a* divided by *b* equals *c* divided by *d*" or "*a* is to *b* as *c* is to *d*." Keep in mind that a proportion is an equation and may be dealt with as such.

In the proportion $\dfrac{a}{b} = \dfrac{c}{d}$ or $a : b = c : d$, *a*, *b*, *c*, and *d* are respectively the first, second, third, and fourth **terms.** *a* and *c* are **numerators;** *b* and *d* are **denominators.** The first and fourth terms, *a* and *d*, are called the **extremes,** and the second and third, *b* and *c*, the **means,** of the proportion.

EXERCISES

1. Name the terms, the numerators, the denominators, the means, and the extremes of the following proportions:

a $\dfrac{3}{4} = \dfrac{6}{8}$ b $\dfrac{2}{3} = \dfrac{6}{9}$ c $\dfrac{m}{n} = \dfrac{p}{q}$ d $\dfrac{AB}{CD} = \dfrac{RS}{PQ}$

2. In the following proportions give (1) the sum of the means, (2) the sum of the extremes, (3) the sum of the numerators, (4) the sum of the denominators, (5) the product of the numerators, (6) the product of the denominators, (7) the product of the means, and (8) the product of the extremes:

a $\dfrac{2}{3} = \dfrac{4}{6}$ b $\dfrac{3}{5} = \dfrac{9}{15}$ c $\dfrac{5}{7} = \dfrac{10}{14}$ d $\dfrac{5}{3} = \dfrac{20}{12}$

Note that for each proportion in Ex. 2, the product of the means is equal to the product of the extremes.

■ Proportional Segments

△ *Two lines are divided **proportionally** if the segments of one have the same ratio as the corresponding segments of the other.*

In the figure at the right AC and BD are divided *proportionally* if $AE : EC = BE : ED$.

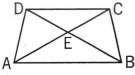

The postulate on page 330 may now be stated: **A line parallel to one side of a triangle divides the other two sides proportionally.**

Theorem 52 may be stated: **The bisector of an angle of a triangle divides the opposite side into segments which are proportional to the other two sides.**

EXERCISES

1. Assume AC and BD in the figure above to be divided proportionally, and find the length of ED when $AE = 6$, $EC = 5$, and $BE = 7$.

2. In Ex. 1, how long is AC if $AE = 8$, $BE = 9$, and $ED = 7$?

3. In $\triangle ABC$, CD bisects $\angle C$ (D is on AB). Compute the length of BD when $AC = 12$, $BC = 10$, and $AD = 5$.

4. Construct two line segments so that they will be in the ratio $4 : 3$.

EXTRA

5. Find the number of degrees in each of two complementary angles whose ratio is $2 : 7$.

SUGGESTION: $2x + 7x = 90$.

6. Two supplementary angles are in the ratio of 5 to 7. How many degrees are there in each angle?

7. If the sum of two lines is 20 in. and their ratio is $2 : 3$, how long is each?

8. If $DE \parallel AC$, $AD : DB = 3 : 4$, and $BC = 8$, how long are CE and BE?

9. If $DE \parallel AC$, DB is 3 units more than AD, $CE = 2$, and $EB = 3$, how long is AB?

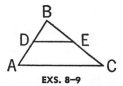

EXS. 8–9

PROPORTIONAL SEGMENTS

335

■ Properties of Proportions

The following exercises will illustrate certain facts about proportions which will be proved in later sections:

1. In the proportion $\frac{3}{5} = \frac{6}{10}$, find the product of the means and the product of the extremes. Note that the two products are equal.

2. In the proportion $\frac{3}{5} = \frac{6}{10}$, invert each ratio. You will get $\frac{5}{3}$ and $\frac{10}{6}$. Are the terms still in proportion — that is, do they still form a proportion? Invert the ratios in several other proportions.

3. In the proportion $\frac{3}{5} = \frac{6}{10}$, write the numerators as one ratio and the denominators as another. You will get $\frac{3}{6}$ and $\frac{5}{10}$. Are the terms still in proportion? Do the same with several other proportions.

4. In the proportion $\frac{3}{5} = \frac{6}{10}$, find the sum of each numerator and the corresponding denominator and divide each sum by the denominator. You will get $\frac{8}{5}$ and $\frac{16}{10}$. Are the terms still in proportion? Do the same with several other proportions.

5. In the proportion $\frac{5}{3} = \frac{10}{6}$, subtract each denominator from the corresponding numerator and divide each difference by the denominator. You will get $\frac{2}{3}$ and $\frac{4}{6}$. Are the terms still in proportion?

6. In the proportion $\frac{3}{5} = \frac{6}{10}$, find the sum of the first term and the third term, and divide it by the sum of the second and fourth terms. You will get $\frac{9}{15}$. Is this ratio equal to the two original ratios?

7. Written algebraically, the theorems suggested by Exs. 1–6 are as follows: If $\frac{a}{b} = \frac{c}{d}$, then —

a $ad = bc$ **b** $\dfrac{b}{a} = \dfrac{d}{c}$ **c** $\dfrac{a}{c} = \dfrac{b}{d}$

d $\dfrac{a+b}{b} = \dfrac{c+d}{d}$ **e** $\dfrac{a-b}{b} = \dfrac{c-d}{d}$ **f** $\dfrac{a+c}{b+d} = \dfrac{a}{b} = \dfrac{c}{d}$

8. Try to state these **proportion theorems** in words.

Note: The proofs of the following eight proportion theorems are **optional.** The statements may be accepted after numerical illustrations are given.

<table>
<tr><td>PROPORTION
THEOREM
1</td><td>*In any proportion, the product of the extremes is equal to the product of the means.*</td></tr>
</table>

This means that if $\dfrac{a}{b} = \dfrac{c}{d}$, then $ad = bc$.

Proof. If $\dfrac{a}{b} = \dfrac{c}{d}$, then $\cancel{b}d \times \dfrac{a}{\cancel{b}} = b\cancel{d} \times \dfrac{c}{\cancel{d}}$, or $ad = bc$.

EXAMPLE: If $\dfrac{2}{3} = \dfrac{5}{x}$, then $2x = 15$ and $x = 7\frac{1}{2}$.

<table>
<tr><td>PROPORTION
THEOREM
2</td><td>*If the product of two numbers is equal to the product of two other numbers, either pair may be made the means and the other pair the extremes of a proportion.*</td></tr>
</table>

This means that if $ab = cd$, then $\dfrac{a}{c} = \dfrac{d}{b}$.

Proof. If $ab = cd$, then $\dfrac{a\cancel{b}}{\cancel{b}c} = \dfrac{\cancel{c}d}{b\cancel{c}}$ or $\dfrac{a}{c} = \dfrac{d}{b}$.

<table>
<tr><td>PROPORTION
THEOREM
3</td><td>*If the numerators of a proportion are equal, the denominators are equal. If the denominators are equal, the numerators are equal.*</td></tr>
</table>

Proof. If $\dfrac{a}{x} = \dfrac{a}{y}$, then $ay = ax$ and $y = x$.

If $\dfrac{x}{a} = \dfrac{y}{a}$, then $ax = ay$ and $x = y$.

The terms of a proportion are also in pro-portion by inversion; that is, the second term is to the first as the fourth is to the third.

This means that if $\dfrac{a}{b} = \dfrac{c}{d}$, then $\dfrac{b}{a} = \dfrac{d}{c}$.

Proof. If $\dfrac{a}{b} = \dfrac{c}{d}$, then $ad = bc$. If we now divide both sides of this equation by ac, we get $\dfrac{\not{a}d}{\not{a}c} = \dfrac{b\not{c}}{a\not{c}}$ or $\dfrac{b}{a} = \dfrac{d}{c}$.

The terms of a proportion are also in pro-portion by alternation; that is, the first term is to the third as the second is to the fourth.

This means that if $\dfrac{a}{b} = \dfrac{c}{d}$, then $\dfrac{a}{c} = \dfrac{b}{d}$.

Proof. If $\dfrac{a}{b} = \dfrac{c}{d}$, then $ad = bc$. If we now divide both sides of this equation by cd, we get $\dfrac{a\not{d}}{c\not{d}} = \dfrac{b\not{c}}{\not{c}d}$ or $\dfrac{a}{c} = \dfrac{b}{d}$.

The terms of a proportion are also in pro-portion by addition; that is, the sum of the first and second terms is to the second term as the sum of the third and fourth is to the fourth.

This means that if $\dfrac{a}{b} = \dfrac{c}{d}$, then $\dfrac{a+b}{b} = \dfrac{c+d}{d}$.

Proof. If $\dfrac{a}{b} = \dfrac{c}{d}$, then $\dfrac{a}{b} + 1 = \dfrac{c}{d} + 1$, and $\dfrac{a+b}{b} = \dfrac{c+d}{d}$.

At the top of the next page is another corollary to the postulate on page 330. It is also a corollary to Proportion Theorem 6 and is proved by means of that theorem.

A line parallel to one side of a triangle divides the other two sides so that either side is to one of its segments as the other is to the corresponding segment.

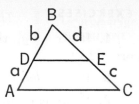

Since $DE \parallel AC$, $\dfrac{a}{b} = \dfrac{c}{d}$. Why?

Then $\dfrac{a+b}{b} = \dfrac{c+d}{d}$. Proportion Theorem 6.

1. If $AB = 14$, $AD = 6$, $BC = 10$, and $DE \parallel AC$, then $14 : 6 = 10 : EC$. Why?

2. If $AB = 12$, $DB = 8$, $BC = 9$, and $DE \parallel AC$, then $BE = \underline{\ ?\ }$.

PROPORTION THEOREM 7

The terms of a proportion are also in proportion by subtraction; that is, the first term minus the second is to the second as the third minus the fourth is to the fourth.

This means that if $\dfrac{a}{b} = \dfrac{c}{d}$, then $\dfrac{a-b}{b} = \dfrac{c-d}{d}$.

Proof. Subtract 1 from both sides of the equation $\dfrac{a}{b} = \dfrac{c}{d}$. The rest of the proof is left for you.

PROPORTION THEOREM 8

If three terms of one proportion are equal respectively to the three corresponding terms of another proportion, then the remaining term of the first is equal to the remaining term of the second.

This means that if $\dfrac{a}{b} = \dfrac{x}{c}$ and $\dfrac{a}{b} = \dfrac{y}{c}$, then $x = y$.

Proof. Solve for x in one proportion and for y in the other. The rest of the proof is left for you.

EXERCISES

1. If $6x = 5y$, then $x : y = $ _?_ : _?_.   (Use Proportion Theorem 2.)

2. If $ax = by$, then $x : y = $ _?_ : _?_.

3. Write each of the following proportions by inversion:

$$\frac{2}{3} = \frac{10}{15} \qquad\qquad \frac{m}{n} = \frac{p}{q} \qquad\qquad AB : CD = PQ : RS$$

4. Write by alternation: $\frac{3}{7} = \frac{9}{21}$, $r : s = t : x$

5. Write by addition: $\dfrac{3}{5} = \dfrac{9}{15}$, $\dfrac{AB}{BC} = \dfrac{RS}{ST}$

6. Write by subtraction: $\dfrac{12}{7} = \dfrac{24}{14}$, $\dfrac{7+x}{x} = \dfrac{5}{2}$

7. If $\dfrac{m}{n} = \dfrac{2}{7}$ and $\dfrac{r}{n} = \dfrac{2}{7}$, then $m = $ _?_.

8. Solve for x.   Use Proportion Theorem 1.

a $\dfrac{3}{5} = \dfrac{4}{x}$ b $\dfrac{2}{x} = \dfrac{3}{7}$ c $\dfrac{21-x}{x} = \dfrac{1}{2}$

d $\dfrac{20-x}{x} = \dfrac{2}{3}$ e $\dfrac{a}{b} = \dfrac{c}{x}$ f $\dfrac{a}{x} = \dfrac{b}{c}$

g $\dfrac{2a}{3b} = \dfrac{5c}{2x}$ h $\dfrac{3m}{2x} = \dfrac{n}{m}$ i $\dfrac{a-x}{x} = \dfrac{b}{c}$

j $\dfrac{a+x}{x} = \dfrac{b}{c}$ k $\dfrac{2a-3x}{2x} = \dfrac{2b}{3a}$ l $\dfrac{3x-2a}{2x} = \dfrac{2b}{3a}$

9. In the figure $DE \parallel AB$.   In each row below supply the missing length.

	AD	DC	BE	EC
a	3	2	6	?
b	7	3	?	5
c	2	?	3	4
d	$\frac{4}{3}$	$\frac{1}{2}$	4	?

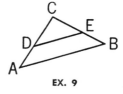

EX. 9

10. If BD bisects $\angle B$, and AC, BC, and AB are as follows, how long are AD and DC?

	AC	BC	AB
a	12	10	5
b	21	9	18
c	25	14	21

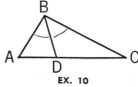

EX. 10

340   RATIO AND PROPORTION

11. In the figure for Ex. 9 on page 340, $DE \parallel AB$ and the lengths of lines are as follows. Supply the missing lengths.

	AD	DC	BE	EC
a	a	b	c	?
b	a	?	b	c
c	$2a$	$3b$	$5b$	?
d	$3a$	?	$4a$	$2b$
e	$3m$	$7p$	?	$14q$

12. Write proportions using the letters a, b, c, and x which, when solved for x, will give the following: $x = \dfrac{bc}{a}$; $x = \dfrac{ac}{b}$; $x = \dfrac{ab}{c}$.

■ Special Terms in a Proportion

△ *The fourth term of a proportion is called the* **fourth proportional** *to the other three. When the means of a proportion are the same, either of them is called the* **mean proportional** *between the other two.*

In the proportion $\frac{2}{3} = \frac{4}{6}$, 6 is the fourth proportional to 2, 3, and 4 in the order named.

In the proportion $\frac{4}{6} = \frac{6}{9}$, 6 is the mean proportional between 4 and 9. Make a similar statement concerning $a : b = b : c$.

EXAMPLE 1: Find the fourth proportional to 3, 5, and 7. (Solve the proportion $\dfrac{3}{5} = \dfrac{7}{x}$ for x.)

EXAMPLE 2: Find the mean proportional between 3 and 12. (If $\dfrac{3}{x} = \dfrac{x}{12}$, then $x^2 = 36$ and $x = 6$.)

EXERCISES

1. Find the fourth proportional to —

a 3, 4, 7   b 2, 1, 5   c 8, 10, 6

d a, b, c e $2a, 3b, 4a$ f $\frac{1}{2}, \frac{2}{3}, \frac{3}{4}$

2. Find the mean proportional between —

a 4 and 9   b 2 and 18   c 2 and 8

d 16 and 4   e $3a$ and $12a$ f a and b

3. Construct an accurate figure for each of the following statements, write the hypothesis and conclusion, and test the conclusion by measurement and division.

a If in any circle one chord bisects another, either segment of the bisected chord is the mean proportional between the segments of the other chord.

b In any right triangle the altitude upon the hypotenuse is the mean proportional between the segments of the hypotenuse.

■ Square Root

In finding the mean proportional between two numbers, you will need to work with square roots.

△ *The* **square root** *of a number is a number which when multiplied by itself will give the original number.* The symbol for square root is $\sqrt{}$, called a radical sign.

EXAMPLES: $\sqrt{36} = 6$ because $6 \times 6 = 36$

$\sqrt{a^2} = a$ because $a \times a = a^2$

Approximate square roots. The square roots of most numbers cannot be found exactly, but may be expressed by use of the radical sign. If $x^2 = 20$, $x = \sqrt{20}$, a number between 4 and 5.

The square root of a number can be approximated to any degree of precision. $\sqrt{3}$ lies between 1 and 2, since $1^2 = 1$ and $2^2 = 4$. It lies between 1.7 and 1.8 because $1.7^2 = 2.89$ and $1.8^2 = 3.24$. It lies between 1.73 and 1.74 because $(1.73)^2 = 2.993$ and $(1.74)^2 = 3.028$. We say that $\sqrt{3} = 1.73$ to the nearest hundredth. Why? Show that 1.732 equals $\sqrt{3}$ to the nearest thousandth.

Table of square roots. A table of square roots of numbers from 1 to 250 is provided on page 532. The square roots are given to the nearest thousandth.

Find the square root of each of the following numbers to the nearest hundredth. The answer to the first one is 2.24.

| 5 | 27 | 56 | 93 | 115 | 183 | 207 | 241 |

Square root of a fraction. The square root of a fraction is obtained by first finding the square root of the numerator and of the denominator and then indicating the quotient of the two square roots, or actually performing the division.

EXAMPLE 1: $\sqrt{\dfrac{9}{25}} = \dfrac{\sqrt{9}}{\sqrt{25}} = \dfrac{3}{5}.$ Check $\dfrac{3}{5} \times \dfrac{3}{5} = \dfrac{9}{25}$

EXAMPLE 2: $\sqrt{\dfrac{2}{3}} = \dfrac{\sqrt{2}}{\sqrt{3}} = \dfrac{1.414}{1.732} = \underline{\ ?\ }$

This is a long process. See Example 3 for a better way.

EXAMPLE 3: $\sqrt{\dfrac{2}{3}} = \sqrt{\dfrac{6}{9}} = \dfrac{\sqrt{6}}{\sqrt{9}} = \dfrac{\sqrt{6}}{3} = \dfrac{2.449}{3} = .82$ (to hundredths)

Example 3 suggests the following rule:

Before taking the square root of a fraction, change its form, if necessary, so that the denominator is a square.

EXERCISES

1. Find the mean proportional between each of the following pairs of numbers. Leave the answers in radical form (for example, $\sqrt{20}$).

a 5, 4   b 4, 3   c 9, 2
d 3, 9   e 8, 5   f 15, 3

2. Find the mean proportional between each of the following pairs of numbers. Using the table of square roots on page 532, give the answers to the nearest hundredth.

a 12, 6   b 9, 15   c 8, 25
d 19, 12   e 21, 11   f 13, 17

3. Find to the nearest hundredth the square root of each of the following fractions: $\dfrac{1}{2}, \dfrac{1}{3}, \dfrac{1}{4}, \dfrac{3}{2}, \dfrac{5}{6}, \dfrac{5}{8}, \dfrac{7}{16}, \dfrac{11}{12}$

4. Find the mean proportional between each of the following pairs of fractions. Leave the answers in a form for quick computation. $\left(\text{For example, leave } \sqrt{\dfrac{3}{5}} \text{ as } \dfrac{\sqrt{15}}{5}.\right)$

a $\dfrac{2}{3}, \dfrac{3}{4}$ b $\dfrac{3}{2}, \dfrac{1}{8}$ c $\dfrac{5}{3}, \dfrac{2}{5}$
d $\dfrac{1}{6}, \dfrac{5}{3}$ e $\dfrac{5}{6}, \dfrac{7}{10}$ f $\dfrac{7}{12}, \dfrac{1}{4}$

5. Solve the following proportions for x. Leave the answer in a form for quick computation.

a $\dfrac{3}{x} = \dfrac{2x}{5}$ b $\dfrac{7}{3x} = \dfrac{x}{8}$ c $\dfrac{5}{2x} = \dfrac{3x}{11}$

d $\dfrac{2x}{7} = \dfrac{4}{5x}$ e $\dfrac{7x}{3} = \dfrac{3}{4x}$ f $\dfrac{3x^2 + 7}{3x} = \dfrac{5x}{4}$

6. CD is the mean proportional between AD and DB.

a If $AD = 9$ units and $DB = 4$ units, how long is CD?

b If $AD = 10$ units and $DB = 22$ units, how long is CD?

c If $AD = 19$ in. and $BD = 11$ in., how long is CD to the nearest hundredth?

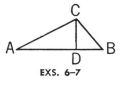

EXS. 6–7

7. AC is the mean proportional between AD and AB.

a If $AD = 8$ and $AB = 18$, how long is AC?

b If $AD = 13$ and $AB = 17$, how long is AC to the nearest hundredth?

8. $CE = 2AD$ and $DE \parallel AB$.

a If $CD = 3$ and $EB = 2$, find AD.

b If $CD = 4$ and $EB = 7$, find AD.

c If $CD = 5$ and $EB = 8$, find AD.

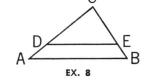

EX. 8

Give the answers to the nearest hundredth.

■ Square Roots in Earlier Times — *Optional*

Ancient and medieval mathematicians used various methods for finding the approximate values of square roots. They could not say, for example, that $\sqrt{10} = 3.162$ to the nearest thousandth because the symbolism of decimal fractions was not yet invented. The best they could do was to express the approximate square roots using common fractions.

The rule most commonly used was $\sqrt{A} = \sqrt{a^2 + r}$ when a^2 is the nearest square less than A and r is the excess of A over a^2. They then said that $\sqrt{a^2 + r} = a + \dfrac{r}{2a}$, an incorrect statement, but not far wrong when r is small.

By this method $\sqrt{52}$ would be $\sqrt{49 + 3} = 7 + \frac{3}{14} = 7\frac{3}{14}$. This compares favorably with $\sqrt{52} = 7.211$ taken from the table.

Another approximation was $\sqrt{A} = \dfrac{1}{2}\left(a + \dfrac{A}{a}\right)$. Using this formula $\sqrt{52} = \frac{1}{2}(7 + \frac{52}{7}) = \frac{1}{2}(7 + 7\frac{3}{7})$ or $7\frac{3}{14}$.

Try both of these formulas with $\sqrt{70}$.

Can you show that $a + \dfrac{r}{2a}$ and $\dfrac{1}{2}\left(a + \dfrac{A}{a}\right)$ are two forms of the same formula, remembering that $r = A - a^2$?

Construction Problem   **Constructing the fourth proportional to three given line segments.**

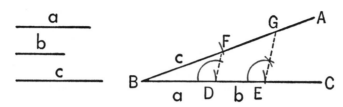

Given   segments a, b, and c.

Required   to construct the fourth proportional to a, b, and c.

Analysis.   If x represents the fourth proportional, we wish to find x so that $a : b = c : x$. This suggests the use of the postulate on page 330.

Construction.

1. Draw any angle ABC.
2. On BC take $BD = a$ and $DE = b$. On BA take $BF = c$.
3. Draw DF and construct $EG \parallel DF$.
4. FG is the required fourth proportional.

Proof. $EG \parallel DF$. $\dfrac{a}{b} = \dfrac{c}{FG}$.   (Postulate, page 330.) FG is the fourth proportional to a, b, c.   (Definition of fourth proportional.)

EXERCISES

1. Draw three line segments m, n, and p. Construct the fourth proportional to m, n, and p.

2. Construct the fourth proportional to lines that are 1 in., 2 in., and 3 in. long. Check the result by measurement.

EXTRA

3. Given line segments a, b, and c. Construct a segment x so that $x = \dfrac{ab}{c}$.

4. Given line segments m and n. Construct a segment x so that $x = \dfrac{m^2}{n}$.

FOURTH PROPORTIONAL   **345**

Construction Dividing a line segment into parts that have the
Problem same ratio as two given segments.

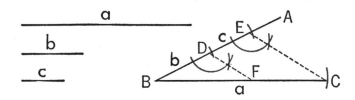

Given segments a, b, and c.

Required to divide a into parts which have the ratio $b : c$.

Analysis. Let $BC = a$. We wish to find a point F on BC so
that $BF : FC = b : c$.

This suggests the use of Postulate, page 330.

Construction.

1. Draw any angle ABC with $BC = a$.
2. On BA take $BD = b$ and $DE = c$.
3. Draw EC.
4. Construct $DF \parallel EC$.
5. Then $BF : FC = b : c$. Why?

EXERCISES

1. Draw $a = 5$ in., $b = \frac{1}{2}$ in., and $c = \frac{3}{4}$ in. Using straightedge
and compass only, divide a into parts that have the ratio $b : c$.

2. Draw a line segment AB. Using straightedge and compass
only, find a point C on AB so that the two parts of AB are in
the ratio $2 : 3$.

3. Draw a line segment AB. Using straightedge and compass
only, find a point C on AB so that $AC = \frac{2}{3}AB$.

EXTRA

4. Draw any triangle ABC and near it draw a line DE. Construct another triangle DEF so that $AB : DE = BC : EF$ and
$AB : DE = CA : FD$.

5. Draw $\triangle ABC$ and any two line segments m and n. Construct $\triangle DEF$ so that the corresponding sides of $\triangle ABC$ and
$\triangle DEF$ will be in the ratio $m : n$.

The proof of Theorem 53 is *optional*.

THEOREM 53 | *If a line divides two sides of a triangle proportionally, it is parallel to the third side.*

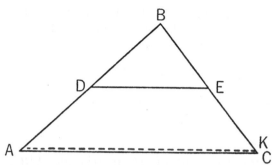

Given $\triangle ABC$ in which $\dfrac{BD}{DA} = \dfrac{BE}{EC}$.

To prove $DE \parallel AC$.

Plan. The proof is by coincidence (page 316).

Proof. Through A construct $AK \parallel DE$.

STATEMENTS	REASONS
1. $DE \parallel AK$.	1. Construction.
2. $\dfrac{BD}{DA} = \dfrac{BE}{EK}$.	2. Why?
3. $\dfrac{BD}{DA} = \dfrac{BE}{EC}$.	3. Given.
4. $EC = EK$.	4. Proportion Theorem 8.
5. K and C are the same point.	5. They are both at the same distance from E in the same direction.
6. AK coincides with AC.	6. Why?
7. $DE \parallel AC$.	7. See statement 1.

COROLLARY If a line divides two sides of a triangle so that either side is to one of its segments as the other side is to the corresponding segment, it is parallel to the third side.

Proof. If $\dfrac{BA}{DA} = \dfrac{BC}{EC}$, then $\dfrac{BA - DA}{DA} = \dfrac{BC - EC}{EC}$. Why?

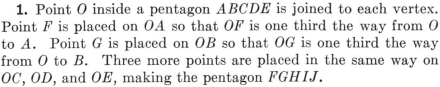

Problems for Pacemakers

1. Point O inside a pentagon $ABCDE$ is joined to each vertex. Point F is placed on OA so that OF is one third the way from O to A. Point G is placed on OB so that OG is one third the way from O to B. Three more points are placed in the same way on OC, OD, and OE, making the pentagon $FGHIJ$.

Prove that angle ABC equals angle FGH.

2. Transform the proportion $\dfrac{a}{b} = \dfrac{c}{x}$ into three other proportions where x occurs as the first, second, and third terms respectively.

3. Three line segments a, b, and c are given. Construct a line x so that $2ab = cx$.

4. D is the middle point of AC in triangle ABC. R is on AB, S is on BC. If DR and DS bisect angle ADB and angle BDC, respectively, then RS is parallel to AC.

5. A diameter DC of a circle is perpendicular to a chord AB. Through H, any point on AB, lines DH and CH are drawn and extended to meet the circle at E and F, respectively.

Prove $\dfrac{AF}{AE} = \dfrac{FB}{BE}$.

6. Side BC of triangle ABC is extended to form exterior angle ACD. Line CE bisects angle ACD and intersects side AB extended at point E.

Prove that $\dfrac{AC}{CB} = \dfrac{EA}{EB}$.

7. The bisectors of the base angles of an isosceles triangle meet the equal sides at D and E.

Prove that DE is parallel to the base of the triangle.

8. Given that $a : b = c : d$, prove that
$$(a + b) : (a - b) = (c + d) : (c - d).$$

9. Given that $a : b = b : c$, prove that
$$(ac - 1) : (b - 1) = (b + 1) : 1.$$

10. Given that $a : b = c : d$, prove that
$$(a - 1) : b = (bc - d) : bd.$$

11. Given that $a : b = c : d$, prove that
$$(a + 1) : 1 = (bc + d) : d.$$

12. Solve for x. $ab : b = (b - cx) : (bc - x)$.

SUPPLEMENTARY EXERCISES

1. Mr. Anderson and Mr. Browning started a clothing business. They decided that the division of profits should be in the ratio 5 : 3. What did that mean?

2. If Mr. Anderson's share (Ex. 1) at the end of the first year was $6000, what was Mr. Browning's share?

3. If Mr. Browning's share was $9000 at the end of the second year, what was Mr. Anderson's share?

4. If the total profit for the third year was $24,000, what was the share of each?

5. Which would be a better ratio from the point of view of Mr. Browning, 5 : 3 or 10 : 6? 5 : 3 or 6 : 4? 5 : 3 or 3 : 2?

6. State the proportion $m : n = p : q$, by inversion, alternation, addition, and subtraction.

7. If $\dfrac{a}{b} = \dfrac{c}{d}$, does $\dfrac{a}{c} = \dfrac{b}{d}$? Why?

8. In $\triangle ABC$, BD bisects $\angle B$ (D is on AC). If $AB = 12$, $BC = 8$, and $AC = 15$ units, how long are AD and DC?

9. Find the fourth proportional to —

a 3, 4, and 7 b $\frac{1}{2}$, $\frac{2}{3}$, and $\frac{3}{4}$

10. Find the mean proportional between —

a 5 and 6 b 24 and 32

Give the answers to the nearest hundredth.

11. Find the mean proportional between —

a $\frac{1}{2}$ and $\frac{2}{3}$ b $\frac{4}{5}$ and $\frac{3}{2}$

Leave the answers in a form for easy computation.

12. Find the value of x in each of these proportions:

a $\dfrac{4}{5} = \dfrac{6}{x}$ b $\dfrac{x}{a} = \dfrac{c+d}{c-d}$

13. What is the ratio of x to y in the following equations?

a $2x = 4y$ b $\dfrac{x+y}{x-y} = \dfrac{4}{3}$

14. Divide a given line into segments which have the ratio 3 : 4.

15. Given line segments a, b, and c. Construct x so that $a : b = c : x$.

16. Given line segments a, b, and c. Construct x so that $a : b = x : c$.

17. Given line segments a, b, and c. Construct x so that $x : a = c : b$.

18. Given line segments a, b, and c. Construct x so that $x = \dfrac{ac}{b}$.

19. Given line segments a and b. Construct x so that $x = \dfrac{b^2}{a}$.

20. Given a line segment equal to the sum of two lines, a and b, and their ratio $m : n$ (m and n being two given lines). Find a and b.

21. Given a line segment equal to the difference between two lines, a and b, and their ratio $m : n$. Find a and b.

22. Construct a triangle with sides a, b, and c, given two sides, a and b, and the fact that $b : c = 2 : 3$.

23. Construct a triangle, given two sides, a and b, and the fact that $b : c = 3 : 4$.

24. Construct a triangle, given two sides a and b and the fact that $b : c = m : n$ (m and n being two given lines).

■ Proportional Lines in Three Dimensions — *Optional*

On the next page is a theorem about proportional lines in three dimensions. It is analogous to the corollary on page 331.

To prove this theorem you must assume that you have already established a previous theorem: *If two parallel planes are cut by a third plane, the lines of intersection are parallel; that is, if plane PQ* ∥ *plane RS then AB* ∥ *CD.* Its proof depends also upon the postulate on page 330.

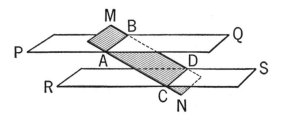

If two lines are cut by three parallel planes, the corresponding segments are proportional.

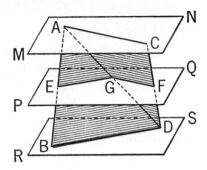

Given AB and CD, two lines cut by parallel planes MN, PQ, and RS at A, E, B, and C, F, D, respectively.

To prove   that $\dfrac{AE}{EB} = \dfrac{CF}{FD}$.

The *plan* is to form two triangles ABD and ADC with a common side AD, each with a line parallel to the base, and form two proportions of which one ratio will be common.

Proof.   Draw AD intersecting PQ at G. The plane made by AB and AD will intersect plane PQ in EG and plane RS in BD. The plane made by AD and CD will intersect plane PQ in GF and plane MN in AC.

STATEMENTS	REASONS
1. EG is $\parallel$ to BD.	1. See theorem on preceding page.
2. FG is $\parallel$ to AC.	2. Why?
3. Hence $\dfrac{AE}{EB} = \dfrac{AG}{GD}$.	3. Postulate, page 330.
4. Also, $\dfrac{CF}{FD} = \dfrac{AG}{GD}$.	4. Why?
5. $\dfrac{AE}{EB} = \dfrac{CF}{FD}$.	5. Why?

Use the figure above to help you complete:

1. If $AE = 3$ in., $EB = 5$ in., and $CF = 4$ in., $FD = \underline{\ ?\ }$.
2. If $AE = 2$ in., $EB = CF$, and $FD = 3$ in., $CD = \underline{\ ?\ }$.

I. Vocabulary

1. Illustrate the use of the following words:

Ratio   Subtraction in a proportion
Proportionally   Proportion
Means   Terms of a proportion
Inversion   Extremes
Fourth proportional   Alternation
Addition in a proportion   Mean proportional

II. Postulate

2. $DE \parallel AB$. Then $\dfrac{5}{4} = \dfrac{3}{CE}$. Why?

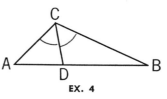

III. Proportion theorems

3. State the theorem suggested by each of the following:

a If $\dfrac{a}{b} = \dfrac{c}{d}$, then $ad = bc$ **b** If $ab = cd$, then $\dfrac{a}{c} = \dfrac{d}{b}$

c If $\dfrac{a}{x} = \dfrac{a}{y}$, then $x = y$ **d** If $\dfrac{a}{b} = \dfrac{c}{d}$, then $\dfrac{b}{a} = \dfrac{d}{c}$

e If $\dfrac{a}{b} = \dfrac{c}{d}$, then $\dfrac{a}{c} = \dfrac{b}{d}$ **f** If $\dfrac{a}{b} = \dfrac{c}{d}$, then $\dfrac{a+b}{b} = \dfrac{c+d}{d}$

g If $\dfrac{a}{b} = \dfrac{c}{d}$, then $\dfrac{a-b}{b} = \dfrac{c-d}{d}$ **h** If $\dfrac{a}{b} = \dfrac{x}{c}$ and $\dfrac{a}{b} = \dfrac{y}{c}$, then $x = y$

IV. Theorems

4. If CD bisects $\angle C$, then $\dfrac{AD}{DB}$ equals what other ratio? Why? What construction lines do you need?

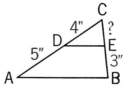

EX. 4

5. If $\dfrac{AD}{DC} = \dfrac{BE}{CE}$, what is the relation between DE and AB? State the theorem.

V. Special terms in a proportion

6. Find the fourth proportional to 3, 6, and 9.

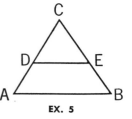

EX. 5

7. Find the mean proportional between 2 and 8.

8. Find the mean proportional between 3 and 4 and give your answer to the nearest hundredth.

VI. Construction problems

9. Draw three unequal line segments and construct their fourth proportional.

10. Draw three unequal line segments a, b, and c. Divide a into two segments that have the ratio $b : c$.

Testing Your Understanding

TEST 1

Give the reason that applies. For Exs. 1, 3, 7, 9, 10, and 11 state a geometric proposition from this chapter.

1. If $DE \parallel AB$, $AD = 2$, $DC = 3$, and $BE = 1\frac{1}{2}$, then $CE = 2\frac{1}{4}$.

2. If $\dfrac{4}{5} = \dfrac{3}{x}$, then $4x = 15$.

3. CD bisects $\angle C$. If $AC = 8''$, $BC = 5''$, and $AB = 6\frac{1}{2}''$, then $AD = 4''$.

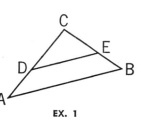

EX. 1

4. If $\dfrac{a}{b} = \dfrac{c}{d}$, then $\dfrac{a}{c} = \dfrac{b}{d}$.

5. If $\dfrac{AB}{CD} = \dfrac{x}{RS}$ and $\dfrac{AB}{CD} = \dfrac{y}{RS}$, then $x = y$.

6. If $2x = 3y$, then $x : y = 3 : 2$.

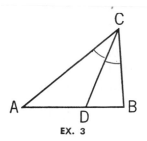

EX. 3

7. If, in the figure for Ex. 1, $DE \parallel AB$, then $AC : CD = BC : CE$.

8. If $AD : CD = CD : DB$, then CD is the mean proportional between AD and DB.

9. If, in the figure for Ex. 1, $AD : DC = BE : EC$, then $DE \parallel AB$.

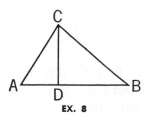

EX. 8

10. If $AC = CB$ and $\angle 1 = \angle 2$, then $AD = DB$.

11. $BE \parallel CF \parallel DG$. If $EF = 2$, $FG = 3$, and $BC = 1\frac{1}{2}$, then $CD = 2\frac{1}{4}$.

12. If $\dfrac{15 - x}{x} = \dfrac{2}{3}$, then $\dfrac{15}{x} = \dfrac{5}{3}$.

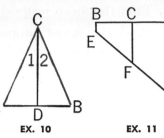

EX. 10　　　　EX. 11

TEST 2

Be ready to give reasons for your answers:

1. $AB : BC = 4 : \underline{?}$
　　$AB : AC = \underline{?} : \underline{?}$
　　$BC : AC = \underline{?} : \underline{?}$
　　$AC : \underline{?} = 7 : 4$
　　$\underline{?} : AB = 3 : 4$

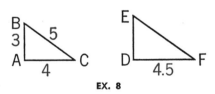

EX. 1

2. AB is 20 in. long and C is on AB. If $AC : CB = 3 : 4$, then $AC = \underline{?}$ in.

3. The fourth proportional to 5, 6, and 7 is $\underline{?}$.

4. The mean proportional between 6 and 7 is $\underline{?}$. (Give the answer to the nearest hundredth.)

5. In $\triangle ABC$, $DE \parallel AC$ (D on AB, E on BC). If $AB = 8$ cm., $BC = 11$ cm., and $AD = 2$ cm., then $BE = \underline{?}$ cm.

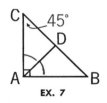

EX. 7

6. CD bisects $\angle C$ of $\triangle ABC$. If $AC = 2$ units and $BC = 3$ units, then $AD : DB = \underline{?} : \underline{?}$.

7. $CA \perp AB$, $\angle C = 45°$, and AD bisects $\angle A$. $CD : DB = 1 : \underline{?}$.

EX. 8

8. If $DE : AB = DF : AC$ and $BC : EF = AC : DF$, then $DE = \underline{?}$ and $EF = \underline{?}$.

9. $DE \parallel AB$ and $CE = 3AD$. If $CD = 3$ in. and $EB = 2$ in., $AD = \underline{?}$ in. (to the nearest hundredth).

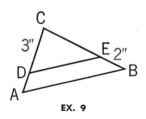

EX. 9

CHAPTER 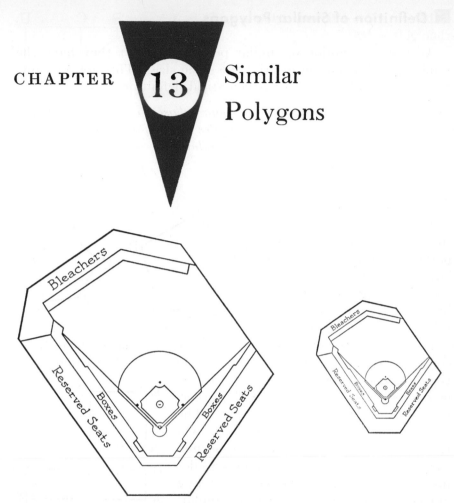 Similar
Polygons

HERE ARE two plans of a baseball park drawn to different scales.
They have the same shape, but one is smaller than the other.

Measure, in inches, three lines along the outside of the section
marked "Reserved Seats" in the larger figure. Measure the same
lines in the smaller figure. What do you note concerning the ratios
of corresponding distances in the two figures?

Measure corresponding angles on these two plans. What do
you note concerning the corresponding angles?

You have noted that on these two plans the corresponding
distances are in the same ratio and the corresponding angles are
equal. This is true of any two plane figures that have the same
shape. Such figures are said to be *similar*.

SIMILAR FIGURES

■ Definition of Similar Polygons

An intuitive notion of similar polygons is that they have the same shape but not necessarily the same size. This notion, however, is not sufficient as a mathematical definition.

△ **Similar polygons** are polygons whose corresponding angles are equal and whose corresponding sides are in proportion.

The symbol for *similar to* or *is similar to* is ∼.

$ABCDE \sim A'B'C'D'E'$, if **a** $\angle A = \angle A'$, $\angle B = \angle B'$, etc.; and

b $\dfrac{AB}{A'B'} = \dfrac{BC}{B'C'} = \dfrac{CD}{C'D'}$, etc.

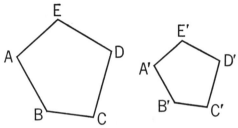

Note that the definition of similar polygons has two parts. In order to be similar, not only must the corresponding angles be equal, but also the corresponding sides must be in proportion.

In the case of two polygons of more than three sides one of these conditions may be fulfilled and the other not. The square and the rectangle at the right have the angles of one equal to the angles of the other, but the sides are not proportional. The polygons are obviously not similar. On the other hand, the two pentagons pictured below have their corresponding sides in the ratio 2 : 1, but the corresponding angles are not equal. They are not similar.

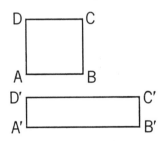

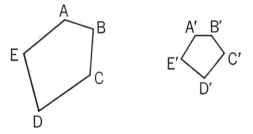

In the case of two triangles, however, one condition cannot be fulfilled without the other. This is a matter for proof and will be considered later in the chapter.

■ Using the Definition of Similar Polygons

On the preceding page you learned the definition of similar polygons. It is in two parts. Since definitions are always reversible, the following two statements are also correct.

1. *Corresponding angles of similar polygons are equal.*
2. *Corresponding sides of similar polygons are in proportion.*

Do you remember the definition of congruent triangles? The definition requires that all six pairs of corresponding parts be equal. But you discovered that if certain three pairs are equal the other pairs are necessarily equal. When *s.s.s.* = *s.s.s.*, *s.a.s.* = *s.a.s.*, or *a.s.a.* = *a.s.a.*, not only these three pairs are equal in every case, but also the other three pairs. You will find a similar situation in connection with the definition of similar triangles.

EXERCISES

1. $\triangle ABC \sim \triangle A'B'C'$, AB corresponds to $A'B'$, BC to $B'C,'$ and AC to $A'C'$. What angles are equal? Write three proportions involving the sides of these triangles.

2. The sides of a triangle are 6, 4, and 5 in. In a similar triangle, the side corresponding to the 6-inch side is 9 in. Find the lengths of the other two sides. ($4 : x = 6 : 9$ and $5 : y = 6 : 9$.)

3. Draw two triangles that are similar but not congruent. Draw two triangles that are similar and congruent.

4. Are similar triangles always congruent? Are congruent triangles always similar? (Test this last question by means of the definition of similar triangles.)

5. Prove that all equilateral triangles are similar. (Are the angles of one equal to the angles of the other? If $AB = BC = CA$ and $DE = EF = FD$, does $\dfrac{AB}{DE} = \dfrac{BC}{EF} = \dfrac{CA}{FD}$?)

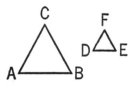

6. Prove that all squares are similar.

7. Are all rectangles similar?

8. The sides of a triangle are a, b, and c units. Find the sides of a similar triangle in which the side corresponding to a is d.

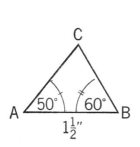 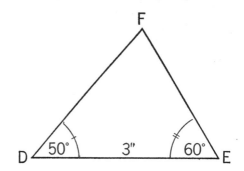

1. Make $\triangle ABC$ so that $AB = 1\frac{1}{2}''$, $\angle A = 50°$, and $\angle B = 60°$.

2. Make $\triangle DEF$ so that $DE = 3''$, $\angle D = 50°$, and $\angle E = 60°$.

3. Do these triangles appear to have the same shape? Do they appear to be similar?

4. Measure or compute $\angle C$ and $\angle F$. $\angle C = \angle F = \underline{\ ?\ }°$.

5. You made the ratio of AB to $DE = \frac{1}{2}$ or .5. If you have been accurate, you will find by measurement and division that $\frac{AC}{DF}$ and $\frac{CB}{FE}$ also equal .5.

You started with two particular triangles in which two angles of one were equal to two angles of the other. Then you showed that the third angles were equal and the corresponding sides were in proportion.

According to the definition, then, these triangles are similar.

Try the above experiment again with two other triangles. This time for $\triangle ABC$ make $AB = 1''$, $\angle A = 40°$, and $\angle B = 70°$; and for $\triangle DEF$ make $DE = 3''$, $\angle D = 40°$, and $\angle E = 70°$.

By measurement and division find the ratio of each pair of corresponding sides.

Are the corresponding sides in proportion?
Are the corresponding angles equal?
Are these triangles similar? Why?

Theorem 54, which follows, shows that these relationships hold in general; that is, when two angles of one triangle are equal to two angles of another, the third angles are equal and the corresponding sides are in proportion. Hence, the triangles are similar.

Two triangles are similar if two angles of one are equal to two angles of the other.

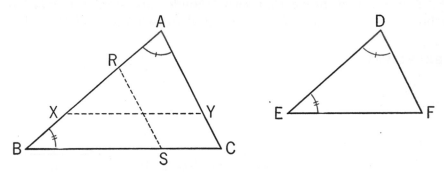

Given △ABC and △DEF with ∠A = ∠D and ∠B = ∠E.
To prove that △ABC ∼ △DEF.

Discussion and plan. You are given two angles of one triangle equal to two angles of another triangle. In order to prove that the triangles are similar, you must show that the conditions of the definition of similar triangles are fulfilled. You must show that the third pair of angles are equal and that the corresponding sides are in proportion. To do the latter you will use the postulate on page 330 and prove two ratios equal to the same ratio.

Proof. Place △DEF in the position AXY with ∠D coinciding with its equal ∠A.

STATEMENTS	REASONS
1. ∠AXY = ∠E = ∠B.	1. Given.
2. $XY \parallel BC$.	2. Theorem 10.
3. $\dfrac{AB}{AX} = \dfrac{AC}{AY}$ or $\dfrac{AB}{DE} = \dfrac{AC}{DF}$.	3. Postulate, page 330.

Place △DEF in the position RBS with ∠E coinciding with its equal ∠B.

4. ∠BRS = ∠D = ∠A.	4. Given.
5. $RS \parallel AC$.	5. Theorem 10.
6. $\dfrac{AB}{RB} = \dfrac{BC}{BS}$ or $\dfrac{AB}{DE} = \dfrac{BC}{EF}$.	6. Postulate, page 330.
7. $\dfrac{AB}{DE} = \dfrac{BC}{EF} = \dfrac{AC}{DF}$.	7. Axiom 2, page 84.
8. ∠C = ∠F.	8. Why?
9. △ABC ∼ △DEF.	9. Definition.

<u>COROLLARY</u> **Two right triangles are similar if an acute angle of one is equal to an acute angle of the other.**

You can now prove that two triangles are similar if you can show that two angles of one are equal to two angles of the other.

EXERCISES

1. In $\triangle ABC$, D and E are taken on AC and BC respectively, so that $DE \parallel AB$. Prove that $\triangle ABC \sim \triangle DEC$.

2. $DE \perp AB$ and $CB \perp AB$. Prove that $\triangle ABC \sim \triangle AED$.

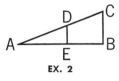

EX. 2

3. Angle B is a right angle and $DE \perp AC$. Prove that $\triangle ABC \sim \triangle AED$.

4. In acute triangle ABC, the altitudes BD and AE meet at F. Prove that **a** $\triangle AEC \sim \triangle BDC$, **b** $\triangle BFE \sim \triangle AFD$, and **c** $\triangle ADF \sim \triangle AEC$.

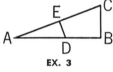

EX. 3

5. In trapezoid $ABCD$ with bases AB and DC, the diagonals intersect at O. Prove that $\triangle DOC \sim \triangle AOB$. Is there another pair of similar triangles in this figure?

6. Two chords AC and BD intersect at E within a circle. Prove that $\triangle ABE \sim \triangle CED$.

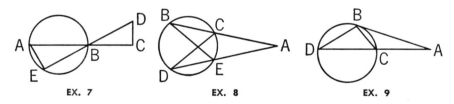

EX. 7   EX. 8   EX. 9

7. AB is a diameter, ABC and EBD are straight lines, $DC \perp AC$. Prove that $\triangle AEB \sim \triangle BCD$.

8. BCA and DEA are secants. Prove that $\triangle ABE \sim \triangle ADC$.

9. DCA is a secant and BA is a tangent. Prove that $\triangle ABC \sim \triangle ADB$.

10. BDE bisects $\angle B$ of inscribed $\triangle ABC$. Prove that **a** $\triangle ABD \sim \triangle EBC$ and **b** $\triangle EDC \sim \triangle EBC$.

11. Prove that two isosceles triangles with equal vertex angles are similar.

EX. 10

Note: For a minimum course the *proofs* of the next two theorems, Theorems 55 and 56, may be omitted.

THEOREM
55

Two triangles are similar if an angle of one is equal to an angle of the other, and the sides including these angles are in proportion.

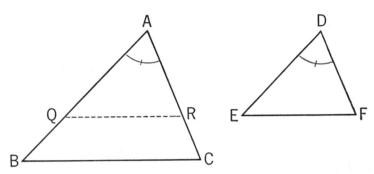

Given $\triangle ABC$ and $\triangle DEF$ with $\angle A = \angle D$ and $\dfrac{AB}{DE} = \dfrac{AC}{DF}$.

To prove that $\triangle ABC \sim \triangle DEF$.

The *plan* is to prove that two angles of one are equal to two angles of the other.

Proof. Place $\triangle DEF$ in the position AQR with $\angle D$ coinciding with its equal $\angle A$.

STATEMENTS	REASONS
1. $\dfrac{AB}{DE} = \dfrac{AC}{DF}$ or $\dfrac{AB}{AQ} = \dfrac{AC}{AR}$.	1. Given.
2. $QR \parallel BC$.	2. Corollary, page 347.
3. $\angle B = \angle AQR$ or $\angle E$.	3. Theorem 14.
4. $\angle A = \angle D$.	4. Given.
5. $\triangle ABC \sim \triangle DEF$.	5. Theorem 54.

EXERCISES

1. Prove that two isosceles triangles are similar if their vertex angles are equal, by using Theorem 55.

2. Prove that two right triangles are similar if the sides adjacent to the right angles are proportional.

3. In $\triangle ABC$ and $\triangle A'B'C'$, $\angle A = \angle A'$, $\angle B = \angle B'$, $AD = DB$, and $A'D' = D'B'$. Prove that $\triangle ACD \sim \triangle A'C'D'$.

Two triangles are similar if their corresponding sides are in proportion.

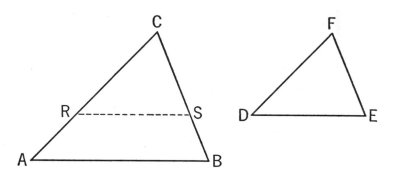

Given $\triangle ABC$ and $\triangle DEF$ with $\dfrac{AB}{DE} = \dfrac{BC}{EF} = \dfrac{CA}{FD}$.

To prove that $\triangle ABC \sim \triangle DEF$.

The *plan* is to mark off $CR = FD$ and $CS = FE$, to prove that $\triangle RSC \sim \triangle ABC$, and to prove that $\triangle DEF \cong \triangle RSC$.

Proof. Mark off $CR = FD$ and $CS = FE$. Draw RS.

STATEMENTS	REASONS
1. $\dfrac{CA}{FD} = \dfrac{BC}{EF}$ or $\dfrac{CA}{CR} = \dfrac{BC}{SC}$.	1. Given and construction.
2. In $\triangle ABC$ and $\triangle RSC$, $\angle C = \angle C$.	2. Identity.
3. $\triangle RSC \sim \triangle ABC$.	3. Theorem 55.
4. $\dfrac{CA}{CR} = \dfrac{AB}{RS}$.	4. Page 357, Statement 2.
5. $\dfrac{CA}{FD} = \dfrac{AB}{DE}$.	5. Given.
6. $RS = DE$.	6. Proportion Theorem 8.
7. $\triangle CRS \cong \triangle DEF$.	7. *s.s.s.* = *s.s.s.*
8. $\triangle ABC \sim \triangle DEF$.	8. Substituting for $\triangle CRS$ the congruent $\triangle DEF$.

Note: The proof of this theorem will be simpler for you if you will remember that RS must be proved equal to DE before you can state that $\triangle CRS$ and DEF are congruent.

■ Proving Four Lines Proportional

Just as you used *congruent* triangles to prove two corresponding sides are *equal*, you will use *similar* triangles to prove that two pairs of lines have the same ratio; that is, that the four lines are *in proportion*.

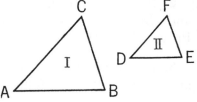

EXAMPLE 1: Suppose $\triangle I \sim \triangle II$ and the sides similarly placed correspond to each other, then

$$\frac{AB}{DE} = \frac{BC}{EF}, \quad \frac{BC}{EF} = \frac{CA}{FD},$$

and $\frac{CA}{FD} = \frac{AB}{DE}$ because in similar triangles the corresponding sides are in proportion.

The numerators of each proportion are sides of $\triangle I$ and the denominators are sides of $\triangle II$.

The numerator and the denominator in each ratio are corresponding sides.

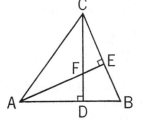

EXAMPLE 2: In $\triangle ABC$, CD and AE are altitudes.

Prove that $\frac{AE}{CD} = \frac{EB}{DB}$.

Choose two triangles which contain these four lines. The numerators should be sides of one triangle and the denominators sides of the other. Here AE and EB are sides of $\triangle AEB$. CD and DB are sides of $\triangle CDB$.

Prove that $\triangle AEB \sim \triangle CDB$. Then $AE : CD = EB : DB$.

Make sure that AE and CD are corresponding sides; that is, that they are opposite equal angles. (AE and CD are both opposite the identical angle B.) Similarly, make sure that EB and DB are corresponding sides.

EXAMPLE 3: In the figure for Example 2 show that $\frac{AE}{AB} = \frac{CD}{CB}$.

Here the numerators are not in the same triangle. Rewrite the proportion by alternation and get $\frac{AE}{CD} = \frac{AB}{CB}$. Then you see that you should prove $\triangle AEB \sim \triangle CDB$.

EXERCISES

1. $AB \perp BCD$, $DE \perp BCD$, and ACE is a straight line. Prove that $\triangle ABC \sim \triangle EDC$. State three proportions involving the sides of these triangles.

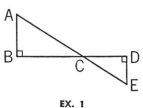

EX. 1

2. In $\triangle ABC$, D and E are taken on AC and BC respectively so that $DE \parallel AB$. Prove that $AC : DC = AB : DE$.

3. In the acute triangle ABC, the altitudes CD and BE meet at F. Prove that the following proportions are true:

a $AE : AD = BE : CD$ b $AB : EB = AC : CD$
c $CF : BF = EF : DF$ d $CF : CE = BF : BD$
e $CF : AB = EF : AE$ f $CE : CF = BE : AB$

4. Prove that the diagonals of a trapezoid divide each other proportionally.

5. Two chords AB and CD intersect within a circle at E. Prove that $AE : EC = DE : EB$.

6. CBA and CDE are two secants of a circle from an external point C. One secant meets the circle at B and A, the other at D and E. Prove that $AC : EC = DC : BC$.

7. BA and BDC are a tangent and a secant to a circle from an external point B. The tangent meets the circle at A and the secant meets the circle at D and C. Prove that AB is the mean proportional between BC and BD.

8. $CD \perp AB$ and $\angle ACB$ is a right angle.

a Prove that CD is the mean proportional between AD and DB.
b Prove that AC is the mean proportional between AB and AD.
c Prove that BC is the mean proportional between AB and DB.

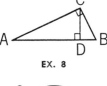

EX. 8

9. $\triangle ABC$ is inscribed in a circle and CD is drawn to D, the middle point of arc AB. Prove that $AC : CD = AE : BD$.

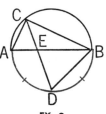

EX. 9

10. Prove: Two triangles are similar if their sides are parallel to each other.

11. Prove: Two triangles are similar if their sides are perpendicular to each other.

12. C is the vertex of the right angle of $\triangle ABC$. $BD \perp AB$ and meets AC extended at D. $AE \perp AB$ and meets BC extended at E. Prove that $\triangle ACE \sim \triangle BCD$.

13. Prove: If two triangles are similar, the bisectors of any two corresponding angles have the same ratio as any two corresponding medians.

■ A Diagonal Scale — *Optional*

By the aid of a diagonal scale shown here it is possible to measure to the nearest hundredth of an inch. The truth of this statement may be shown by means of similar triangles.

$ABCD$ is a square 1 inch on each side. Each side is divided into 10 equal parts and lines drawn as shown. All the horizontal lines are parallel and all the slanting lines are parallel. The horizontal sides of the resulting parallelograms are each .1 of an inch.

The horizontal distance from 9 to E is .01 inch. From 9 to the second diagonal is .01 + .1 or .11 inch. And so on.

The horizontal distance from 8 to F is .02 inch. From 8 to the second diagonal is .02 + .1 or .12 inch. And so on.

What is the horizontal distance from 7 to G? from 7 to the second diagonal?

Similar statements can be made for other horizontal distances. We shall prove one of them: that the distance from 1 to H is .09 inch.

$$\triangle AKD \sim \triangle 1HD. \quad \text{Why?}$$

Then $\dfrac{AD}{1D} = \dfrac{AK}{1H}$ where $AD = 1$ inch, $1D = .9$ inch, and $AK = .1$ inch.

So $\dfrac{1}{.9} = \dfrac{.1}{1H}$ and $1H = .09$ inch.

How far is M from AD? How far is N from AD? How far is P from AD?

Corresponding altitudes of similar triangles have the same ratio as any two corresponding sides.

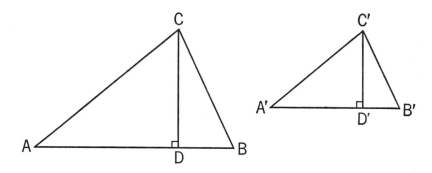

Given   similar triangles ABC and $A'B'C'$ with $CD \perp AB$ and $C'D' \perp A'B'$.

To prove   that $\dfrac{CD}{C'D'} = \dfrac{AC}{A'C'} = \dfrac{BC}{B'C'} = \dfrac{AB}{A'B'}$.

The *plan* is to prove that $\triangle ADC \sim \triangle A'D'C'$.

Proof.

STATEMENTS	REASONS
1. $\triangle ABC \sim \triangle A'B'C'$.	1. Given.
2. $\angle A = \angle A'$.	2. Why?
3. $CD \perp AB$, $C'D' \perp A'B'$.	3. Given.
4. $\triangle ADC \sim \triangle A'D'C'$.	4. Corollary, page 360.
5. $\dfrac{CD}{C'D'} = \dfrac{AC}{A'C'}$.	5. Why?
6. $\dfrac{AC}{A'C'} = \dfrac{BC}{B'C'} = \dfrac{AB}{A'B'}$.	6. Page 357, Statement 2.
7. $\dfrac{CD}{C'D'} = \dfrac{AC}{A'C'} = \dfrac{BC}{B'C'} = \dfrac{AB}{A'B'}$.	7. Axiom 1, page 84.

EXERCISES

1. If, in the figure above, $AB = 8$, $A'B' = 6$, and $CD = 5$ in., how long is $C'D'$?

2. If, in the figure above, $AB = 10''$ and $A'B' = 7''$, what is the numerical value of the ratio $CD : C'D'$?

■ Products of Line Segments

To prove that the product of two segments is equal to the product of two other segments, first prove by means of similar triangles that the four segments are proportional. Then apply the fact that the product of the means is equal to the product of the extremes in a proportion.

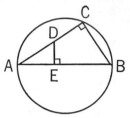

In the figure at the right AB is a diameter and $DE \perp AB$. You are to prove that $AE \times AB = AC \times AD$.

First prove $\triangle ABC \sim \triangle ADE$. Then $AE : AC = AD : AB$ and $AE \times AB = AC \times AD$. Why?

EXERCISES

1. Prove: In any triangle the product of any altitude and the side upon which it is drawn is equal to the product of any other altitude and the side upon which it is drawn.

2. Prove: In any parallelogram the product of any altitude and the side upon which it is drawn is equal to the product of any other altitude and the side upon which it is drawn.

3. Prove that the product of the two arms of a right triangle is equal to the product of the hypotenuse and the altitude upon the hypotenuse.

EXTRA

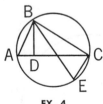

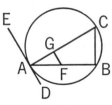

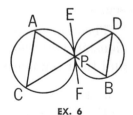

EX. 4   EX. 5   EX. 6

4. $\triangle ABC$ is inscribed in a circle, BE is a diameter, and $BD \perp AC$. Prove that $AB \times BC = BD \times BE$.

5. DE is tangent to the circle at A, $FG \parallel DE$. Prove that $AF \times AB = AG \times AC$.

6. EF is the common tangent to the circles at P. APB and CPD are straight lines. Prove that $AP \times PD = CP \times PB$.

Before you study Theorems 58, 59, 60

1. In this circle chords AB and CD intersect at E. $AE = 2$ cm., $EB = 3$ cm., $CE = 1\frac{1}{2}$ cm., and $ED = 4$ cm. (scale $\frac{1}{2} = 1$).

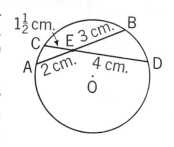

Note that $2 \times 3 = 6$ and that $1\frac{1}{2} \times 4 = 6$. If you draw any other chord through E and measure the two segments made by the point E, you will find that the product is 6.

We say that the product of the segments of one chord is equal to the product of the segments of the other chord. We mean, of course, the product of the *measures* of the segments of the chords.

Theorem 58 proves that this relationship between intersecting chords holds in general.

2. In this figure $AC = 10$ cm. and $BC = 4$ cm. $10 \times 4 = 40$. $EC = 8$ cm. and $DC = 5$ cm. (scale $\frac{1}{2} = 1$). 8×5 is also 40. Again we are talking about the *measures* of the lines, not the lines themselves. In this case $AC \times BC = EC \times DC$; that is, one whole secant times its external segment equals the other whole secant times its external segment.

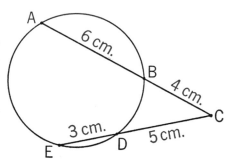

Theorem 59 proves that this relationship between intersecting secants and their segments holds in general.

3. In this figure $\overline{AB}^2 = DB \times CB$. ($\overline{AB}^2$ means AB square.) AB is tangent to the circle.

Use the dimensions given on the figure to show that the above statement is correct for this one special case.

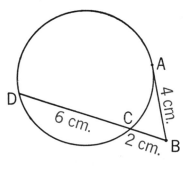

Theorem 60 proves that this relationship between an intersecting secant and tangent holds in general.

If two chords intersect within a circle, the product of the segments of one is equal to the product of the segments of the other.

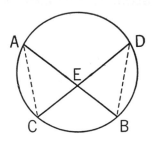

Given   chords AB and CD intersecting at E.

To prove   that $AE \times EB = CE \times ED$.

The *plan* is to draw AC and BD and prove the triangles similar.

Proof.   The proof is left for you.

EXERCISES

Use the figure at the right for the following exercises:

1. $AE = 4$, $EB = 3$, and $CE = 2$ units.   What is the length of ED?   ($AE \times EB = CE \times ED$ or $12 = 2x$. $x =$ _?_)

2. $AE = 5$, $EB = 4$, and $ED = 10$ units.   Find CE.

3. $AE = 2\frac{1}{2}$, $EB = 3\frac{1}{3}$, and $ED = 6$ units.   Find CE.

4. $AE = 6.4$, $EB = 5.3$, and $CE = 3.2$ units.   Find ED.

5. $AE = 9$ units, $EB = 4$ units, and $CE = ED$.   Find CE and ED.   ($x^2 = 36$, $x =$ _?_)

6. If $AE = 4$ units, $EB = 3$ units, and $CE = ED$, how long is ED?   Write the answer first in radical form; then find the square root to the nearest hundredth.   (See table, page 532.)

EXTRA

7. $AE = \frac{1}{2}$ unit, $EB = \frac{2}{3}$ unit, and $CE = ED$.   Find ED to the nearest hundredth.

8. $AE = \frac{3}{5}$ unit, $EB = \frac{2}{3}$ unit, and $CE = ED$.   Find CE to the nearest hundredth.

If from a point outside a circle two secants are drawn, the product of one secant and its external segment is equal to the product of the other secant and its external segment.

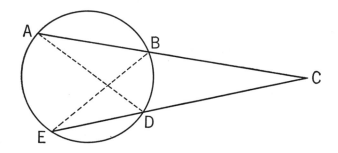

Given   secants CBA and CDE from the external point C.
To prove   that $AC \times BC = EC \times DC$.
The *plan* is to prove that $\triangle ACD \sim \triangle ECB$.
Proof.   The proof is left for you.

EXERCISES

Use the figure at the right for the following exercises:

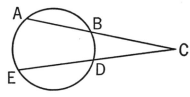

1. If $AC = 9$, $BC = 4$, and $DC = 2$ units, find EC.   ($AC \times BC = EC \times DC$ or $9 \times 4 = 2x$. $x = \underline{\ ?\ }$)

2. If $AC = 9$, $BC = 3$, and $EC = 12$ units, find DC.

3. If $AB = 5$, $BC = 4$, and $DC = 2$ units, find EC.   (Note that $AC = 9$ units.)

4. If $AB = 6$, $BC = 3$, and $DC = 2$ units, find ED.   (First find EC.)

5. If $AB = 8$, $BC = 6$, and $DC = 4$ units, find ED.

6. If $AC = 5\frac{1}{2}$, $BC = 1\frac{3}{4}$, and $DC = 2\frac{1}{4}$ units, find EC.

7. If $AB = 2\frac{2}{3}$, $BC = 2\frac{1}{2}$, and $DC = 1\frac{3}{4}$ units, find ED.

EXTRA

8. If $AC = a$, $BC = b$, and $DC = c$, find ED and EC.

9. If $AB = a$, $BC = b$, and $EC = c$, find DC and ED.

■ Quadratic Equations

If, in the figure, $AB = 6$ units, $CE = 2$ units, and $ED = 4$ units, to find AE and EB involves a kind of equation we have not yet discussed. If we let $AE = x$, then $EB = 6 - x$ and, by Theorem 58, $x(6 - x) = 8$ or $6x - x^2 = 8$. This can be changed to $x^2 - 6x + 8 = 0$.

Such an equation involving the unknown to the second power and no higher (that is, it has x^2 but not x^3 or x^4) is called a **quadratic equation.**

The simplest kind of quadratic equation contains the unknown to the second power only. Examples of such equations are $x^2 = 9$, $x^2 + 3 = 4$, and $\dfrac{x^2}{2} = 8$.

To solve $x^2 = 9$, take the square root of both sides; then $x = +3$ or -3. (This may be written ± 3.)

If $\dfrac{x^2}{2} = 8$, then $x^2 = 16$ and $x = \pm 4$.

All such equations can be simplified to the form $x^2 = a$, and can be solved by taking the square root of both sides. Then $x = \pm \sqrt{a}$.

You have already solved quadratic equations which are as simple as this type.

EXERCISES

Solve the following equations. When the square roots cannot be found exactly, leave the answers in radical form.

EXAMPLE: $x^2 = 18$

$x = \pm \sqrt{18}$

1. $x^2 = 25$

2. $x^2 = 144$

3. $x^2 = 20$

4. $x^2 = 156$

5. $2x^2 = 72$

6. $3x^2 = 75$

7. $4x^2 = 52$

8. $x^2 + 7 = 16$

9. $2x^2 + 3 = 5$

10. $3x^2 - 5 = 10$

11. $5x^2 + 2 = 3x^2 + 6$

12. $7x^2 - 9 = 2x^2 + 16$

13. $4x^2 + 3 = x^2 + 18$

14. $4x^2 = x^2 + 25$

■ Solution by Factoring

Quadratic equations which involve both x^2 and x can be solved in a variety of ways. When they are in the form $x^2 + ax + b = 0$ and $x^2 + ax + b$ is factorable, the method is as follows:

EXAMPLE 1: Solve $x^2 + 6x + 8 = 0$ for x.

$$x^2 + 6x + 8 = (x + 4)(x + 2)$$

So we have $(x + 4)(x + 2) = 0$.

The product of two factors is zero if, and only if, one of the factors is zero. Hence $(x + 4)(x + 2)$ will equal zero when $x + 4 = 0$ and when $x + 2 = 0$.

If $x + 4 = 0$, $x = -4$ and if $x + 2 = 0$, $x = -2$.

These are the two roots of $x^2 + 6x + 8 = 0$.

Check $x = -4$ and $x = -2$ to see if they satisfy the equation.

EXAMPLE 2: Solve $x^2 - x = 12$ for x.

First write the equation as $x^2 - x - 12 = 0$
Then factor the left side. $(x - 4)(x + 3) = 0$
Then $x - 4 = 0$ and $x + 3 = 0$ and $x = 4$ or $x = -3$
Check these values in the given equation.

EXERCISES

Solve these quadratic equations by factoring:

1. $x^2 + 4x - 12 = 0$
2. $x^2 - 6x + 8 = 0$
3. $x^2 + 8x + 12 = 0$
4. $x^2 + 5x - 14 = 0$
5. $x^2 - 4x - 45 = 0$
6. $x^2 + 6x = 27$
7. $x^2 - 8x + 15 = 0$
8. $x(x - 2) = 8$
9. $x(x + 4) = 5$
10. $x^2 = 14x - 40$
11. $x^2 = 2x + 63$
12. $x^2 + 10x = -16$

For Exercises 13–14, use the figure for Exercises, page 369.

13. If $AB = 9$, $CE = 2$, and $ED = 10$ units, how long are AE and EB?

14. If $CD = 16$, $AE = 6$, and $EB = 8$ units, how long are CE and ED?

For Exercises 15–16, use the figure for Exercises, page 370.

15. If $AB = 10$, $ED = 5$, and $DC = 3$ units, how long is BC?
16. If $ED = 12$, $AB = 3$, and $BC = 4$ units, how long is CD?

THEOREM	*If from a point outside a circle a secant and a*
60	*tangent are drawn, the product of the secant and its external segment is equal to the square of the tangent.*

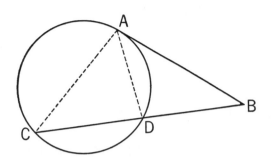

Given   tangent BA and secant BDC from an external point B.
To prove   that $\overline{AB}^2 = CB \times DB$.
The *plan* is to prove that $\triangle CBA \sim \triangle ABD$.
Proof.   The proof is left for you.

Theorem 60 does not depend upon Theorem 59.   If Theorem 59 were proved after Theorem 60 instead of before, it could be proved this way. If AB is a tangent,
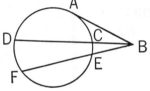
$$DB \times CB = \overline{AB}^2$$
$$FB \times EB = \overline{AB}^2$$
Hence $DB \times CB = FB \times EB$.

EXERCISES

Use the figure at the right for these exercises:

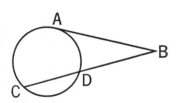

1. If $CB = 9$ and $DB = 4$ units, how long is AB?

2. If $CD = 5$ and $DB = 4$ units, how long is AB?

3. $CD = 6$ and $DB = 3$ units.   Find AB and leave the answer in radical form.

4. $CD = 2$ and $DB = 3$ units.   Find AB to the nearest hundredth.

In any right triangle the altitude upon the hypotenuse is the mean proportional between the segments of the hypotenuse.

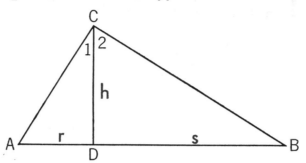

Given   triangle ABC with right angle at C, $CD \perp AB$. $AD = r$, $DB = s$, and $CD = h$.
To prove   that $r : h = h : s$.
The *plan* is to prove that $\triangle ADC \sim \triangle CDB$.
Proof.   The proof is left for you.

If the altitude upon the hypotenuse of a right triangle is drawn, either arm is the mean proportional between the whole hypotenuse and the segment of the hypotenuse adjacent to the arm.

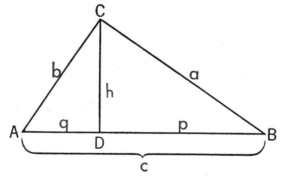

Given $\triangle ABC$ with right angle at C, $CD \perp AB$.
To prove   that $c : b = b : q$ and $c : a = a : p$.
The *plan* is to prove $\triangle ADC \sim \triangle ABC$ and $\triangle BDC \sim \triangle ABC$.
Proof.   The proof is left for you.

Practice the following proportions using the figure for Theorem 62. Point to the lines as you say them.

$$q : h = h : p, \quad c : b = b : q, \quad c : a = a : p$$

These are the proportions resulting from Theorems 61 and 62.

EXERCISES

In the figure, $\angle C$ is a right angle and $CD \perp AB$:

1. $AD = 9$ and $DB = 4$ units. Find DC. $(AD : DC = DC : DB$ or $9 : x = x : 4.)$

2. If $AB = 12$ and $DB = 3$ units, what is the length of BC? $(AB : BC = BC : DB$ or $12 : x = x : 3.)$

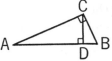

3. $AB = 16$ and $AD = 4$ units. Find AC.

4. If $AD = 20$ and $DC = 10$ units, what is DB?

5. $AD = 9$ and $AC = 16$ units. Find DB. (First find AB.)

6. $AD = 9$ and $DB = 4$ units. Find AC and BC, first in radical form and then to the nearest tenth.

7. $AD = 18$ and $DB = 2$ units. Find DC. Find AC and BC to the nearest tenth.

Construction Problem   Constructing the mean proportional between two given line segments.

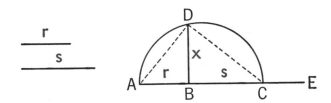

Given   segments r and s.
Required   to construct the mean proportional to r and s.
Construction.

1. Draw a line AE and mark off $AB = r$ and $BC = s$.
2. Upon AC as diameter construct a semicircle.
3. At B construct $BD \perp AC$.
4. BD is the required mean proportional.

Proof.   The proof is left for you.

1. Draw two line segments and construct the mean proportional between them.

2. Draw any triangle and construct the mean proportional between the base and the altitude upon that base.

3. On squared paper draw a rectangle with base 9 units and altitude 4 units. Construct the mean proportional between the base and the altitude. Using this mean proportional as a side, draw a square on squared paper. Count the small squares in the rectangle and in the square. How do the numbers of small squares compare?

4. Show how the mean proportional between two line segments may be constructed, using Theorem 62.

5. Draw two lines, a and b. Construct the mean proportional between $3a$ and $2b$. How long in terms of a and b is the mean proportional?

6. Given that $a : x = x : b$, find the value of x in terms of a and b. Construct the mean proportional between two line segments, a and b. What is the length, in terms of a and b, of this mean proportional?

7. Given two line segments, s and t. Construct a line equal to $\sqrt{st}$.

EXTRA

8. Given two line segments, s and t. Construct a line equal to $\sqrt{6st}$.

9. Given two line segments, r and s. Construct a line equal to $\dfrac{\sqrt{rs}}{3}$.

10. Given two lines, a and b. Construct a line equal to $2\sqrt{ab}$.

11. Given two lines, x and y. Construct a line equal to $\sqrt{\dfrac{xy}{3}}$.

12. Construct a line whose square will be equal to the product of the base and altitude of a given rectangle.

13. Take any line as a unit of length. Call it 1 (one). Construct a line equal to $\sqrt{2}$.

14. Using any line as a unit of length construct a line equal to $\sqrt{6}$.

15. Using any line as a unit of length construct a line equal to $\sqrt{5}$.

16. Draw a short line and call it a. Construct a line equal to $a\sqrt{2}$.

17. Draw a short line and call it a. Construct a line equal to $a\sqrt{3}$.

18. Using any line as a, construct a line equal to $a\sqrt{5}$.

Before you study Theorem 63

1. Construct a right angle ACB with AC equal to 3 inches and BC equal to 4 inches. If you do this accurately, you will find that $AB = 5$ inches.

Note that $3^2 + 4^2 = 5^2$; that is, $9 + 16 = 25$.

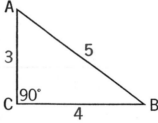

2. Do this exercise again making AC equal to 6 cm. and BC equal to 8 cm. Does $AB = 10$ cm.? Does $6^2 + 8^2 = 10^2$?

3. If you construct a right triangle with the two arms equal to 5 units and 12 units, you will find that the hypotenuse is 13 units. Does $5^2 + 12^2 = 13^2$?

4. Make a right triangle with arms 4 cm. and 5 cm. Let the hypotenuse be x. Then x^2 should equal $4^2 + 5^2 = 16 + 25 = 41$. If $x^2 = 41$, $x = \sqrt{41}$. From the table, $\sqrt{41} = 6.4$. Is the hypotenuse of your triangle 6.4 cm.? It should be if your work is accurate.

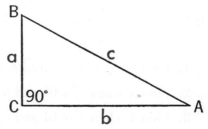

Notice that in all of the right triangles which you have constructed $c^2 = a^2 + b^2$.

Theorem 63 shows that this relationship is general.

In any right triangle, the square of the hypotenuse is equal to the sum of the squares of the arms.

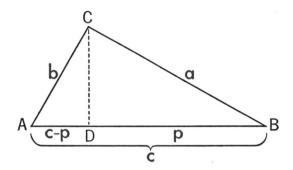

Given   right triangle ABC with the right angle at C.

To prove   that $c^2 = a^2 + b^2$.

The *plan* is to find the value of a^2 and b^2 by means of Theorem 62 and to add the results.

Proof.   Draw the altitude CD.   Let $DB = p$; then $AD = c - p$.

STATEMENTS	REASONS
1. $c : a = a : p$.	1. Theorem 62.
2. $a^2 = cp$.	2. Why?
3. $c : b = b : (c - p)$.	3. Theorem 62.
4. $b^2 = c^2 - cp$.	4. Why?
5. $a^2 + b^2 = c^2$.	5. Axiom 3, page 84.

This theorem is known as the Pythagorean (pǐ-thăg′ŏ-rē′ăn) Theorem after Pythagoras (about 580 B.C.), a Greek philosopher and mathematician, who had a secret society of mathematicians at Crotona, Italy.

Since $c^2 = a^2 + b^2$, then also $a^2 = c^2 - b^2$ and $b^2 = c^2 - a^2$. Why? If we solve for c, a, and b in these equations, we have

$$c = \sqrt{a^2 + b^2}, \quad a = \sqrt{c^2 - b^2}, \quad b = \sqrt{c^2 - a^2}$$

1. Find c when $a = 3$ and $b = 4$.

2. Find a when $c = 10$ and $b = 6$.

3. Find b when $c = 13$ and $a = 12$.

The following numerical exercises are solved by means of the Pythagorean Theorem. If a right triangle is not indicated by the given lines, you should draw auxiliary lines so that you will have a right triangle. In case your answer is a square root that you cannot find exactly, give the answer to the nearest tenth.

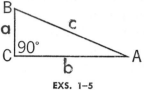

EXS. 1–5

1. If $a = 6$ and $b = 8$ units, how long is c?

2. If $a = 10$ and $b = 24$ units, how long is c?

3. If $a = 4$ and $b = 6$ units, how long is c?

4. If $c = 25$ and $a = 15$ units, how long is b?

5. If $c = 7$ and $b = 4$ units, how long is a?

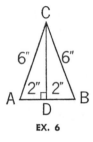

EX. 6

6. If in an isosceles triangle each of the equal arms is 6 in. and the base is 4 in., how long is the altitude upon the base? (Use right triangle ADC.)

7. If in an isosceles triangle the base is 4 in. and the altitude upon the base is 4 in., how long is each of the equal arms?

8. In an equilateral triangle each side is 10 in. How long is the altitude?

9. In an equilateral triangle each side is 3 cm. How long is the altitude? (SUGGESTION: $\sqrt{3^2 - (\frac{3}{2})^2} = \sqrt{9 - \frac{9}{4}} = \sqrt{\frac{27}{4}} = \frac{\sqrt{27}}{2}$.)

10. The sides of five equilateral triangles are 12, 8, 16, 7, and 5 units respectively. How long is the altitude in each case?

11. In a circle whose radius is 5 in., a chord is 4 in. from the center. Find the length of the chord. (Use right triangle OAC.)

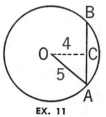

EX. 11

12. A chord 24 in. long is 4 in. from the center of a circle. How long is the radius of the circle?

■ Proofs of Pythagorean Theorem — *Optional*

The Pythagorean Theorem is a famous one historically. Professional and amateur mathematicians have vied with each other to produce proofs. Several hundred of these proofs are now known. We reproduce three of them here.

1. ABC is the given right triangle with right angle at C. Use the hypotenuse AB as a radius to draw the circle. Extend lines as shown.

Outline of proof. The reasons are left for you.

$$AF = c, \ AE = c, \ DC = a$$

Since $DC \times CB = EC \times CF$,

$$a \times a = (c - b)(c + b)$$
$$a^2 = c^2 - b^2$$

or $\qquad\qquad a^2 + b^2 = c^2$

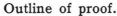

2. ABC is the given right triangle with right angle at C. BC is shorter than AB, so mark off $EB = BC$. $DE \perp AB$.

Outline of proof.

$\triangle BDC \cong \triangle BDE$ and $DC = DE$.

$\triangle ADE \sim \triangle ABC$ so $\dfrac{BC}{DE} = \dfrac{CA}{AE}$

and $\dfrac{CA}{AE} = \dfrac{AB}{AD}$. Hence $\dfrac{a}{k} = \dfrac{b}{c - a}$

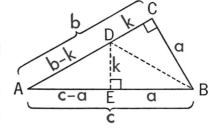

and $\dfrac{b}{c - a} = \dfrac{c}{b - k}$. From these two equations you get $bk = ac - a^2$ and $b^2 - bk = c^2 - ac$. Adding: $b^2 - bk + bk = c^2 - ac + ac - a^2$, which becomes $b^2 = c^2 - a^2$ or $a^2 + b^2 = c^2$.

3. ABC is the given right triangle with right angle at C. Use BC as a radius for the circle.

Outline of proof.

$\dfrac{c - a}{b} = \dfrac{b}{c + a}$, $\quad b^2 = c^2 - a^2$,

or $b^2 + a^2 = c^2$.

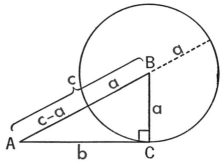

■ Simplification of Radicals

In the work which follows you will need to simplify radicals and to rationalize denominators.

If a number can be separated into two factors, one of which is a square, its square root can be written as the product of a whole number and a square root.

EXAMPLE 1: Since $12 = 4 \times 3$, $\sqrt{12} = \sqrt{4 \times 3} = \sqrt{4}\sqrt{3} = 2\sqrt{3}$

EXAMPLE 2: $\sqrt{50} = \sqrt{25 \times 2} = \sqrt{25}\sqrt{2} = 5\sqrt{2}$

Check the correctness of each of the following:

a $\sqrt{18} = 3\sqrt{2}$ b $\sqrt{24} = 2\sqrt{6}$

c $\sqrt{27} = 3\sqrt{3}$ d $\sqrt{3a^2} = a\sqrt{3}$

e $\sqrt{3x^4} = x^2\sqrt{3}$ f $\sqrt{a^2b} = a\sqrt{b}$

■ Rationalizing Denominators

The fraction $\dfrac{8}{\sqrt{3}}$ may be put in better form for computation by multiplying the numerator and the denominator by $\sqrt{3}$. Thus, $\dfrac{8}{\sqrt{3}} = \dfrac{8 \times \sqrt{3}}{\sqrt{3} \times \sqrt{3}} = \dfrac{8\sqrt{3}}{3}$. Since $\sqrt{3}$ is an *irrational number* (the square root of 3 cannot be found exactly), the process by which we get rid of the radical in the denominator is called *rationalizing*.

To rationalize the denominator of a fraction in the form $\dfrac{a}{\sqrt{b}}$, multiply the numerator and the denominator by $\sqrt{b}$.

Check the correctness of each of the following:

a $\dfrac{7}{\sqrt{6}} = \dfrac{7\sqrt{6}}{6}$ b $\dfrac{12}{\sqrt{3}} = 4\sqrt{3}$ c $\dfrac{3b}{\sqrt{a}} = \dfrac{3b\sqrt{a}}{a}$

To rationalize the denominator of a fraction such as $\dfrac{7}{\sqrt{12}}$ you could multiply the numerator and the denominator by $\sqrt{3}$. Explain. Or you could first write $\dfrac{7}{2\sqrt{3}}$ and then proceed.

Write the following as the product of a rational and an irrational number:

1. $\sqrt{8}$
2. $\sqrt{20}$
3. $\sqrt{32}$
4. $\sqrt{40}$

5. $\sqrt{44}$
6. $\sqrt{45}$
7. $\sqrt{48}$
8. $\sqrt{60}$

9. $\sqrt{72}$
10. $\sqrt{5a^2}$
11. $\sqrt{a^2 b}$
12. $\sqrt{mn^2}$

In the following exercises rationalize the denominators:

13. $\dfrac{2}{\sqrt{3}}$
14. $\dfrac{5}{\sqrt{2}}$
15. $\dfrac{6}{\sqrt{3}}$
16. $\dfrac{9}{\sqrt{3}}$

17. $\dfrac{8}{\sqrt{5}}$
18. $\dfrac{15}{\sqrt{6}}$
19. $\dfrac{a}{\sqrt{3}}$
20. $\dfrac{a}{\sqrt{b}}$

Solve these equations and simplify the answers:

21. $4x^2 = x^2 + 9$
22. $4x^2 = x^2 + 81$
23. $4x^2 = x^2 + 36$

24. $4x^2 = x^2 + 4$
25. $4x^2 = x^2 + 16$
26. $4x^2 = x^2 + 25$

Below are two corollaries to Theorem 63.

COROLLARY 1 **In an isosceles right triangle the hypotenuse is equal to one of the equal arms times $\sqrt{2}$.**

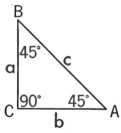

Since $a = b$, $c = \sqrt{a^2 + a^2} = \sqrt{2a^2} = a\sqrt{2}$.
Hence if $a = 5$, $c = 5\sqrt{2}$.

COROLLARY 2 **In an isosceles right triangle either of the equal arms is equal to the hypotenuse divided by $\sqrt{2}$.**

By Corollary 1, $AB = BC\sqrt{2}$; hence $BC = \dfrac{AB}{\sqrt{2}}$.

If $AB = 7$, $BC = \dfrac{7}{\sqrt{2}} = \dfrac{7\sqrt{2}}{2}$.

EXERCISES

1. Give at sight the value of c (figure above) when a is as follows: 1, 2, 3, 4, 6, 7, 8, a.

2. Give at sight the value of a (figure above) when c is as follows: 2, 4, 6, 8, 10, 3, 5, 7, 9, a.

THEOREM
64

In a right triangle, if one angle is 30°, the hypotenuse is twice the side opposite the 30° angle.

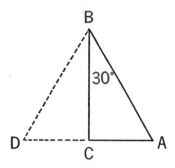

Given   rt. $\triangle ABC$ with right angle at C and $\angle B = 30°$.

To prove   that $AB = 2AC$.

Plan.   Make $\angle CBD = \angle CBA$. Continue AC to BD. Show that each angle of $\triangle ABD = 60°$ and hence $DA = AB = BD$. Prove that $AD = 2AC$ (Theorem 3) and substitute AB for AD.

Proof.   The proof is left for you.

EXERCISES

1. If $b = 1$, $c =$ _?_.   Since $a = \sqrt{c^2 - b^2}$, $a =$ _?_.

2. If $c = 8$ units, $b = \dfrac{c}{2} =$ _?_. $a =$ _?_.

3. $a = 6$ units. $b =$ _?_ and $c =$ _?_.   (Let $b = x$ and $c = 2x$).

<u>COROLLARY 1</u>   If one angle of a right triangle is 30°, the side opposite the 60° angle is equal to $\sqrt{3}$ times the side opposite the 30° angle.

If $AC = s$, then $AB = 2s$ and $BC = \sqrt{4s^2 - s^2} = \sqrt{3s^2} = s\sqrt{3}$.   Hence if $AC = 4$ in., $BC = 4\sqrt{3}$ in.

<u>COROLLARY 2</u>   If one angle of a right triangle is 30°, the side opposite the 30° angle is equal to the side opposite the 60° angle divided by $\sqrt{3}$.

By Corollary 1, $BC = AC\sqrt{3}$.   Hence $AC = \dfrac{BC}{\sqrt{3}}$.

THEOREM	*In a right triangle, if the hypotenuse is twice one*
65	*of the arms, the angle opposite that arm is 30°.*

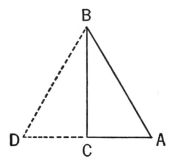

Given   right triangle with right angle at C and $AB = 2AC$.

To prove $\angle CBA = 30°$.

Plan.   Continue AC, making $CD = AC$.   Draw BD.   Prove that $AB = AD$ (both equal $2AC$).   Prove that $AB = BD$ by congruent triangles.   Then show that $\angle A = 60°$ and $\angle CBA = 30°$.

Proof.   The proof is left for you.

Theorems 64 and 65 do not involve similar triangles.   They are placed here because they are so often used in connection with the Pythagorean Theorem.

■ Using 45° and 30°–60° Right Triangles

If, in a right triangle, one of the angles is 45° or 30° and the length of one side is given, the length of each of the other two sides can be found by inspection.

Can you explain the following examples?

EXAMPLE 1:   If $a = 3$, then $b = 3$, and $c = 3\sqrt{2}$

EXAMPLE 2:   If $c = 5$, then $b = \dfrac{5}{\sqrt{2}}$, and $a = \dfrac{5}{\sqrt{2}}$

$$\left(\text{Then } b = a = \dfrac{5\sqrt{2}}{2}\right)$$

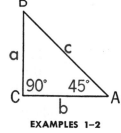

EXAMPLES 1–2

384   SIMILAR POLYGONS

EXAMPLE 3: If $a = 2$, then $c = 4$, and $b = 2\sqrt{3}$

EXAMPLE 4: If $c = 6$, then $a = 3$, and $b = 3\sqrt{3}$

EXAMPLE 5: If $b = 7$, then $a = \dfrac{7}{\sqrt{3}}$, and $c = \dfrac{14}{\sqrt{3}}$. (Then $a = \dfrac{7\sqrt{3}}{3}$ and $c = \frac{14}{3}\sqrt{3}$)

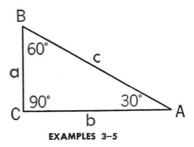

EXAMPLES 3–5

EXERCISES

1. In the following table a is given. Copy the table and fill in the blanks. The first two columns are done for you.

a	1	2	3	4	5	6	$\frac{1}{2}$	$1\frac{1}{2}$	$2\frac{1}{2}$
b	1	2	?	?	?	?	?	?	?
c	$\sqrt{2}$	$2\sqrt{2}$	?	?	?	?	?	?	?

2. In this table c is given. Copy the table and fill in the blanks. The first two are done for you.

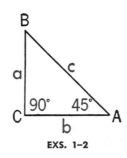

EXS. 1–2

c	1	2	3	4	5	6	7	8
a	$\dfrac{1}{\sqrt{2}}$	$\dfrac{2}{\sqrt{2}}$	?	?	?	?	?	?
b	$\dfrac{1}{\sqrt{2}}$	$\dfrac{2}{\sqrt{2}}$	?	?	?	?	?	?

3. Copy and fill in the blanks:

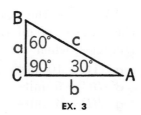

EX. 3

a	1	2	3	4	5	6	$\frac{1}{2}$	$1\frac{1}{2}$
c	2	4	?	?	?	?	?	?
b	$\sqrt{3}$	$2\sqrt{3}$	?	?	?	?	?	?

USING 45° AND 30°–60° TRIANGLES

4–5. Copy these two tables and fill in the blanks:

c	1	2	3	4	5	6	7
a	$\frac{1}{2}$	1	$\frac{3}{2}$	?	?	?	?
b	$\frac{1}{2}\sqrt{3}$	$\sqrt{3}$	$\frac{3}{2}\sqrt{3}$	?	?	?	?

b	1	2	3	4	5	6	7
a	$\dfrac{1}{\sqrt{3}}$	$\dfrac{2}{\sqrt{3}}$	?	?	?	?	?
c	$\dfrac{2}{\sqrt{3}}$	$\dfrac{4}{\sqrt{3}}$	?	?	?	?	?

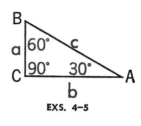

EXS. 4–5

6. Find the length of the diagonal of a square whose side is 6 ft. (Note the 45° right triangle.)

7. If a side of a square is 11 ft., how long is the diagonal?

8. If the diagonal of a square is 8 ft., how long is a side?

9. If the diagonal of a square is 15 ft., how long is a side?

10. A baseball diamond is a square 90 ft. on a side. How far is it from second base to the home plate?

11. $\triangle ABC$ is equilateral. If $AC = 4$ in., how long is the perpendicular CD?

12. $\triangle ABC$ is equilateral. If the perpendicular $CD = 6$ in., how long is AC?

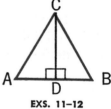

EXS. 11–12

13. $\triangle ACB$ is a right triangle. $CD \perp AB$, and $\angle A = 30°$.

  a $\angle 1 = \underline{?}°$; $\angle 2 = \underline{?}°$; $\angle B = \underline{?}°$.

  b If $CD = 6$ units, how long are AC, AD, DB, and BC?

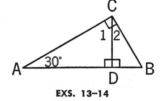

EXS. 13–14

EXTRA

14. Using the figure for Ex. 13, give the lengths of all the sides of the three triangles, when

a $AC = 10$ units	**b** $AC = 9$ units	**c** $BC = 4$ units
d $BC = 5$ units	**e** $DC = 8$ units	**f** $DC = 5$ units
g $BD = 6$ units	**h** $AB = 24$ units	**i** $AD = 8$ units

SIMILAR POLYGONS

1. Prove: The product of two sides of a triangle is equal to the product of the diameter of the circumscribed circle and the altitude upon the third side of the triangle.

2. BC is the base of isosceles triangle ABC. AD is drawn from the vertex angle to point D on the base BC or BC extended so that angle BAD equals angle B. Prove that AB is the mean proportional between BC and BD.

3. AB equals BC in the isosceles triangle ABC. BD is drawn from the vertex B to any point D of the base. Prove that $\overline{AB}^2 = \overline{BD}^2 + AD \cdot DC$. (SUGGESTION: Circumscribe circle about triangle ABC. Draw the diameter from B and extend BD to the circle. Use Exercise 1 above.)

4. Prove: If the lengths of the two arms of a right triangle are in the ratio of one to two, the altitude upon the hypotenuse will divide the hypotenuse in the ratio of one to four.

5. Two parallel chords are 16 inches and 30 inches long respectively. If the distance between their middle points is 23 inches, what is the radius of the circle?

6. In triangle ABC, K is a point on BC so that CK equals one third CB and H is a point on AB so that AH equals one half AB. CH and AK intersect in E. Prove that $EK = \frac{1}{4}AK$.

7. Two tangents CA and CB are drawn to a circle. From a point D in the minor arc AB, perpendiculars DE, DF, and DG are drawn to AB, AC, and BC respectively. Prove that DE is a mean proportional between DF and DG.

8. The diameter AB of a circle is extended through B to C so that BC is equal to a radius. From B and C tangents are drawn to the circle. The tangent from C touches the circle at E and the tangent from B at F. AE extended meets the tangent from B at D. Prove that triangle DEF is equilateral.

9. A rectangle is 5 inches by 3 inches. A line segment 4 inches long is moved about with its ends always on the perimeter of the rectangle. Find the locus of the mid-point of this segment.

10. From A and B, the extremities of the hypotenuse of the right triangle ABC, the lines AD and BE are drawn perpendicular to AB. Point D lies on BC extended, and point E lies on AC extended. Prove triangle BCE similar to triangle ACD.

1. Given that $\triangle ABC$ is similar to $\triangle DEF$ with $\angle A = \angle E$ and $\angle B = \angle D$. State three proportions that are true.

2. A tower casts a shadow 84 ft. long when a vertical 10-foot pole casts a shadow 7 ft. long on level ground. How high is the tower?

3. Prove: If one of two similar triangles is isosceles, the other is also.

4. In a circle whose radius is 8 inches, chords are drawn through a point 3 inches from the center. What is the product of the segments of each of these chords?

5. Two concentric circles have radii that are 6 in. and 10 in. In the larger circle a chord is drawn tangent to the smaller circle. What is its length?

6. In $\triangle ABC$, $\angle B = 90°$, $\angle A = 30°$, and $BD \perp AC$. If $AB = 6$ in., how long are BC, BD, AD, and DC?

7. The altitude of an equilateral triangle is 4 in. What is its perimeter?

8. Write the following as the product of a rational and an irrational number:

a $\sqrt{24}$ 　　　　　　 b $\sqrt{27}$ 　　　　　　 c $\sqrt{50}$

9. Rationalize the denominator:

a $\dfrac{4}{\sqrt{3}}$ 　　　　　 b $\dfrac{3}{\sqrt{2}}$ 　　　　　 c $\dfrac{2}{3\sqrt{5}}$

10. Given segments a and b, construct $\sqrt{5ab}$.

11. In $\triangle ABC$, $AC = BC$ and on CA, D is taken so that $DB = AB$. Prove that $AC \times DA = \overline{AB}^2$.

12. Prove: If two circles are tangent internally, all chords of the greater circle drawn from the point of contact are divided proportionally by the smaller circle.

13. The centers of two circles whose radii are 8 and 6 in. are 21 in. apart. How long is the common internal tangent?

14. Another converse of Theorem 64 is: If one side of a triangle is twice another side and the angle opposite the shorter of these two sides is 30°, then the triangle is a right triangle. Is this true? Can you prove it?

15. Prove that corresponding altitudes of similar triangles have the same ratio as the corresponding sides.

16. Prove: The perpendicular from any point on a circle to a diameter of a circle and terminated by it is the mean proportional between the segments of the diameter.

17. $\triangle ABC$ is a right triangle with right angle at C, $EA \perp AB$, and $DB \perp AB$. ACD and BCE are straight lines. Prove that the following proportions are true:

EX. 17

a $AB : AE = BC : AC$ **b** $AB : BD = AC : BC$
c $AB : BE = BD : AD$ **d** $AC : BD = CE : AB$

18. AB is a diameter of a circle and BC is a tangent. AC meets the circle at D. **a** Prove that BD is a mean proportional between AD and DC. **b** Prove that AB is a mean proportional between AC and AD.

19. AC and AD are tangents. Prove: AB is a mean proportional between BC and BD.

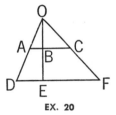

EX. 19

20. The transversals OD, OE, and OF are cut by parallel lines AC and DF. Prove that $AB : DE = BC : EF$. (SUGGESTION: Show that the two ratios are equal to the same ratio.)

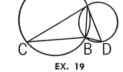

21. Prove: Each of the triangles formed by joining the middle points of the sides of a triangle is similar to the given triangle.

EX. 20

22. $\triangle ABC$, inscribed in a circle, has $AB = BC$. A line from B to any point E on arc AC meets AC at D. Prove that $BD : AB = AB : BE$.

23. $ABCDE$ and $A'B'C'D'E'$ are two similar pentagons. AB corresponds to $A'B'$, BC to $B'C'$, etc. From A and A' both diagonals are drawn. Prove that $\triangle ABC \sim \triangle A'B'C'$, $\triangle ACD \sim \triangle A'C'D'$, and $\triangle ADE \sim \triangle A'D'E'$.

24. Using the same figure as for Ex. 23, prove that if $\triangle ABC \sim \triangle A'B'C'$, $\triangle ACD \sim \triangle A'C'D'$, and $\triangle ADE \sim \triangle A'D'E'$, then the two pentagons are similar.

■ Similar Polygons in a Three-Dimensional Figure—*Optional*

Here is a situation where you find similar polygons in three dimensions.

If a pyramid is cut by a plane parallel to its base, the section formed is a polygon similar to the base.

You are given a pyramid $V-ABCDE$ cut by a plane parallel to the base intersecting the lateral edges at A', B', C', D', and E'.

You are to prove that $A'B'C'D'E'$ is similar to $ABCDE$. To do this you must prove two things:

1. The corresponding angles are equal, and
2. The corresponding sides are in proportion.

What angles must you prove equal?

What sides must you prove to be in proportion?

You can prove this theorem only if you know some previously proved theorems such as:

When two parallel planes are cut by a third plane, the lines of intersection are parallel. (What lines does this make parallel?)

Angles whose sides are parallel each to each are either equal or supplementary (in this case equal). What angles are equal?

Can you show that $\dfrac{A'B'}{AB} = \dfrac{VB'}{VB}$ and $\dfrac{B'C'}{BC} = \dfrac{VB'}{VB}$ and so

$\dfrac{A'B'}{AB} = \dfrac{B'C'}{BC}$. Are the polygons similar?

Chapter Summary

I. Definition

1. Under what conditions will quadrilateral $ABCD$ be similar to quadrilateral $A'B'C'D'$?

II. Theorems

2. State three theorems that begin: Two triangles are similar if . . .

3. State the theorem or theorems suggested by each of the following figures and the statement(s) under each.

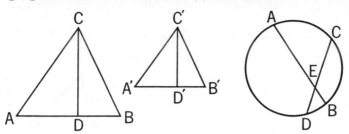

a $\triangle ABC \sim \triangle A'B'C'$, CD and $C'D'$ are altitudes.

b AB and CD are chords.

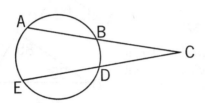

c CBA and CDE are secants.

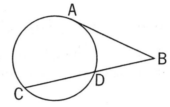

d BA is a tangent. BDC is a secant.

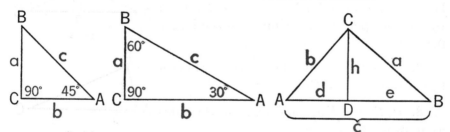

e (1) $c = a\sqrt{2}$

   (2) $a = \dfrac{c}{\sqrt{2}}$

f (1) $c = 2a$

   (2) $b = a\sqrt{3}$

   (3) $a = \dfrac{b}{\sqrt{3}}$

g $AC \perp CB$, $CD \perp AB$

   (1) $\dfrac{d}{h} = \dfrac{?}{e}$

   (2) $\dfrac{c}{b} = \dfrac{b}{?}$

   (3) $\dfrac{c}{?} = \dfrac{a}{e}$

   (4) $c^2 = a^2 + ?$

4. Write and solve a numerical exercise for each theorem above.

5. Complete: In a right triangle, if the hypotenuse is twice one of the arms, the angle opposite that arm is _?_.

III. Construction Problem

6. Construct the mean proportional between lines a and b.

TEST 1

Which of these statements are True *and which are* False?

1. If $\angle B = \angle E$, then $\triangle ABC \sim \triangle DEF$.

2. With the angles as shown, $\triangle ABC \sim \triangle DEF$.

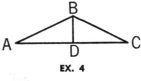

EX. 1

3. In $\triangle ABC$ and $\triangle DEF$, $\angle A$ and $\angle D$ are right angles and $\triangle ABC \cong \triangle DEF$. If $\frac{AC}{AB} = 1$, $\angle F = 45°$.

4. If $BD \perp AC$, $\triangle ABD \sim \triangle BDC$.

5. A 4×6 rectangle is similar to a 5×7 rectangle, since the angles are all equal.

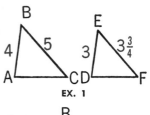

EX. 2

6. If the sides of regular pentagon $ABCDE$ are each $1''$ and the sides of regular pentagon $FGHMN$ are each $2''$, then the smaller pentagon is similar to the larger pentagon.

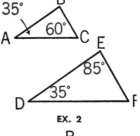

EX. 4

7. $AC = BC$ and $AB = BD$. Therefore $\triangle ABD \sim \triangle ACB$.

8. $D, E,$ and F are midpoints of the sides as shown. Therefore

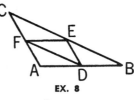

EX. 7

$$\frac{FE}{AB} = \frac{FD}{BC} = \frac{DE}{AC} \text{ and } \triangle FED \sim \triangle ABC.$$

9. AB is a diameter and $CD \perp AB$. Therefore $CD = \sqrt{ab}$.

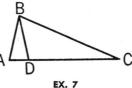

EX. 8

10. AB and CD are two chords intersecting at E. If $AE = 5''$, $EB = 6''$, and $CE = 4''$, then $ED = 7''$.

11. If in right triangle ABC the hypotenuse $BC = 6''$ and $AB = 2''$, then $AC = \sqrt{40}$.

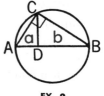

EX. 9

SIMILAR POLYGONS

TEST 2

You may leave answers in radical form.

1. $DE \parallel AB$, $AD = 2''$, $DC = 3''$, and $DE = 3''$, then $AB =$ _?_ in.

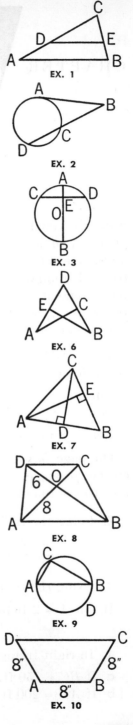

EX. 1

2. AB is a tangent and BCD is a secant. If $BC = 3''$ and $AB = 4''$, then $DC =$ _?_ in.

EX. 2

3. AB is a diameter perpendicular to CD. If $CD = 8''$ and $AE = 2''$, the radius of the circle is _?_ in.

EX. 3

4. In $\odot O$ chord $AB = 6''$ and the radius of the circle is $4''$. The chord is _?_ in. from the center of the circle.

5. In a square each side of which is $1''$, the diagonal equals _?_ in.

EX. 6

6. $\angle A = \angle B$. If $DC = \frac{3}{4}''$, $DE = \frac{3}{4}''$, and $AC = 1''$, then $BE =$ _?_ in.

7. $CD \perp AB$ and $AE \perp BC$. If $AB = 4''$ and $BC = 3''$, then $BE =$ _?_ times BD.

EX. 7

8. $ABCD$ is a trapezoid. If $OB = 2OD$, $OC =$ _?_.

EX. 8

9. If arc $ACB =$ arc ADB and AC is equal to a radius, then $\angle A =$ _?_ °.

EX. 9

10. $ABCD$ is an isosceles trapezoid in which $\angle A = 120°$. The altitude of the trapezoid is _?_ in.

EX. 10

CHAPTER **14** Numerical Trigonometry

Some of you have studied numerical trigonometry in a previous year. You know that it deals with the measurement of sides and angles of triangles and relationships among them. It is used to find unknown distances which are inaccessible for direct measurement. In this chapter you will study the numerical trigonometry of right triangles.

Can you do these exercises?

1. In the triangle at the right what is the value of —

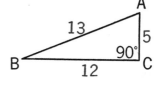

tan B	sin B	cos B
tan A	sin A	cos A

Leave your answers as fractions.

On page 531 there is a table containing tangents, sines, and cosines of angles from 1° to 90°. The values in the table are correct to the fourth decimal place.

2. Using the table on page 531, find the value of the following:

tan 24°	sin 24°	cos 24°
tan 76°	sin 76°	cos 76°

3. Using the table, complete —

If tan A = 2.1445, $\angle A$ = _?_.   If sin A = .4226, $\angle A$ = _?_.
If cos A = .2756, $\angle A$ = _?_.

4. In right triangle ABC, $\angle C$ is the right angle.

a If BC = 150 ft. and $\angle B$ = 28°, how long is AC?
b If AB = 200 ft. and $\angle B$ = 32°, how long is AC?

■ The Tangent Ratio

Here are two right triangles in which $\angle B = \angle B'$. The triangles are similar. Why?

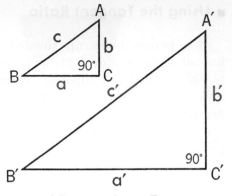

Hence, $\dfrac{b}{a} = \dfrac{b'}{a'}$. Why?

No matter how large or how small the right triangles are, if $\angle B = \angle B'$, the ratio $\dfrac{b}{a}$ is

constant. In other words, the ratio $\dfrac{\text{side opposite } \angle B}{\text{side adjacent } \angle B}$ is always the same just as long as $\angle B$ remains the same. As the angle varies the ratio varies. The ratio is called the tangent of $\angle B$ (written "tan B").

△ *The* **tangent** *of an acute angle in a right triangle is the quotient found (or indicated) by dividing the* **side opposite the angle** *by the* **side adjacent to the angle.**

Note: The phrase *side adjacent to the angle* does not refer to the hypotenuse.

In the figure tan $B = \dfrac{b}{a}$ and tan $A = \dfrac{a}{b}$.

The values of the tangents in the box are taken from the table on page 531. (They are given here to the nearest hundredth.)

Note that as the angle increases the tangent increases. By drawing figures, you can see that if the angle is very small, the side opposite the angle is very short, and so the tangent of a small angle is small. When the angle comes close to 90°, the hypotenuse is nearly parallel to the side opposite the angle. This makes the side opposite very long. Hence the tangent of an angle close to 90° is large.

tan 20° = .36
tan 30° = .58
tan 40° = .84
tan 45° = 1.00
tan 50° = 1.19
tan 60° = 1.73

By use of the table on page 531 complete the following:

a tan 32° = _?_　　　**b** tan 75° = _?_　　　**c** tan 85° = _?_
d If tan A = .4663, A = _?_　　**e** If tan A = 1.1918, A = _?_
f If tan A = .2126, A = _?_　　**g** If tan A = 2.6051, A = _?_

■ Using the Tangent Ratio

If a person looks up toward an object, the angle which his line of sight makes with a horizontal line in the same vertical plane is called the **angle of elevation.** If he looks down toward an object, the angle with the horizontal is called the **angle of depression.** ∠A in Figure 1 is an *angle of elevation* if the observer is at A. ∠BAC in Figure 2 is an *angle of depression*, the observer being at A.

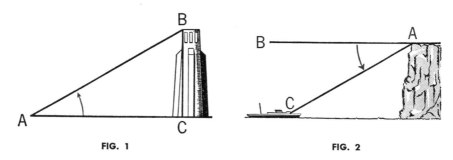

FIG. 1   FIG. 2

EXAMPLE 1: At a point 280 ft. from the base of a tower, the angle of elevation is 32°. Find the height of the tower. (Fig. 1)

$$\frac{CB}{AC} = \tan 32° \quad \text{(Definition)}$$

Then $\frac{CB}{280} = .6249$ (Substituting numerical values.

Tan 32° = .6249 is found from the table on page 531.)

CB = 280(.6249)

CB = 175 ft. (To the nearest foot)

EXAMPLE 2: At what angle, to the nearest degree, does a road rise from the horizontal if it rises 200 ft. in a horizontal distance of one tenth of a mile?

$$\text{Tan } B = \frac{CA}{BC} = \frac{200}{528}$$

Tan B = .3789   (By division)

If we look in the tables, we see that tan 20° = .3640 and tan 21° = .3839. Since .3789 is nearer .3839 than .3640, ∠B is nearer 21° than 20°.

The angle is 21° to the nearest degree.

EXERCISES

1. Find b in the right triangle ABC when a and $\angle B$ are as follows. Give answers to the nearest whole number.

a $a = 142$ ft., $\angle B = 36°$
b $a = 385$ yd., $\angle B = 24°$
c $a = 556$ in., $\angle B = 62°$
d $a = 842$ yd., $\angle B = 44°$

EXS. 1–2

2. Find a in the right triangle ABC when b and $\angle A$ are as follows. Give answers to the nearest tenth. (Note that a is the side opposite the angle and b is the side adjacent.)

a $b = 16.5$ in., $\angle A = 32°$ **b** $b = 98.3$ ft., $\angle A = 70°$
c $b = 64.3$ yd., $\angle A = 51°$ **d** $b = 19.7$ cm., $\angle A = 38°$

3. Solve the following equations for a. Give answers to the nearest tenth.

a $\dfrac{3.2}{a} = 4.6$ **b** $\dfrac{8.4}{a} = 2.8$ **c** $\dfrac{7.6}{a} = 4.5$ **d** $\dfrac{1.6}{a} = 4.2$

4. Find a in the right triangle ABC when b and $\angle B$ are as follows. Give answers to the nearest hundredth. (If you wish to avoid long division, you can find the number of degrees in $\angle A$ and use tan A instead of tan B.)

a $b = 3.24$, $\angle B = 25°$ **b** $b = 8.62$, $\angle B = 60°$
c $b = 5.91$, $\angle B = 72°$ **d** $b = 4.53$, $\angle B = 36°$

5. In order to find the width of a river, a 216-ft. base line AC is measured along the bank. The point B is located on the opposite bank so that $\angle ACB$ is a right angle. $\angle CAB$ is found to be 55°. What is the width of the river?

6. The angle of elevation of the top of a tree from a point 50 ft. from its foot is 42°. What is the height of the tree?

7. A road rises 352 ft. in a horizontal distance of one-half mile. At what angle, to the nearest degree, does the road rise from the horizontal?

8. A tree 198 ft. high casts a shadow 132 ft. long. What is the angle of elevation of the sun to the nearest degree?

USING THE TANGENT RATIO

■ The Sine Ratio

A second important ratio of the sides of a right triangle is the sine ratio. In any right triangle, large or small, just so long as $\angle B$ is constant the ratio $\dfrac{b}{c}$ is constant. As the angle changes the ratio changes. This ratio is called the sine of $\angle B$ (written "sin B").

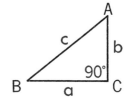

△ *The **sine** of an acute angle in a right triangle is the quotient obtained (or indicated) by dividing the **side opposite the angle** by the **hypotenuse**.*

In the figure sin $B = \dfrac{b}{c}$ and sin $A = \dfrac{a}{c}$.

Note that as the angle increases the value of the sine increases (see table, page 531).

The sine of a small angle is small. The sine of an acute angle can never be equal to or greater than 1 since the side opposite the angle must always be less than the hypotenuse. However, if the angle is very close to 90°, the sine is very close to 1. Check with the table.

From the table find the value of the following:

a sin 22°   **b** sin 52°   **c** sin 79°

If sin $A = .4563$, what is A to the nearest degree?

EXAMPLE: If a kite is flying with 200 ft. of string out and the string makes an angle of 38° with the horizontal, how high above the ground is the kite? (Assume that the string is straight.)

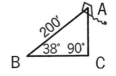

$\dfrac{CA}{BA} = $ sin 38°   (Definition)

$\dfrac{CA}{200} = .6157$ (Substituting numerical values)

CA = 200 × .6157
CA = 123 ft.   (To the nearest foot)

■ The Cosine Ratio

In a right triangle ABC, with the right angle at C, the ratio

$$\frac{\text{side adjacent to } \angle B}{\text{hypotenuse}}$$

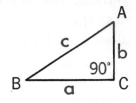

is called the *cosine of* $\angle B$ (written "cos B").

△ The **cosine** *of an acute angle in a right triangle is the quotient obtained (or indicated) by dividing the **side adjacent** to the angle by the hypotenuse.*

In the triangle, $\cos B = \dfrac{a}{c}$ and $\cos A = \dfrac{b}{c}$.

Note that as the angle increases the cosine decreases (see table, page 531). The cosine of an acute angle is never equal to or greater than 1. (Why?) The cosine of a very small angle is very close to 1, and the cosine of an angle near 90° is very small.

EXAMPLE: In a circle whose radius is 24.0 in., a chord AB makes an angle of 35° with the radius drawn to A.
How long is the chord?
Draw OC from the center perpendicular to AB.

$\dfrac{AC}{AO} = \cos 35°$ (Definition)

Then $\dfrac{AC}{24.0} = .8192$

AC = 24(.8192) = 19.66 (to nearest hundredth)
AB = 2AC = 39.3 (to the nearest tenth)

EXERCISES

1. In right triangle ABC, find b when c and $\angle B$ are as follows. Give answers to the nearest whole number.

a $c = 462$ ft., $\angle B = 49°$ **b** $c = 215$ yd., $\angle B = 57°$
c $c = 857$ yd., $\angle B = 65°$ **d** $c = 361$ ft., $\angle B = 21°$

2. In right triangle ABC, find a when c and $\angle A$ are as follows. Give answers to the nearest tenth.

a $c = 21.2$, $\angle A = 18°$
b $c = 45.3$, $\angle A = 27°$
c $c = 93.2$, $\angle A = 68°$
d $c = 48.9$, $\angle A = 37°$

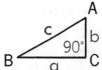

3. A guy wire 120 ft. long runs from the ground to the top of a pole. It makes an angle of 64° with the line drawn to the foot of the pole. Assuming that the ground is level and the pole vertical, what is the height of the pole?

4. How high does an airplane rise in flying 9000 ft. upward along a straight path inclined 29° from the horizontal?

5. A road rises 350 ft. in a distance of 3000 ft. along the road. What angle, to the nearest degree, does it make with the horizontal?

6. If the radius of a circle is 72.4 ft., what is the length of a chord whose arc is 44°?

7. In a certain isosceles triangle the equal sides are each 5.2 in. long and the base is 3.6 in. long. What is the size of the vertex angle, to the nearest degree?

8. In right triangle ABC, $\angle C$ is the right angle. Find a when c and $\angle B$ are as follows:

a $c = 485$ ft., $\angle B = 62°$ b $c = 213$ yd., $\angle B = 41°$
c $c = 12.3$, $\angle B = 55°$ d $c = 36.1$ cm., $\angle B = 18°$

■ Using the Trigonometric Ratios

The sine, cosine, and tangent of an angle are called *trigonometric ratios*. As long as the angle is of a given size, these ratios are constant. As the angle changes, the ratios change. You have seen how each of these ratios is used in problems. In the exercises on the next two pages you will first have to choose the correct ratio — sine, cosine, or tangent — to be used in solving each problem. The following exercises will give you training in making this choice.

Complete the following sentences:

1. If I am given $\angle B$ and the side opposite and wish to find the side adjacent, I will use the _?_ ratio. If I wish to find the hypotenuse, I will use the _?_ ratio.

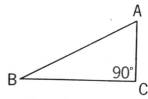

2. If I am given $\angle A$ and the side adjacent and wish to find the hypotenuse, I will use the _?_ ratio. If I wish to find the side opposite, I will use the _?_ ratio.

3. If I am given ∠B and the hypotenuse and wish to find the side adjacent, I will use the _?_ ratio. If I wish to find the side opposite, I will use the _?_ ratio.

4. If I am given the side opposite ∠B and the side adjacent to ∠B and wish to find ∠B, I will use the _?_ ratio.

5. If I am given the hypotenuse and the side adjacent to ∠B and wish to find ∠B, I will use the _?_ ratio.

6. If I am given the hypotenuse and the side opposite ∠A and wish to find ∠A, I will use the _?_ ratio.

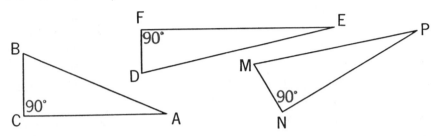

7. Using the figures above, write the sine, cosine, and tangent of each of the acute angles in terms of the sides of the triangles. $\left(\text{For example, } \sin M = \dfrac{NP}{MP}.\right)$

EXERCISES

1. The angle of elevation of the top of a monument from a point on level ground 43 ft. from the foot of the monument is 52°. How high is the monument?

2. From the top of a cliff 116 ft. high the angle of depression of a boat is 24°. What is the distance along the line of sight from the observer to the boat?

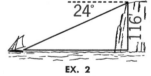

EX. 2

3. From a ship's masthead 155 ft. high the angle of depression of a buoy is 23°. What is the distance from the ship to the buoy?

4. In a certain circle the radii to the ends of a chord 52 ft. long form an angle of 110°. How long is the radius of the circle?

5. A ladder 40 ft. long resting upon the ground reaches a point 32 ft. high upon a vertical wall. Find the angle at which the ladder is inclined from the horizontal.

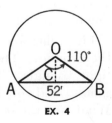

EX. 4

6. When the angle of elevation of the sun is 55°, a tree casts a shadow 55 ft. long on level ground. How tall is the tree?

7. The shadow of a vertical pole 32 ft. high is 40 ft. on level ground. Find the angle of elevation of the sun.

EX. 6

8. The equal sides of an isosceles triangle are each 48.2 in., and each base angle is 72°. Find the altitude upon the base.

9. The equal sides of a roof, *AC* and *BC*, make an angle of 30° with the horizontal. If *AC* is 50 ft. long, how long is *AB*, the span of the roof?

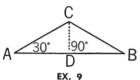

EX. 9

10. The altitude upon the base of an isosceles triangle is 12.4 in. and the base is 16.4 in. How many degrees are there in each base angle?

11. A chord 1.2 ft. long makes an angle of 25° with the radius drawn to one end of the chord. How long is the radius of the circle and how far is the chord from the center?

12. How long is the shorter altitude of a parallelogram if the sides are respectively 13 ft. and 27 ft. and the angle between them is 69°?

13. The angle of elevation of the top of a tower from a point 250 ft. away from its foot and on a level with it is 37°. How high is the tower?

14. If the radius of a circle is 835 ft., what is the length of a chord whose arc is 46°?

15. As seen from a ship sailing due west at the rate of 9 mi. an hour a lighthouse is due south at 8 P.M. At 10 P.M. the lighthouse is 34° east of south. How far is the ship from the lighthouse at 10 P.M.?

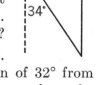

16. The top of a mountain known to be 13,500 ft. above sea level is observed at an angle of elevation of 32° from a point 7120 ft. above sea level. What is the distance along the line of sight between the two points?

17. A flagpole is broken and the top has fallen over and touches the ground. The two parts of the pole and the ground form a right triangle. The upper part makes an angle of 32° with the ground and touches it at a point 69 ft. from the foot of the pole. What was the original height of the pole?

18. What is the angle of elevation of the sun when a vertical pole 32 ft. high casts a shadow 43 ft. long on level ground?

19. Two tangents to a circle are each 324 ft. long and form an angle of 70°. How long is the radius of the circle?

20. If the angle of climb of a plane taking off from an airport is 5°, how far will the plane travel through the air to gain an altitude of 1500 ft.?

21. A plane is flying due east at 120 mi. an hour. At 10:00 A.M. the course of the plane makes an angle of 14° with a tower. Ten minutes later the course of the plane is at right angles to the tower. Find the shortest distance from the course of the plane to the tower.

■ An Interesting Puzzle — *Optional*

Here is a way you apparently can change 64 square inches into 65 square inches by cutting a figure into four pieces and putting them together again in a different arrangement. Do you think that such a thing is possible?

Using squared paper, cut out a square 8 units on a side. Use a unit large enough to work with easily. Then cut along the lines as shown in Fig. 1 making two triangles and two quadrilaterals. Rearrange the pieces as shown in Fig. 2. This new figure appears to be a rectangle with length 13 units and width 5 units. Its area is 65 square units as compared to the original 64 square units.

Is something wrong? If so, what is it?

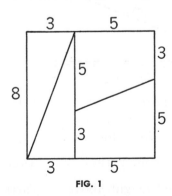

FIG. 1

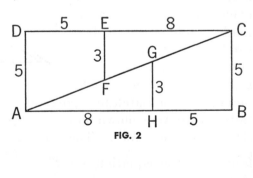

FIG. 2

SUGGESTION: How many degrees are there in ∠ECF? in ∠GCB?

■ Trigonometry and Satellites — *Optional*

Whenever scientists produce a worthwhile invention, usually there is some aspect of mathematics in the background. Radar is an example of an invention based on the principles of radio, electronics, physics, and mathematics. The word RADAR comes from the capitalized letters in "RAdio Detection And Ranging."

Basically radar works like this: If a person faces a flat surface such as the side of a building and calls out, the echo of his voice will return to him soon afterward. This echo occurs because the sound waves, created by the voice, travel through the air, strike the side of the building, and "bounce" back to be heard. Sound waves travel through air at approximately 1100 feet per second. If a person hears the echo two seconds after his call, he knows that the surface is approximately 1100 feet away. Why?

This "echo" principle is used in radar but radar uses a special type of high frequency radio wave which travels at the speed of light, 186,000 miles per second. Radar waves are "beamed" in predetermined directions and are sent in short powerful bursts or "pulses." A pulse may be only one or two microseconds long (1 microsecond = 1 millionth of a second).

This pulse of radio energy travels through the air in a straight line. If there is an object in its path, the object will cause some of the waves to bounce back to the sending source. Very accurate electronic timing devices measure the time interval between the sending of a pulse and the reception of the echo.

Radar is useful for tracing the path of airplanes and can furnish contact even with a small manmade satellite. If such a satellite were circling the earth, as shown in the diagram, radar devices could

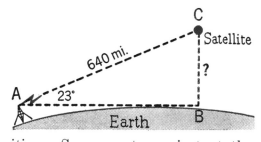

determine the satellite's position. Suppose at any instant the radar angle were shown on the "scope" to be 23° and the distance AC to be 640 miles. Then in right $\triangle ABC$, side BC could be found by the equation $\sin 23° = \dfrac{BC}{640}.$ Under these conditions $BC = \underline{\ ?\ }$ to the nearest mile. (The actual height above the earth may be obtained from specially prepared tables.)

1. AC is a diameter of a circle and AD a tangent. BC is drawn from one end of the diameter to a point B on AD. Angle CBA is 40°. CB crosses the circle at E. CE is 10 inches. Find the length of the radius of the circle.

2. A ladder 30 feet long is resting against a wall. The ladder makes an angle of 60° with the horizontal ground. If the foot of the ladder is drawn away 3 feet, how far down the wall will the top of the ladder descend?

3. In a right triangle ABC, angle C is a right angle and CD is perpendicular to AB. If tan A is $\frac{3}{4}$ and AC is 12, what are the lengths of BC, CD, and AD?

4. Tan $A = \frac{5}{3}$, cos $B = \frac{3}{5}$, $AC = 6$. Find DB, AD, and BC.

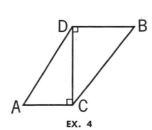

EX. 4

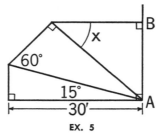

EX. 5

5. The dimensions are as indicated in the figure. **a** Find angle x. **b** Find AB.

6. $ABCD$ is a parallelogram. The dimensions are as in the figure. Find x.

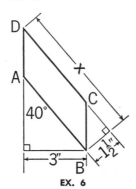

EX. 6

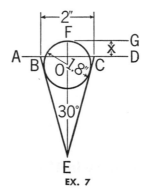

EX. 7

7. $ABCD$ is a straight line. $\angle ABE = \angle ECD$. O is the center of the circle. $FG \perp EOF$. The circle is tangent to BE and EC. Use the given dimensions to find x.

1. If a pilot glides from an altitude of 8300 ft., and the angle of glide is 8°, how far does he glide in making a landing?

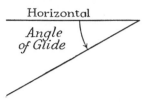

Horizontal

Angle of Glide

2. A spotter finds that the angle of elevation of a plane reported to be directly above a certain point is 22°. If the point over which the airplane is reported is 7250 ft. from the spotter, at what altitude is the plane flying?

3. The angle of depression from a plane to an airport marker is 17°. The plane is flying at an altitude of 980 ft. How far is the plane from the marker at the time the sight is taken?

4. A plane is flying a course of 35° at a speed of 125 mi. an hour. How far east does it fly in 25 minutes? How far north?

5. The angle of climb of a plane taking off from a runway is 7°. From the point of take-off to a high-tension line is 1500 ft. How high will the plane be when it is over the high-tension line?

6. There is an obstruction 100 ft. high at the end of a runway. If the pilot wants to clear it by at least 50 ft., how far away from the obstruction must the plane leave the ground if the angle of climb is 6°?

7. A glider travels 4550 ft. in gliding from an altitude of 360 ft. What is the angle of glide?

8. From the top of a mountain 3240 ft. high the angles of depression of two farmhouses due east of the observer are 23° and 47°. What is the horizontal distance between the two houses?

9. Is sin 60° twice as great as sin 30°?

10. Is tan 75° = tan 45° + tan 30°?

11. Show by the use of a right triangle that the sine of any acute angle is equal to the cosine of its complement.

12. Is tangent 66° more or less than tan 40° + tan 26°?

■ Trigonometry in Three Dimensions

Often the right triangles to be solved by means of trigonometry lie in two different planes. To do exercises involving such triangles you should be able to *see* them in more than one plane.

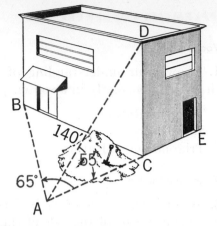

BC is a horizontal line, the base of the front of a building 140 ft. long. *CD* is a vertical line, the corner of the building. *EC* is another horizontal line, the base line of an adjacent side of the building. *CA* is an extension of *EC*, so that ∠*BCA* = 90°. ∠*DCA* is also a right angle. *DA* is a slanting line. Horizontal ∠*BAC* and vertical ∠*DAC* can both be measured by a transit set at point *A*. ∠*BAC* = 65° and ∠*DAC* = 55°. The question is: How long is *CD*?

Do you see the horizontal △*ABC* and the vertical △*ADC*? Are they right triangles? If so, which angles are the right angles?

In △*ADC* you know the size of ∠*DAC*. You can find the length of *CD* if you can find the length of *CA*.

In △*ABC* you know the size of ∠*BAC* and the length of *BC*. Hence you can find the length of *CA*. How long is *CD*?

By means of an electronic device called *Tacan*, a pilot is given the distance and the bearing of his plane from a known transmitting tower as shown in the illustration. From the scale of the map find the distance to Avon airport. If the plane is 5000 feet above ground, what is the angle of glide to the nearest degree?

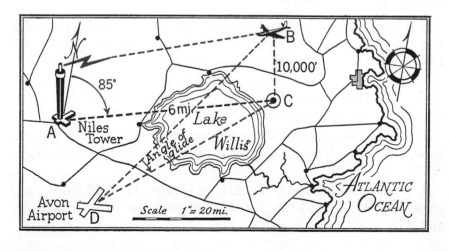

TRIANGLES IN DIFFERENT PLANES

I. Vocabulary

1. Show your understanding of the following terms by using each of them correctly in a sentence. Be sure you can spell them.

Tangent Ratio	Cosine Ratio
Sine Ratio	Angle of Elevation
Trigonometric Ratios	Angle of Depression

II. Trigonometric Ratios

2. What is the value of each of the following ratios in terms of the side of the triangle?

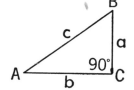

tan A	sin A	cos A
tan B	sin B	cos B

3. Which of the following increase as the angle increases?

tan x $\qquad$ cos x $\qquad$ sin x

III. Using the Table

4. Using the table of trigonometric ratios, write the value of each of the following:

tan 50° $\qquad$ sin 35° $\qquad$ cos 40°

5. What is the value of x to the nearest degree?

If tan x = 1.345 $\qquad$ If sin x = .2134 $\qquad$ If cos x = .3156

IV. Using Trigonometric Ratios

6. From a point on level ground 150 feet from the foot of a flag pole, the angle of elevation of the top of the pole is 50°. How high is the pole to the nearest foot?

7. In a circle whose radius is 20.3 inches a chord 32.0 inches is drawn. How many degrees to the nearest degree is the angle between the radii drawn to the ends of this chord?

8. In right triangle ABC the right angle is at C. CD is perpendicular to AB. If angle A is 35° and AD is 4 inches, how long is AB?

9. In parallelogram $ABCD$, AB is 8 inches, AD is 12 inches, and angle A is 42°. Find the distance between the parallel lines BC and AD.

Which of these statements are True *and which are* False?

1. $AC = 7$, $BC = 11$, and $\angle 1 = \angle 2 = \angle 3$ = $\angle 4 = 90°$. Then $\dfrac{DE}{BE} = \dfrac{MN}{BN} = \dfrac{OP}{BP} = \dfrac{7}{11}$.

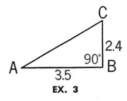

EX. 1

2. In $\triangle ABC$, $\angle C$ is a right angle, AB = 5 in., and $AC = 3$ in. Then $\tan B = \frac{3}{4}$.

3. Tan $C = \dfrac{2.4}{3.5}$. (See figure.)

4. The tangent of any angle from 40° to 89° is greater than 1.

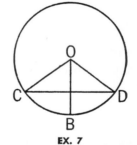

EX. 3

5. If in right triangle ABC, $\angle B = 89.9°$, tan B is very small.

6. AB is parallel to the horizontal line CD. If an observer is standing at B, the angle of depression of an object at C is 35°.

7. OB is a radius 5 in. long and is perpendicular to CD which is 8 in. long. Then $\sin C = \frac{3}{5}$.

EX. 6

8. As an angle varies from 0° to 90°, the cosine of the angle increases.

9. The sine of an acute angle may be as large as 5.

10. If tan $A = .7459$, $\angle A$ is greater than 45°.

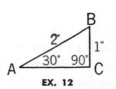

EX. 7

11. In $\triangle ABC$, $\angle C$ is 90°. If $\angle A = 40°$ and $AC = 500$ ft., then BC is less than 500 ft.

12. Cos 30° $= \dfrac{\sqrt{3}}{2}$.

13. In $\triangle ABC$, $\angle C$ is a right angle. Then the product $(\tan A)(\tan B) = 1$.

EX. 12

CHAPTER **15** Areas of
Polygons

You ARE already familiar with the rules and formulas for finding areas of some polygons. Can you match the formulas on the right below with the corresponding figure name on the left?

FIGURE	AREA FORMULA
a Trapezoid	1. $A = lw$
b Parallelogram	2. $A = bh$
c Rectangle	3. $A = \frac{1}{2}bh$
d Triangle	4. $A = \frac{1}{2}h(a + b)$

In this chapter you will review what you have already studied about areas to gain a more mature understanding of the subject. Then you will proceed to relationships that are new to you. The development in the first part of the chapter is without deductive proofs. The proofs are given later in the chapter.

Note: For a minimum course, the proofs of all the theorems in this chapter are optional.

■ Meaning of Area

For several years you have used the units of measure of surfaces, such as the square inch, the square yard, or the square centimeter. Each of these units is a square whose side is one unit of length.

△ *The **unit of measure of a surface** is a square whose side is one unit of length.*

A polygon always encloses a portion of a plane. The measure of that portion of surface is called the area of the polygon. The **area of a polygon** is, then, the number of square units contained in the surface bounded by the polygon.

There are, of course, formulas for finding the areas of polygons, but the *fundamental meaning* of area is better understood if you count squares instead of using the formulas.

Find the areas of the figures below by counting the squares.

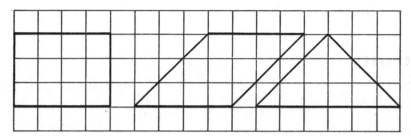

Counting squares is tedious and usually inaccurate. In the figures above the dimensions of the polygons are integral. If the dimensions were fractional the task would be harder but not impossible. When one dimension is, for example, $\sqrt{3}$ units or $\sqrt{12}$ units, counting squares can give only approximate areas.

■ Equal Figures

There is a difference in meaning between *equal* figures and *congruent* figures.

△ **Equal figures** *are figures that have the same area.*

The equal sign, =, is used for equal in area. It is interesting to note that the symbol for congruent, ≅, is an equal sign with the sign for similar above it. Congruent figures are both equal in area and similar.

Although all congruent figures are equal, equal figures are not necessarily congruent. For example, if a parallelogram is divided by a diagonal and the two triangles are replaced as shown, the figure formed is equal but not congruent to the original figure.

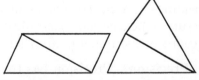

The two figures above are equal, because they are made up of congruent parts.

Two polygons are equal if they are composed of respectively congruent parts.

EXAMPLE: In the figure, *AD* = *DC* and *BE* = *EC*, *DEF* is a straight line such that *EF* = *DE*. Then it is easy to see that *ABC* = *ABFD*. *ABC* is made up of *ABED* and △I. *ABFD* is made up of *ABED* and △II. And △I ≅ △II.

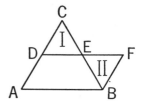

EXERCISES

1. *ABCD* is a parallelogram. *AR* ⊥ *BC* and *DS* ⊥ *BC*. Is △I congruent to △II? Is *ARSD* = *ABCD*? (Give an informal discussion, not a formal proof.)

2. *ABCD* is a trapezoid and *DE* = *EC*. *BEG* and *ADG* are straight lines. Is △I ≅ △II? Is *ABG* = *ABCD*?

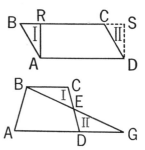

■ Precision in Measurement

Before beginning computation with the formulas of this chapter some of you will want to study the following discussion on precision and accuracy in measurement.

Measurements are never exact. You can measure to the nearest quarter of an inch, to the nearest tenth, or even to the nearest millionth if your instruments are so designed. But you are never justified in saying, for example, that a length is exactly 5.62 inches. This is due to many factors, among them man's inability to produce exact instruments and inability to make exact readings. A measurement of 5.62 inches means that the correct result is nearer 5.62 than 5.61 or 5.63 inches. Numbers used to record measurements are therefore *approximate numbers.*

Precision. Precision has to do with the size of the unit of measure employed. For example, 2.13″ is more precise than 2.1″ because the unit is hundredths of an inch in the first measurement and only tenths of an inch in the second. The precision of a measurement is indicated by the way the measurement is recorded. If a measurement is 2 inches to the nearest tenth of an inch, it is recorded as 2.0 inches. If it is 2 inches to the nearest hundredth, it is recorded as 2.00 inches; and so on. A recorded length of 15.623 inches means that the measurement is correct to thousandths of an inch.

Significant figures. The measurement 2.0 inches is said to be correct to two *significant figures,* 2.00 to three *significant figures*, and 15.623 to five *significant figures*.

Scientists tell us that the sun is 9.29×10^7 or 92,900,000 miles away from the earth. This distance is, of course, in round numbers and is given to the nearest hundred thousand miles. The number contains only three significant figures; the zeros are not significant. They show only the place or position of the three significant figures, 9, 2, and 9. If you round off to two significant figures, you would say that the sun is 9.3×10^7 or 93,000,000 miles away. This distance would be correct to the nearest million miles or two significant figures.

All the digits of a recorded number are significant figures except for zeros in certain special cases. Note the following concerning zeros in numbers.

a .0046 or 0.0046 has two significant figures. The zeros are not significant because they show only the place value of the 4 and the 6.

b 3.00 has three significant figures. The zeros are significant. If the number was intended to have two significant figures, it would have been written 3.0. A recorded number of 3.00 inches means that a length has been measured to the nearest hundredth of an inch.

c 3007 has four significant figures. The zeros are significant. They lie between two digits that are significant.

d In a number like 4000 it is impossible to tell whether there is one significant figure or two, three, or four significant figures. More has to be known about the number before the significant figures can be determined. If the number 4000, for example, is given as 4×10^3, the number contains only one significant figure; and if given as 4.0×10^3, the number contains two significant figures.

■ Accuracy in Computation with Approximate Numbers

Another word used in connection with approximate numbers is **accuracy.** The degree of accuracy is determined by the number of significant figures. Thus 31, 3.1, .31, and .031 are all of the same degree of accuracy because each contains two significant figures.

The result of computation with approximate numbers cannot be more accurate than the numbers themselves. For example, to give the product of the approximate numbers 3.15 and 2.26 as 7.1190 would be to indicate greater precision than is justified. The product should be given as 7.12, rounding off the product to the same number of significant figures as in the given numbers.

The study of accuracy in the results of computation with approximate numbers requires mathematics beyond the scope of this book. It will be entirely satisfactory for your purposes to abide by the following arbitrary rules:

In finding the product or quotient of two approximate numbers, keep only as many figures in the result as there are in the given number which has the least number of significant figures.

EXAMPLES: In multiplying 5.23 by 2.78, keep three figures in the product. In multiplying 2.94 by 1.2, keep two figures.

In a series of multiplications or divisions or a combination of both, keep one more figure in each product or quotient than in the less precise factor until the final answer is reached.

In rounding off numbers, if the first figure dropped (counting from the left) **is 5, 6, 7, 8, or 9, increase the preceding figure by 1; if it is 0, 1, 2, 3, or 4, do not increase the preceding figure.**

EXAMPLES: In rounding off, 2.367 becomes 2.37. 2.364 becomes 2.36. 2.365 becomes 2.37.

In this book you will use these rules only when approximate numbers are expressed as decimals, as 3.1 or 4.25.

EXAMPLES: Using decimals,
$$4.25 \times 3.1 \div 6.5 = 2.0 \text{ (approximately)}$$

Using mixed numbers,
$$4\tfrac{1}{4} \times 1\tfrac{3}{4} \div 2\tfrac{1}{8} = 3\tfrac{1}{2}$$

■ Area of a Rectangle

You have often used the fact that the area of a rectangle is equal to the length times the width. This means that if you measure the length of a rectangle and find that it is a certain number of inches long, and if you measure the width of the rectangle and find it to be a certain number of inches wide, and if, further, you multiply these two *numbers* together (not the inches), you will get a *number* which shows how many square inches are contained within the rectangle.

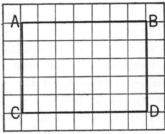

ABDC is a rectangle. If *AB* is 7 inches long, a row of 7 squares 1 inch on a side may be placed along *AB*. If *AC* is 5 inches long, 5 such rows can be made, 1 row for each inch. If there are 5 rows, 7 squares in a row, the total is 35 squares. The area is therefore 35 square inches.

This same relationship holds no matter what the linear dimensions are. They may be fractional (expressed as common or decimal fractions) or they may be lengths like $\sqrt{2}$ or $\sqrt{5}$; the area will always be the length times the width.

Postulate **The area of a rectangle is equal to the product of its length and its width.** ($A = lw$)

EXERCISES

1. Find the areas of rectangles with the following lengths and widths. Give the answers to **e** and **f** to three figures only.

   a 10 in.; 3 in.   **b** $6\frac{1}{4}$ in.; $5\frac{3}{4}$ in.   **c** $16\frac{3}{8}$ mi.; $10\frac{2}{3}$ mi.
   d 3 ft. 0 in.; 9 in.   **e** 3.24 ft.; 2.62 ft.   **f** 4.23 ft.; 2.56 ft.

2. Find the altitude of rectangles, when the following areas and lengths are given: $\left(\text{If } A = lw, \text{ then } w = \dfrac{A}{l}.\right)$ Give the answers to **c** and **d** to three figures only.

   a 50 sq. in.; 10 in.   **b** $25\frac{3}{4}$ sq. ft.; $5\frac{1}{2}$ ft.
   c 30.7 sq. ft.; 6.25 ft.   **d** 32.3 sq. ft.; 9.82 ft.

3. A newspaper stated that one half a square foot of land sold for 50 cents. At that rate an acre of land would sell for __?__.

■ Area of a Parallelogram

The corollary on page 412 is used to find a formula for the area of a parallelogram which is not a rectangle.

$ABCD$ is a parallelogram with base 11″ and height 8″. Can you find its area?

Draw the first figure on cardboard and cut it out. Cut off $\triangle AED$ and fit it on the right as shown in the second figure. You now have a rectangle whose length is 11″ and whose width is 8″. Its area is 88 square inches.

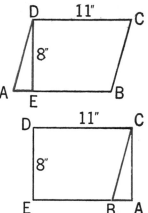

The area of the original parallelogram is the same as the area of the rectangle and so the area of the parallelogram is 88 square inches.

You can get the same result without this reasoning by merely multiplying the original 11 by the original 8.

This same relationship will hold for all parallelograms.

Postulate **The area of a parallelogram is equal to the product of its base and altitude. ($A = bh$)**

A deductive proof of this statement is given on page 421.

Note: Any side of a parallelogram may be regarded as its *base*. The *altitude* is the perpendicular distance between its base and the opposite side.

COROLLARY **Parallelograms with equal bases and equal altitudes are equal in area.**

EXERCISES

1. Draw two parallelograms that have equal bases and equal altitudes, but are not congruent.

2. $ABCD$ is a parallelogram with altitude DE. Assuming any linear unit, find the area when —

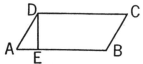

  a $AB = 15$, $DE = 2$
  b $AB = 2\frac{1}{2}$, $DE = 6\frac{1}{3}$
  c $AB = 2.63$, $DE = 1.42$
  d $AB = 10$, $AD = 4$, $\angle A = 30°$
  e $AB = a$, $AD = b$, $\angle A = 60°$

■ Area of a Triangle

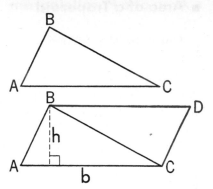

Draw any triangle ABC on cardboard and cut it out. Make $\triangle BCD$ a duplicate of $\triangle ABC$ and place the triangles as shown in the second figure. The resulting figure will be a parallelogram.

If the base of the parallelogram is b and the altitude is h, the area of the parallelogram is bh.

Since the two triangles are the same, one triangle is one half of the parallelogram and the area of either triangle is $\frac{1}{2}bh$. This relationship will hold for all triangles.

Postulate The area of a triangle is equal to one half the product of its base and altitude. $(A = \frac{1}{2}bh)$

A deductive proof of this statement is given on page 421.

From the formula, you can see that —

COROLLARY 1 Triangles with equal bases and equal altitudes are equal.

COROLLARY 2 Triangles which have equal bases in the same straight line and vertices in a line parallel to the bases are equal.

EXERCISES

1. Find the area of $\triangle ABC$ with altitude BE if —
a $AC = 10$, $BE = 4$
b $AC = 12$, $AB = 9$, $\angle A = 60°$
c $AC = 8$, $AB = 5$, $\angle A = 120°$
d $AC = 42$, $AB = 16$, $\angle A = 54°$ (Use table, page 531.)

2. Using the formula $A = \frac{1}{2}bh$, find b when —
a $A = 40$, $h = 8$
b $A = 12$, $h = 6$
c $A = 8\frac{15}{16}$, $h = 3\frac{1}{4}$
d $A = \frac{5}{4}$, $h = 1$

■ Area of a Trapezoid

Consider the following illustration:

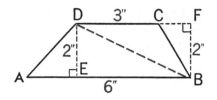

ABCD is a trapezoid in which the lower base *AB* is 6″, the upper base *DC* is 3″, and the height (altitude) *DE* is 2″.

Draw the line *BD* making two triangles *ABD* and *DCB*.

The base of △*ABD* is 6″ and the height is 2″, hence the area is $\frac{1}{2} \times 6 \times 2 = 6$ sq. in.

If you take *DC* as base of △*DCB*, then the height is the perpendicular *BF* meeting *DC* extended. The base of this triangle is 3″ and the height is 2″, hence the area is $\frac{1}{2} \times 3 \times 2 = 3$ sq. in.

Since the trapezoid is made up of the two triangles the area of the trapezoid is 6 sq. in. + 3 sq. in. = 9 sq. in.

To get this result you found the areas of the triangles separately and then added. Since the two altitudes are equal, you would get the same result if you added the two bases first and then multiplied by one half the altitude. That is, $\frac{1}{2}$ of $6 \times 2 + \frac{1}{2}$ of 3×2 is the same as $\frac{1}{2}$ of $(6 + 3) \times 2$. In each case the result is 9.

The above reasoning holds for all trapezoids.

Postulate   **The area of a trapezoid equals one half its height (altitude) times the sum of its bases.**

If the lower base is *b*, the upper base *b′*, and the height *h*, the area is given by the formula

$$A = \tfrac{1}{2}h(b + b')$$

A deductive proof of this statement is given on page 422.

EXERCISE

If *h*, *b*, *b′*, and *A* are the altitude, the bases, and the area respectively of a trapezoid, find the value of the missing letter in each of the following examples: (Assume any linear unit.)

	h	*b*	*b′*	*A*		*h*	*b*	*b′*	*A*
a	2	6	4	?	b	5	3	2	?
c	?	10	8	45	d	?	5	4	$13\frac{1}{2}$
e	4	?	2	20	f	5	10	?	$32\frac{1}{2}$

■ Ratios of Areas of Similar Polygons

When the corresponding sides of two similar triangles are in the ratio 1 : 3 the areas are not in the ratio of 1 : 3, they are in the ratio 1 : 9. (1 and 9 are the squares of 1 and 3.)

This statement is true in general. If the corresponding sides or altitudes are in the ratio $a : b$, the areas are in the ratio $a^2 : b^2$.

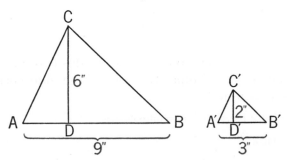

$\triangle ABC \sim \triangle A'B'C'$, CD and $C'D'$ are corresponding altitudes.
If $AB = 9''$, $A'B' = 3''$, and $CD = 6''$, $C'D'$ will have to be $2''$ since the triangles are similar.

The area of $\triangle ABC = \frac{1}{2} \times 9 \times 6 = 27$ sq. in.

The area of $\triangle A'B'C' = \frac{1}{2} \times 3 \times 2 = 3$ sq. in.

The ratio of the sides and the altitudes is $3 : 1$ but the ratio of the areas is $9 : 1$.

AB is 3 times $A'B'$ and CD is 3 times $C'D'$, but the area of $\triangle ABC$ is 9 times the area of $\triangle A'B'C'$.

Postulate   **The areas of two similar triangles have the same ratio as the squares of any two corresponding sides.**

A deductive proof of this statement is given on page 423.

Another way to make this statement is —

The areas of two similar triangles vary as the squares of any two corresponding sides.

EXERCISES

1. The side of a triangle is 4 inches and the corresponding side of a similar triangle 16 inches. What is the ratio of the areas of the triangles?

2. The side of a triangle is 8 inches and the corresponding side of a similar triangle is 12 inches. What is the ratio of the areas of . the triangles?

■ Areas of Similar Polygons

It can be shown that the statement concerning areas of similar triangles on the preceding page is also true of similar polygons in general: that is, *the areas of two similar polygons have the same ratio as the squares of any two corresponding sides.* This proposition will be used but not proved in this book.

EXERCISES

1. The area of a triangle one of whose sides is 3 in. is 24 sq. in. What is the area of a similar triangle whose side corresponding to the 3-in. side is 6 in.?

SUGGESTION: Let x represent the required area.

$$\text{Then } \frac{24}{x} = \frac{3^2}{6^2}.$$

2. Corresponding sides of two similar polygons are 4 in. and 6 in. If the area of the first triangle is 12 sq. in., what is the area of the second?

3. The areas of two similar triangles are 15 sq. in. and 60 sq. in. If one side of the first triangle is 10 in., how long is the corresponding side of the second?

4. If two corresponding sides of similar triangles are 3 ft. and 2 ft., what is the ratio of their areas?

5. If the corresponding sides of two similar pentagons are in the ratio 3 : 4, what is the ratio of their areas?

6. If the areas of two similar triangles are in the ratio 16 : 25, what is the ratio of the corresponding sides?

SUGGESTION: Let x and y represent two corresponding sides.

$$\text{Then } \frac{x^2}{y^2} = \frac{16}{25}. \quad \text{Take the square root of both sides.}$$

7. If the areas of two similar triangles are in the ratio 2 : 1, what is the ratio of the corresponding sides?

8. If the sides of a square are trebled, by what is the area of the square multiplied?

9. If the ratio of the areas of two equilateral triangles is 1 : 2, what is the ratio of their sides?

The area of a parallelogram is equal to the product of its base and altitude.

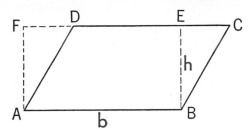

Given $\square ABCD$ with base b and altitude h.
To prove that the area of $\square ABCD = bh$. $(A = bh)$
The *plan* is to show that $ABCD$ is equal to the rectangle $ABEF$.
Prove that $ABEF$ is a rectangle and that its area is bh.
Outline of proof. $ABEF$ is a rectangle. (Why?) $\triangle ADF$ $\cong \triangle BCE$. (Why?) $ABED = ABED$. $ABED$ $+ \triangle ADF$ $= ABED + \triangle BCE$. $ABED + \triangle BCE = ABCD$. $ABED +$ $\triangle ADF = ABEF$. So $ABCD = ABEF$. Area of $ABCD = bh$.

The area of a triangle is equal to one half the product of its base and altitude.

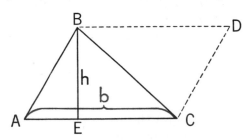

Given $\triangle ABC$ with base b and altitude h.
To prove $A = \frac{1}{2}bh$.
Proof. Draw $BD\|AC$ and $CD\|AB$.

STATEMENTS	REASONS
1. $AB \parallel CD$ and $BD \parallel AC$.	1. Construction.
2. $ABDC$ is a parallelogram.	2. Why?
3. $\triangle ABC = \frac{1}{2}\square ABDC$.	3. Why?
4. $\square ABDC = bh$.	4. Why?
5. $\triangle ABC = \frac{1}{2}bh$, or $A = \frac{1}{2}bh$.	5. Why?

The area of a trapezoid equals one half its altitude times the sum of its bases.

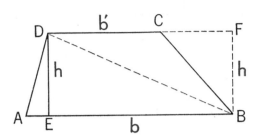

Given   trapezoid $ABCD$ with base $AB = b$, its base $CD = b'$, and its altitude $DE = h$.   Denote its area by A.

To prove   that $A = \frac{1}{2}h(b + b')$.

Proof.   Draw BD.   Draw BF, the altitude of $\triangle BCD$.

STATEMENTS	REASONS
1. $DE = BF = h$.	1. Cor. 3, page 175.
2. $\triangle ABD = \frac{1}{2}bh$.	2. Why?
3. $\triangle BCD = \frac{1}{2}b'h$.	3. Why?
4. $ABCD = \triangle ABD + \triangle BCD$.	4. Why?
5. $ABCD = \frac{1}{2}bh + \frac{1}{2}b'h$.	5. Why?
6. $ABCD = \frac{1}{2}h(b + b')$.	6. Factoring.

EXERCISES

1. Develop the formula for the area of a trapezoid by subtracting the area of the triangle from the area of the parallelogram.

2. Develop the formula for the area of a trapezoid by subtracting the areas of the two triangles from the area of the rectangle.

3. Develop the formula for the area of a trapezoid by subtracting the upper triangle from the large triangle.

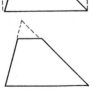

The areas of two similar triangles have the same ratio as the squares of any two corresponding sides.

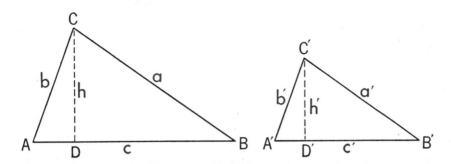

Given that $\triangle ABC \sim \triangle A'B'C'$ with c and c' corresponding sides.

To prove that $\dfrac{\triangle ABC}{\triangle A'B'C'} = \dfrac{c^2}{c'^2}$.

Outline of proof. Draw the corresponding altitudes h and h'.

$\triangle ABC = \dfrac{1}{2}ch$, $\triangle A'B'C' = \dfrac{1}{2}c'h'$. (Why?) $\dfrac{\triangle ABC}{\triangle A'B'C'} = \dfrac{ch}{c'h'} = \dfrac{c}{c'} \times \dfrac{h}{h'}$.

(Axiom 6, page 84.) $\dfrac{h}{h'} = \dfrac{c}{c'}$. (Theorem 57.) $\dfrac{\triangle ABC}{\triangle A'B'C'} =$

$\dfrac{c}{c'} \times \dfrac{c}{c'} = \dfrac{c^2}{c'^2}$. (Substitution.)

EXERCISES

1. Find the area of a square whose side is 25 in.

2. Find the area of a square whose diagonal is $3\sqrt{2}$ in. (You have two right triangles with _?_° in each acute angle.)

3. Find the area of a square whose diagonal is 8 in.

4. The perimeter of a square is 16 ft. Find its area.

5. How long is a side of a square (to the nearest tenth) if the area is 246 sq. in.?

6. The equal sides of an isosceles triangle are each 17 in. and the base is 16 in. Find the area of the triangle.

7. The diagonal and one side of a rectangle are respectively 13 in. and 5 in. Find the area of the rectangle.

8. The diagonal and one side of a rectangle are respectively $\sqrt{74}$ in. and 7 in. Find the area of the rectangle.

9. The equal sides of an isosceles right triangle are each 8 in. Find its area.

10. The hypotenuse of an isosceles right triangle is 10 in. Find its area.

11. The hypotenuse of a right triangle is 29 in. and one side is 20 in. Find its area.

12. Find the area of an equilateral triangle whose side is 8 in. (The altitude forms two 60°–30° right triangles.)

13. The altitude of an equilateral triangle is 4 in. Find its area.

14. The side of an equilateral triangle is 10 in. What is the side of an equilateral triangle with twice the area? with three times the area? with four times the area?

15. Find the area of a rectangle with one side s and diagonal d.

EXTRA

16. Find the area of $\triangle ABC$ in which $BD \perp AC$, when —

    a $AC = 15$, $AB = 10$, and $\angle A = 30°$
    b $AC = 10$, $AB = 8$, and $\angle A = 60°$
    c $AC = 4$, $AB = 3$, and $\angle A = 45°$
    d $AC = 12$, $AB = 8$, and $\angle A = 150°$
    e $AC = 10$, $AB = 7$, and $\angle A = 120°$

17. Find the area of parallelogram $ABCD$ in which $BE \perp AD$, when —

    a $AD = 16$, $AB = 5$, and $\angle A = 30°$
    b $AD = 20$, $AB = 7$, and $\angle A = 60°$
    c $AD = 12$, $AB = 10$, and $\angle A = 45°$
    d $AD = 14$, $AB = 5$, and $\angle A = 135°$

18. What is the area of a rhombus whose diagonals are 10 and 16 inches?

■ Dividing a Triangle into Five Equal Parts — *Optional*

You are given $\triangle ABC$. It is divided into five equal parts by the following procedure.

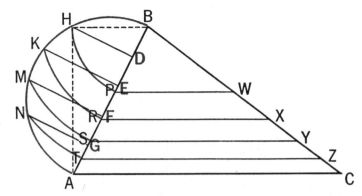

1. One side AB is divided at D, E, F, and G into five equal segments.
2. On AB as a diameter a semicircle is drawn outside the triangle.
3. At D, E, F, and G perpendiculars are constructed meeting the semicircle at H, K, M, and N.
4. With B as center and radii BH, BK, BM, and BN arcs are drawn intersecting AB at P, R, S, and T.
5. Lines through P, R, S, and T drawn parallel to AB divide the area of $\triangle ABC$ into five parts equal in area.

Outline of proof. The proof is started for you. Can you finish it?

$\triangle AHB$ is a right triangle with altitude DH.

Hence $\dfrac{AB}{BH} = \dfrac{BH}{DB}$ or using AB as a unit of measure,

$$\frac{1}{BH} = \frac{BH}{\frac{1}{5}} ; \quad \text{and} \quad \overline{BH}^2 = \frac{1}{5}.$$

In like manner $\overline{BK}^2 = \frac{2}{5}$.

Since $\triangle RBX \sim \triangle PBW$, (Why?) and

$$\frac{\triangle RBX}{\triangle PBW} = \frac{\overline{BR}^2}{\overline{BP}^2} = \frac{\overline{BK}^2}{\overline{BH}^2} = \frac{\frac{2}{5}}{\frac{1}{5}} = \frac{2}{1},$$

then $RXWP = PBW$.

■ Pythagorean Theorem
Proof by Areas — *Optional*

In Chapter 13, you saw several ways of proving the theorem: *The square on the hypotenuse of a right triangle is equal to the sum of the squares on the arms.*

The proof as given here is the one used by Euclid. He used areas. He could not use an algebraic proof because algebra was not sufficiently developed during his lifetime.

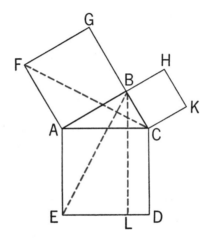

Given. AD is the square on the hypotenuse of right triangle ABC; BF and BK are the squares on the arms BA and BC respectively.

To prove $AD = BF + BK$.

Outline of proof. Draw $BL \parallel AE$. Draw BE and FC.

Prove that $\triangle FAC \cong \triangle BAE$. $\triangle BAE$ and rectangle AL have the same base AE. $\triangle BAE$ and rectangle AL have equal altitudes. (The altitudes lie between the parallels AE and BL.)

Rectangle $AL = 2\triangle BAE$. Why?

Prove that GBC is a straight line parallel to AF.

$\triangle FAC$ and square BF have the same base AF and equal altitudes.

Square $BF = 2\triangle FAC$.

Square $BF =$ rectangle AL. Why?

Also, square $BK =$ rectangle LC.

Hence, by addition, $AD = BF + BK$.

■ Transforming Triangles — *Optional*

By *transforming* a triangle, we mean changing it into an equal triangle of different shape. Corollary 2 on page 417 suggests a method of doing this. If the base of the new triangle is equal to the base of the given triangle and is in the same straight line, and the vertices of the two triangles are in a line parallel to the base, the triangles will be equal.

EXAMPLE 1: Construct a right triangle equal to △ABC with one arm equal to AC.

Through B construct DE ∥ AC. At A construct AB′ ⊥ AC. Then △AB′C is equal to △ABC and is a right triangle with one arm equal to AC.

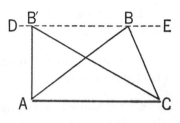

Note that the parallel is drawn through the vertex opposite the side which you wish to retain.

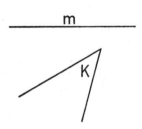
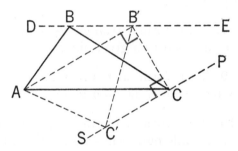

EXAMPLE 2: Transform △ABC into an equal triangle having a given side *m* and a given angle *K*.

The transformation must be done in two steps. Through B construct DE ∥ AC.

With A as center and *m* as radius draw an arc intersecting DE at B′.

△AB′C = △ABC, for it has the same base and an equal altitude.

Since AB′ must now be kept as a base, construct PS through C parallel to AB′.

At B′ construct ∠AB′C′ equal to ∠K and continue the side until it intersects PS at C′.

△AB′C′ = △AB′C = △ABC and has the required parts.

EXERCISES

1. Transform △*ABC* into an equal triangle with one side equal to a given line *m*.

2. Transform △*ABC* into an equal triangle with an angle equal to a given angle *K*.

3. Transform △*ABC* into an equal isosceles triangle, keeping the base.

4. Transform a triangle into an equal right triangle with the base of the given triangle as hypotenuse.

5. Transform a triangle into an equal triangle having as sides two given lines.

6. Transform a triangle into an equal right triangle having a given line as hypotenuse.

7. Transform a triangle into an equal isosceles triangle with a given base.

8. Transform a triangle into an equal isosceles triangle having an arm equal to a given line.

9. Transform a parallelogram into an equal parallelogram having a side equal to a given line.

10. Transform a parallelogram into an equal parallelogram having a given angle.

11. Transform a parallelogram into an equal rhombus.

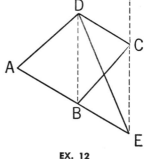

EX. 12

12. Transform quadrilateral *ABCD* into the equal triangle *ADE* by a method suggested by the figure at the right. (*CE* ∥ *DB*.)

13. Transform △*ABC* into an equal rectangle by a method suggested by the figure at the right. (*D* and *E* are the middle points of *AC* and *BC* respectively.) Prove that the construction is correct.

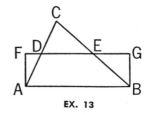

EX. 13

Optional

Transforming a polygon of any number of sides into an equal triangle.

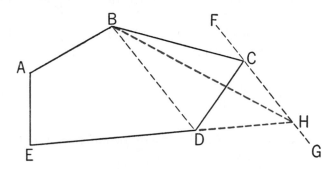

Given polygon *ABCDE*.

Required to transform it into an equal triangle.

Construction. Draw the diagonal *BD* and through *C* construct *FG* ∥ *BD*.

Continue *ED* until it meets *FG* at *H*.

Since △*BCD* and △*BDH* have the same base *BD* and equal altitudes, they are equal. The area of *ABHE* is, therefore, the same as the area of *ABCDE*. But since the side *DH* is a continuation of *ED*, the new polygon has one less side than the original.

This process may be continued until a triangle that is equal to the polygon is reached.

EXERCISES

1. Transform a quadrilateral into an equal triangle.

2. Transform a pentagon into an equal triangle.

3. Transform a hexagon into an equal triangle.

4. Transform a quadrilateral into an equal right triangle.

5. Transform a pentagon into an equal isosceles triangle.

6. Transform a quadrilateral into an equal triangle which shall have a side equal to a given line.

7. Transform a quadrilateral into an equal triangle which shall have an angle equal to a given angle.

8. Transform a quadrilateral into an equal parallelogram.

Given   rectangle *ABCD*.

Required   to transform *ABCD* into an equal square.

Analysis.   The area of rectangle *ABCD* is $AB \times AD$. We must find a line segment of length x so that $x^2 = AB \times AD$.

This is obviously the problem of finding the mean proportional between *AB* and *AD*.

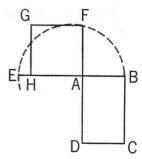

Construction.   Find *AF*, the mean proportional between *AB* and *AD*. See page 375.

On *AF* as a side construct the required square.

Proof.

STATEMENTS	REASONS
1. $AB : AF = AF : AD$.	1. Construction.
2. $\overline{AF}^2 = AB \times AD$.	2. Why?
3. $\overline{AF}^2$ = area of square *AFGH*.	3. Why?
4. $AB \times AD$ = area of rectangle *ABCD*.	4. Why?
5. Square *AFGH* = rectangle *ABCD*.	5. Why?

It is now possible for you to construct a square equal to a polygon of any number of sides. First transform the polygon into an equal triangle. Then change the triangle to an equal rectangle (see Ex. 13, page 428). Finally, construct a square equal to the rectangle.

Draw a pentagon and transform it into an equal square.

EXERCISES

   1. Construct a square equal to one half a given square.

   2. Construct a square equal to one third a given square.

   3. Transform a quadrilateral into an equal square.

   4. Describe a method of constructing a side of a square whose area will be 6 square units. (Assume a length of line as a unit of measure.)

Areas by Means of Trigonometry — *Optional*

When two sides and the included angle of a triangle are given, it is a simple matter to find its area by the use of a formula involving the sine of the angle. This formula is derived as follows:

$\triangle ABC = \frac{1}{2}bh.$

But $\sin C = \dfrac{h}{a}$, or $h = a \sin C.$

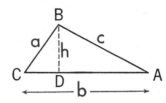

Hence $\triangle ABC = \frac{1}{2}ab \sin C$ (substituting $a \sin C$ for h).

By similar proofs $\triangle ABC = \frac{1}{2}bc \sin A$ or $\frac{1}{2}ac \sin B.$

These formulas are to be used in case the given angle is acute. If the angle is obtuse, the formulas become:

$\triangle ABC = \frac{1}{2}ab \sin (180° - C)$ or $\frac{1}{2}bc \sin (180° - A)$ or $\frac{1}{2}ac \sin (180° - B).$ Prove the first of these formulas, using the figure at the right.

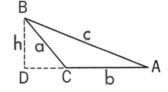

It is proved in a later course in trigonometry that $\sin (180° - A) = \sin A.$

1. Given that $a = 302$ ft., $b = 427$ ft., and $C = 47°$, find the area of the triangle. SUGGESTION: Use the formula $\triangle ABC = \frac{1}{2}ab \sin C$. Then $\triangle ABC = \frac{1}{2}(302)(427)(\sin 47°)$. Use the table.

2. Given that $b = 56.2$ in., $c = 63.9$ in., and $A = 110°$, find the area of the triangle. SUGGESTION: Use the formula $\triangle ABC = \frac{1}{2}bc \sin (180° - A)$. Then $\triangle ABC = \frac{1}{2}(56.2)(63.9)(\sin 70°).$

EXERCISES

1. Find the area of $\triangle ABC$ if: **a** $c = 3.57$ yd., $a = 2.93$ yd., and $\angle B = 31°$; **b** $b = 43.1$ cm., $c = 89.0$ cm., and $\angle A = 129°$.

2. A man owns a triangular piece of land at the intersection of two streets. If the streets intersect at an angle of 65° and he has a frontage of 250 feet on one street and 300 feet on the other, how much land does he own?

3. Show that the area of a parallelogram is $K = ab \sin C$ where a and b are adjacent sides and C is the included angle. Find the area of $\square ABCD$, when $DC = 21''$, $CB = 13''$, and $\angle C = 42°.$

1. Point P divides the side AC of triangle ABC into two segments which have the ratio of 3 to 4. From P lines are drawn parallel to AB and BC. Find the ratio of the area of the parallelogram thus formed to the area of triangle ABC.

2. If a rectangle and an equilateral triangle have equal areas and bases of 6 inches, what is the altitude of the rectangle?

3. Two lines BD and AE intersect at point C. AB is parallel to DE. Prove that the area of triangle ACD equals the area of triangle BCE.

4. D and E are the middle points of AB and BC respectively, of triangle ABC. Two parallel lines are drawn from D and E to intersect AC in F and G. Prove that $DFGE$ is a parallelogram that is equal to one half of triangle ABC.

5. O is any point outside the intersecting lines AB and AD of the parallelogram $ABCD$. If O is joined to each vertex of the parallelogram, then the area of triangle OAC will equal the sum or the difference of the areas of triangles ODA and OAB.

6. The sides of the right angle of a right triangle are 4 inches and 5 inches. The altitude upon the hypotenuse is extended to divide the square, one side of which is the hypotenuse, into two rectangles. Find the areas of these rectangles.

7. Point G is in such a position outside a parallelogram $ABCD$ that when lines are drawn from G to A and D they intersect BC at E and F respectively. Prove that triangles GED and GFA are equal in area.

8. The perimeter of a quadrilateral circumscribed about a circle of radius 4 inches is 60 inches. What is the area of the quadrilateral?

9. Two straight lines BAC and DAE are drawn through the point of contact A of two externally tangent circles. The points $B, E, C,$ and D are on the circles. B and D are on the same circle. Prove that the area of triangle BAE is equal to the area of triangle DAC.

10. The diagonals of the parallelogram $ABCD$ intersect in O. $RSTV$ is a quadrilateral made by joining the midpoints of AO, BO, CO, and DO in succession. Prove that $RSTV$ is a parallelogram whose area is one fourth that of $ABCD$.

1. If two triangles are equal and the base of one is three times the base of the other, what is the ratio of their altitudes?

2. The base of a triangle is 10 in. and the altitude is 5 in. How long is the side of an equal square?

3. The altitude BE of a triangle is 4 in. The base AC is 6 in. BD is a median. Find the areas of $\triangle ABC$, $\triangle ABD$, and $\triangle BDC$.

4. Prove: The median of a triangle divides it into two triangles equal in area.

5. Prove: The line connecting the middle points of the parallel sides of a trapezoid divides it into two trapezoids equal in area.

6. Prove that if a line passes through the point of intersection of the diagonals of a parallelogram, it divides the figure into two parts equal in area.

7. Prove that the diagonals of a parallelogram divide the figure into four triangles equal in area.

8. Prove that the area of a rhombus is equal to one half the product of the diagonals.

9. F, D, and E are the middle points of the sides AB, BC, and CA of $\triangle ABC$. Prove that $AFDE = \frac{1}{2}\triangle ABC$.

10. Prove that the lines connecting in succession the middle points of the sides of a parallelogram form another parallelogram which is equal to one half the given parallelogram.

11. $ABCD$ is a trapezoid. Prove that $\triangle ABC : \triangle ACD = BC : AD$.

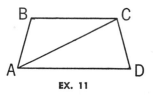

EX. 11

12. Prove that the line joining the middle points of two sides of a triangle forms a triangle which is one fourth the area of the original triangle.

13. Prove: Every straight line drawn through the mid-point of the median of a trapezoid so as to intersect both bases divides the trapezoid into two parts equal in area.

14. E and F are the mid-points of the sides AB and BC of triangle ABC. D is any point on AC. Prove that the area of the quadrilateral $BEDF$ is equal to one half the area of triangle ABC.

■ Areas in Three Dimensions — *Optional*

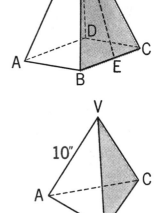

1. The figure at the right represents a square pyramid. It is read $V-ABCD$. $ABCD$ is a square and the triangles VAB, VBC, VCD, and VDA are congruent isosceles triangles. $AB = 6$ in. and $VA = 10$ in.

Can you find the total area; that is, the area of the square base plus the sum of the areas of the four triangles?

SUGGESTION: Draw the altitude VE of $\triangle VBC$ and use the Pythagorean Theorem to find its length.

2. The figure $V-ABC$ is a regular triangular pyramid. This means that the base ABC is an equilateral triangle and the triangles VAB, VBC, and VCA are congruent isosceles triangles.

$AB = 8$ inches and $VA = 10$ inches. Can you find the total area of this pyramid?

Chapter Summary

I. Areas of Polygons

1. Write formulas for the area of each of the following:

Rectangle   Triangle
Parallelogram   Trapezoid

2. On graph paper draw two parallelograms that are equal in area but not congruent.

II. Ratios of Areas of Polygons

3. The altitude of $\triangle I$ is 6 inches and the altitude of $\triangle II$ is 8 inches. The bases of the two triangles are equal. What is the ratio of the areas of the triangles?

4. $\triangle I \sim \triangle II$. The ratio of two corresponding sides is $4:3$. What is the ratio of the areas of the two triangles?

5. One triangle has half the base and half the altitude of another. What is the ratio of their areas?

6. What is the area of an isosceles right triangle whose hypotenuse is $5\sqrt{2}$ inches long?

7. What is the area of an equilateral triangle each of whose sides is 8 inches long?

8. The side of a square is 9 inches. Show that the area of a square drawn upon the diagonal of the given square is twice the area of the given square.

Testing Your Understanding

Answers may be left in radical form:

1. The area of a trapezoid whose bases are 12 in. and 8 in. and whose altitude is 3 in. is _?_ sq. in.

2. If each side of an equilateral triangle is 5 in., the area of the triangle is _?_ sq. in.

3. The altitude of an equilateral triangle is 7 in. Its area is _?_ sq. in.

4. If the diagonal of a square is $\sqrt{2}$ in., the area of the square is _?_ sq. in.

5. Each side of a square is 6 in. The area of a square each of whose sides is equal to a diagonal of the first square is _?_ sq. in.

6. The base of a triangle is 6 in. and the altitude is 4 in. A side of a square whose area is equal to that of the triangle is _?_ in.

7. The area of a triangle is nine times that of a similar triangle. If the shortest side of the larger triangle is 18 in., the shortest side of the smaller triangle is _?_ in.

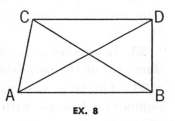

EX. 8

8. $CD \parallel AB$. If the area of $\triangle ABC$ is 20 sq. in., the area of $\triangle ABD$ is _?_ sq. in.

9. $\triangle ABC \sim \triangle DEF$ and BC corresponds to EF. If $BC = 12$ in. and $EF = 3$ in., the ratio of the areas is _?_ : _?_.

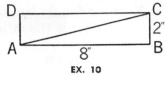

EX. 10

10. $ABCD$ is a rectangle. The area of a square whose side is AC is _?_ sq. in.

11. The area of this trapezoid is _?_ sq. in.

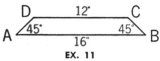

EX. 11

12. Area of $\triangle ADC$ = area of $\triangle DBC$. If $AD = 6$ in., then $DB =$ _?_ in.

13. Parallelogram $ABCD$ is equal in area to parallelogram $MNOP$. If the base and altitude of the first parallelogram are 12 in. and 4 in. and the base of the second is 16 in., then its altitude is _?_ in.

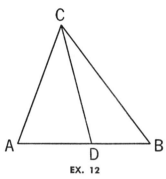

EX. 12

14. In $\triangle ABC$, $\angle A = 120°$, $AB = 12$ in., and $AC = 10$ in. The area of $\triangle ABC$ is _?_ sq. in.

15. Two triangles are equal in area. If the base of one is three times the base of the second, the ratio of the first altitude to the second altitude is _?_ : _?_.

EX. 16

16. $ABCD$ is a square. $DE = EC$, and $\angle E$ is a right angle. The area of $\triangle DCE =$ _?_ sq. units.

17. D and E are the midpoints of AC and BC. Then the ratio of $\triangle DEC$ to $\triangle ABC$ is _?_ : _?_.

EX. 17

18. ABC is a right triangle with right angle at C. If $AB = 15$ in. and $BC = 12$ in., the area of a square whose side is AC is _?_ sq. in.

19. $AB = 5$ in. and the altitude CD is 8 in. The side of a square equal in area to $\triangle ABC$ is _?_ in.

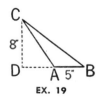

EX. 19

20. In parallelogram $ABCD$, $AB = 8$ in., $AD = 6$ in., and $\angle A = 30°$. The area of the parallelogram is _?_ sq. in.

21. $ABCD$ is a rectangle. $AB = 8$ ft. and $AD = 6$ ft. An equilateral triangle with a side equal to AC would have the area _?_ sq. ft.

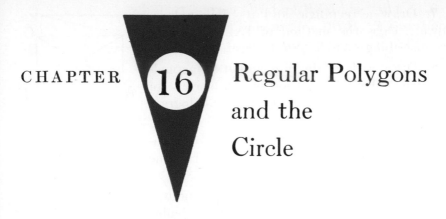

CHAPTER 16

Regular Polygons
and the
Circle

WHAT DO you remember about regular polygons? Can you answer the following questions?

1. What is a regular triangle called?

2. What is a regular quadrilateral called?

3. How many sides and how many angles has a pentagon? If it is a *regular* pentagon, what do you know about the sides and what do you know about the angles?

Do you remember what a polygon inscribed in a circle and what a polygon circumscribed about a circle are?

4. Illustrate a pentagon inscribed in a circle.

5. Illustrate a hexagon circumscribed about a circle.

EXERCISES

1. Prove that an equilateral polygon inscribed in a circle is also equiangular.

2. Is an inscribed equiangular polygon also equilateral?

3. Draw any triangle and circumscribe a circle about it.

4. Draw any square. You can circumscribe a circle about three of its vertices. Will the fourth vertex lie on the circle?

5. Draw any rectangle. You can circumscribe a circle about three of its points. Will the fourth vertex lie on the circle?

6. Draw a square $ABCD$ with the two diagonals AC and BD meeting at O. With O as center and OB as radius draw a circle. Is the circle circumscribed about the square?

EX. 6

7. Draw a rectangle and its diagonals as shown. Does the method of Ex. 6 work for circumscribing a circle about a rectangle?

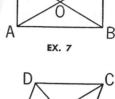
EX. 7

8. Draw a parallelogram and its diagonals as shown. Does the method of Ex. 6 work for circumscribing a circle about a parallelogram that is not a rectangle?

9. Do you think a circle can be circumscribed about a parallelogram such as the one drawn for Ex. 8?

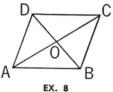
EX. 8

10. When you circumscribe a circle about a triangle do you construct the perpendicular bisectors of the sides or do you bisect the angles?

11. Describe the method of inscribing a circle in a triangle.

Note: For a minimum course, the proofs of Theorems 71, 73, 77, and 78 may be omitted. You should be sure of the meaning and use of these theorems. In each case, read and study what is given and what is to be proved. Also, study the plan of the proof so that you may see how the theorem can be proved.

| THEOREM 70 | *A circle can be circumscribed about any regular polygon.* |

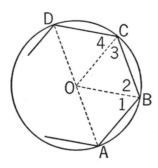

Given any regular polygon $ABCD$ . . .
To prove that a circle can be circumscribed about $ABCD$ . . .
The *plan* is (1) to note that a circle can be constructed through any three vertices such as A, B, and C, and (2) to show that the center of that circle O is as far from a fourth point D as it is from A, B, and C. (The proof is on the opposite page.)

Proof. Construct a circle through points A, B, and C (Const. Prob., page 286). Draw radii OA, OB, OC. Draw OD.

STATEMENTS	REASONS
Consider $\triangle AOB$ and $\triangle COD$.	
1. $AB = CD$.	1. Why?
2. $OB = OC$.	2. Why?
3. $\angle 1 + \angle 2 = \angle 3 + \angle 4$.	3. Why?
4. $\angle 2 = \angle 3$.	4. Why?
5. $\angle 1 = \angle 4$.	5. Why?
6. $\triangle AOB \cong \triangle COD$.	6. Why?
7. $OD = OA$.	7. Why?

Therefore circle O passes through D, and in like manner it can be shown to pass through any other vertex.

**THEOREM
71** | *A circle can be inscribed in any regular polygon.*

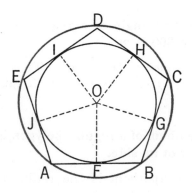

Given the regular polygon $ABCDE$.

To prove that a circle may be inscribed in $ABCDE$.

The *plan.* A circle O can be circumscribed about $ABCDE$. (Theorem 70.) In the figure it is the colored circle.

Draw perpendiculars OF, OG, OH, etc.

$OF = OG = OH = \ldots$.

Draw circle with center O and radius OF. AB, BC, CD, etc. are tangents to this circle.

Proof. The formal proof is left for you.

△ *The **center of a regular polygon** is the common center of its inscribed and circumscribed circles.*

△ *The **radius of a regular polygon** is the radius of its circumscribed circle (OA, OB, OC, etc. in Fig. 1).*

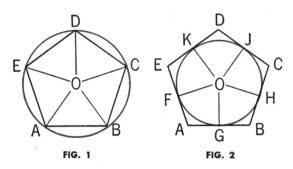

FIG. 1   FIG. 2

△ *The **apothem of a regular polygon** is the radius of its inscribed circle drawn to the point of contact (OF, OG, OH, etc., in Fig. 2).*

△ *The **central angle of a regular polygon** is the angle between the radii drawn to adjacent vertices of the polygon (∠AOB, ∠BOC, ∠COD, etc., in Fig. 1).*

COROLLARY 1   **The central angle of a regular polygon of *n* sides is equal to 360° ÷ *n*.**

The sum of the angles at O is 360°. There are n equal central angles. Hence each angle is 360° ÷ n (Fig. 3).

FIG. 3

COROLLARY 2   **The apothem of a regular polygon is the perpendicular bisector of its side.**

By definition, the apothem is the radius of the inscribed circle drawn to the point of contact. AB is therefore a tangent and OF is perpendicular to it. AB is a chord of the circumscribed circle, so a perpendicular to it from the center bisects it (Fig. 4).

FIG. 4

COROLLARY 3   **The radius of a regular polygon bisects the angle to whose vertex it is drawn.**

In Figure 3 prove two adjacent triangles congruent. (s.s.s. = s.s.s.)

If a circle is divided into any number of equal arcs, the chords of these arcs form a regular polygon of that number of sides.

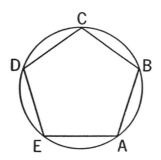

Given ⊙*O* in which arcs *AB*, *BC*, *CD*, *DE*, and *EA* are equal.

To prove that *ABCDE* is a regular polygon.

The *plan*. The chords *AB*, *BC*, . . . are equal and so the polygon is equilateral.

∠*B* is half of arc *CDEA*.

∠*C* is half of arc *DEAB*.

Arc *CDEA* = arc *DEAB* and so ∠*B* = ∠*C*.

Similarly all the angles are equal.

The polygon is equiangular.

Proof. The formal proof is left for you.

COROLLARY 1 **An equilateral polygon inscribed in a circle is a regular polygon.**

COROLLARY 2 **A regular quadrilateral is a square.**

EXERCISES

1. Describe a method of dividing a circle into four equal parts.

2. Describe a method of dividing a circle into six equal parts. Prove that your method is correct.

3. Describe a method of dividing a circle into three equal parts. Prove that your method is correct.

4. How many sides has a regular polygon one of whose angles is 120°?

Construction Problem   Inscribing a square in a circle.

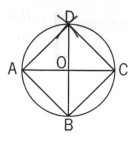

Given   a circle.

Required   to inscribe a square in the circle.

The *plan.* You need to divide the circle into four equal parts in order to use Theorem 72.

Construction and proof are left for you.

To inscribe a square in a circle, construct two perpendicular diameters and join their extremities by straight lines.

By bisecting the arcs made by inscribing a square in a circle, a regular octagon may be inscribed. By continuing the process, regular polygons of $16, 32, 64, \ldots 2^n$ (n being a positive integer) sides may be inscribed.

EXERCISES

1. Inscribe a square in a circle whose radius is 1 inch.
2. Inscribe a regular octagon in a circle whose radius is 2 inches.
3. Can you circumscribe a square about a circle?

Construction Problem   Inscribing a regular hexagon in a circle.

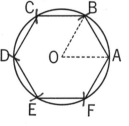

Given   a circle.

Required   to inscribe a regular hexagon in the circle.

The *plan.* You need to divide the circle into six equal parts. This can be done by making six equal central angles, each of which will be 60°. You can construct a 60° angle by constructing an equilateral triangle.

Construction.

1. Draw any radius OA. With A as center and OA as radius draw an arc intersecting the circle at B.

2. With B as center and OA as radius draw an arc intersecting the circle at C. And so on around the circle.

3. Join the points of division of the circle by straight lines. Then $ABCDEF$ is the required regular hexagon.

Outline of proof.

    1. $\triangle AOB$ is equilateral and $\angle O = 60°$. (Why?)

    2. Arc $AB = 60°$ or $\frac{1}{6}$ of the circle. (Why?)

    3. Hence this process divides the circle into six equal parts and $ABCDEF$ is a regular hexagon. (Theorem 72)

To inscribe a regular hexagon in a circle, use the radius as a chord six times in succession. It may be used exactly six times because the arc intercepted by one of the chords is 60°.

COROLLARY 1   **The side of a regular hexagon inscribed in a circle is equal to the radius of the circle.**

COROLLARY 2   **Chords joining the alternate vertices of a regular inscribed hexagon form an equilateral triangle.**

    By bisecting the arcs made by inscribing a regular hexagon in a circle, a regular polygon of 12 sides may be inscribed.

EXERCISES

    1. Inscribe a regular hexagon in a circle whose radius is 1 in. Each side is _?_ in. Each angle contains _?_°.

    2. Inscribe an equilateral triangle in the circle of Ex. 1.

    3. A regular hexagon is inscribed in a circle whose radius is 10 cm. What is the length of the apothem?

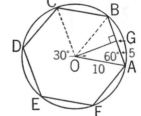

    In order to work efficiently with this figure you should know the following. All the triangles such as AOB, BOC, etc. are equilateral triangles. All the angles of the hexagon, such as $\angle A$, $\angle B$, etc., equal 120°. The radii to the vertices bisect these angles.

    $\triangle AOG$ is a 60°–30° right triangle. $AO = 10$ cm., $AG = 5$ cm., and $OG = $ _?_ cm. See page 383.

    4. An equilateral triangle is inscribed in a circle whose radius is 8 in. What is the length of the apothem? How long is a side of the triangle?

    $\triangle AOD$ is a 60°–30° right triangle. $AO = 8$ in., $OD = 4$ in., and $AD = $ _?_ in. So $AB = $ _?_ in.

    5. What is the length of the apothem of a regular hexagon inscribed in a circle whose radius is 2 in.? 3 in.? 4 in.? a in.?

    6. What is the area of the hexagon for each case of Ex. 5? (Find the area of one equilateral triangle and multiply by 6.)

7. In circles whose radii are 2, 6, 10, and a inches respectively, how long are the sides of the inscribed equilateral triangles?

8. In a circle whose radius is 8 inches, what is the length of each altitude of the inscribed equilateral triangle?

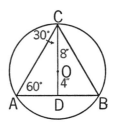

In an equilateral triangle, the altitudes are the same lines as the medians. Hence, if $CO = 8$ in., $OD = 4$ in. (Theorem 43) and the altitude, CD, equals _?_ in.

9. In Ex. 8, how long is AD?

($\triangle ACD$ is a 60°–30° right triangle. $CD = 12$ in. and $AD = \dfrac{12}{?}$ in.)

10. What is the area of the triangle in Ex. 8?

11. In circles whose radii are 2, 6, 10, and a inches, what are the areas of the inscribed equilateral triangles?

12. What is the length of a side of a square inscribed in a circle of radius 4 inches?

$\triangle AOB$ is a 45° right triangle.

13. What is the area of the square in Ex. 12?

14. What is the area of a square inscribed in a circle, whose radius is 6 in.? 3 in.? a in.?

THEOREM 73 | If a circle is divided into three or more equal arcs, the tangents at the points of division form a regular circumscribed polygon.

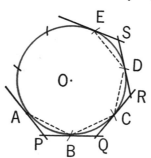

Given circle O with equal arcs AB, BC, CD, etc., and tangents at points A, B, C, etc., intersecting at P, Q, R, etc.

To prove PQR . . . is a regular circumscribed polygon.

The *plan*. Draw chords AB, BC, etc. $\triangle APB \cong \triangle BQC$, etc. and they are isosceles. Hence $PQ = QR$, etc. and $\angle P = \angle Q$, etc.

Proof. The formal proof is left for you.

EXERCISES

1. Divide a circle into six equal parts. Draw radii to the points of division. At the points of division draw lines perpendicular to the radii. You have a regular circumscribed __?__.

2. About a circle whose radius is 2 in., a regular hexagon is circumscribed. What is the length of the apothem? the length of the radius of the hexagon? the area of the hexagon?

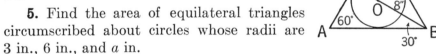

$\triangle GOC$ is a 60°–30° right triangle. $OG = 2$ in., $GC = \dfrac{2}{\sqrt{3}}$ in., $OC = $ __?__. Area $\triangle BOC = $ __?__. Area of the hexagon is 6 times the area of $\triangle BOC$.

3. Find the areas of regular hexagons circumscribed about circles whose radii are 4 in., 6 in., 7 in., 10 in., and a in.

4. Find the area of an equilateral triangle circumscribed about a circle whose radius is 4 in.

$\triangle ABD$ is a 60°–30° right triangle. If $OD = 4$ in., $OB = 8$ in. (Theorem 43), and $BD = 12$ in., $AD = \dfrac{12}{\sqrt{3}}$ in. Area $\triangle ABC = $ __?__ sq. in.

5. Find the area of equilateral triangles circumscribed about circles whose radii are 3 in., 6 in., and a in.

6. What is the area of a square circumscribed about a circle whose radius is 6 inches?

EXTRA

7. What is the ratio of the apothem of an equilateral triangle to the radius of the circumscribed circle?

8. Prove: Any angle of a regular polygon is supplementary to a central angle of the polygon.

9. Prove: In any circle the area of the regular inscribed hexagon is twice the area of the inscribed equilateral triangle.

10. How do the areas of the regular inscribed and the regular circumscribed hexagons of the same circle compare?

11. An equilateral triangle is inscribed in a circle and another is circumscribed about the same circle. What is the ratio of their sides? of their areas?

12. Compare the areas of the isosceles right triangles that are inscribed in and circumscribed about a given circle.

13. Prove by means of algebra: If $\angle A = \dfrac{360°}{n}$ and $\angle B = \dfrac{180°(n-2)}{n}$, then A and B are supplementary angles.

14. Prove: If the successive mid-points of the sides of a regular polygon are joined, the resulting polygon is regular.

15. A regular hexagon is inscribed in a circle whose diameter is a inches. What is the area of the hexagon?

▪ Star Polygons — *Optional*

The figures below are star polygons. Figure 1 begins with a regular pentagon and then the sides are extended until they meet to form a five-pointed star.

Figure 2 begins with a regular hexagon and Figure 3 with a regular octagon.

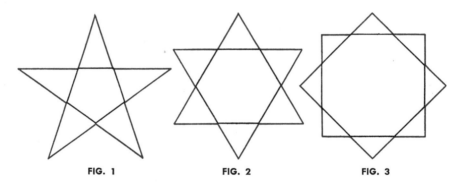

FIG. 1   FIG. 2   FIG. 3

Construct each one of these star polygons.

Why can you not get a star polygon by beginning with an equilateral triangle or a square?

How many degrees are there in each point of each star above?

How many degrees are there in each point of a star polygon constructed from a regular polygon of n sides ($n > 4$)?

The five-pointed star, called a pentagram, was used as a badge or symbol of recognition by the group of mathematicians who studied under Pythagoras.

In the five-star insignia introduced in World War II to indicate the highest rank in the army and navy, the stars are so arranged that their centers lie on a circle and their adjacent points form a pentagon. Can you show how this was done?

THEOREM | *Regular polygons of the same number of sides*
74 | *are similar.*

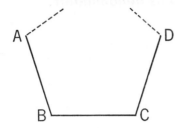 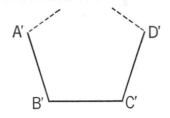

Given regular polygons $ABCD$ . . . and $A'B'C'D'$ . . ., each having n sides.

To prove $ABCD$ . . . $\sim A'B'C'D'$ . . .

The *plan* is to show that the ratios of corresponding sides are equal and that the angles are equal.

Proof.

STATEMENTS	REASONS
1. $AB = BC = CD$, etc.	1. Definition.
2. $A'B' = B'C' = C'D'$, etc.	2. Definition.
3. $\dfrac{AB}{A'B'} = \dfrac{BC}{B'C'} = \dfrac{CD}{C'D'}$, etc.	3. Axiom 6, page 84.
4. Each angle of both polygons equals $\dfrac{(n-2)\ 180°}{n}$.	4. Theorem 18.
5. $ABCD$... $\sim A'B'C'D'$...	5. Definition.

EXERCISES

1. How many degrees are there in the central angles of regular polygons of 4, 5, 6, 8, 10, and 12 sides?

2. Can a circle be inscribed in every equilateral quadrilateral?

3. Can a circle be inscribed in every equiangular quadrilateral?

EXTRA

4. If each side of a regular polygon is doubled to make another regular polygon, what is the effect upon the area?

5. If the area of one regular polygon is 48 sq. in., what is the area of another regular polygon of the same number of sides and half the perimeter?

<table>
<tr><td>THEOREM
75</td><td>In a series of equal ratios the sum of the numerators is to the sum of the denominators as any numerator is to its denominator.</td></tr>
</table>

Given $\dfrac{a}{b} = \dfrac{c}{d} = \dfrac{e}{f} = r$ (the value of the ratio).

To prove $\dfrac{a+c+e}{b+d+f} = r = \dfrac{a}{b} = \dfrac{c}{d} = \dfrac{e}{f}.$

Proof.

STATEMENTS	REASONS
1. $a = br$, $c = dr$, $e = fr$.	1. Axiom 5, page 84.
2. $a + c + e = r(b + d + f)$.	2. Axiom 3, page 84.
3. $\dfrac{a+c+e}{b+d+f} = r$.	3. Axiom 6, page 84.
4. $\dfrac{a+c+e}{b+d+f} = \dfrac{a}{b} = \dfrac{c}{d} = \dfrac{e}{f}.$	4. Why?

<table>
<tr><td>THEOREM
76</td><td>The perimeters of similar polygons have the same ratio as any two corresponding sides.</td></tr>
</table>

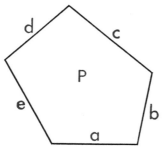 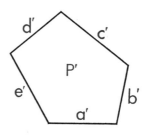

Given similar polygons P and P' with perimeters p and p'.

To prove that $\dfrac{p}{p'} = \dfrac{a}{a'} = \dfrac{b}{b'} = \dfrac{c}{c'}$, etc.

Outline of proof. Since $\dfrac{a}{a'} = \dfrac{b}{b'} = \dfrac{c}{c'}$, etc. (Def. of similar polygons), then $\dfrac{a+b+c, \text{etc.}}{a'+b'+c', \text{etc.}} = \dfrac{a}{a'} = \dfrac{b}{b'} = \dfrac{c}{c'}$, etc. (Theorem 75) and $\dfrac{p}{p'} = \dfrac{a}{a'} = \dfrac{b}{b'} = \dfrac{c}{c'}$, etc.

<table>
<tr><td>THEOREM
77</td><td>The perimeters of two regular polygons of the same number of sides have the same ratio as their radii or as their apothems.</td></tr>
</table>

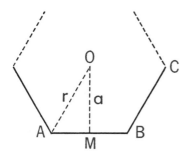 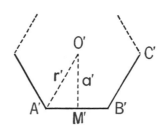

Given regular polygons ABC . . . and $A'B'C'$ . . ., each of n sides, with perimeters p and p', radii r and r', and apothems a and a', respectively.

To prove $\dfrac{p}{p'} = \dfrac{r}{r'} = \dfrac{a}{a'}$.

Proof. Consider polygons ABC . . . and $A'B'C'$ . . .

STATEMENTS	REASONS
1. $\angle A = \angle A'$.	1. Theorem 74.
2. OA bisects $\angle A$ $O'A'$ bisects $\angle A'$	2. Cor. 3, page 440.
3. $\angle OAM = \angle O'A'M'$.	3. Axiom 6, page 84.
4. $OM \perp AB$, and $O'M' \perp A'B'$.	4. Cor. 2, page 440.
5. $\triangle AMO \sim \triangle A'M'O'$.	5. Why?
6. $\dfrac{r}{r'} = \dfrac{a}{a'} = \dfrac{AM}{A'M'}$.	6. Why?
7. $AB = 2AM$, $A'B' = 2A'M'$.	7. Why?
8. $\dfrac{AM}{A'M'} = \dfrac{AB}{A'B'}$.	8. Why?
9. ABC . . . $\sim A'B'C'$ . . .	9. Why?
10. $\dfrac{p}{p'} = \dfrac{AB}{A'B'}$.	10. Theorem 76.
11. $\dfrac{p}{p'} = \dfrac{r}{r'} = \dfrac{a}{a'}$.	11. Axiom 1, page 84.

What is the ratio of the perimeters of two regular pentagons inscribed in circles whose radii are 3 and 4 in.?

The area of a regular polygon is half the product of its apothem and its perimeter.

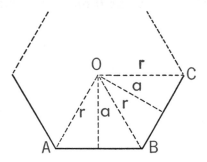

Given   regular polygon ABC . . . of n sides, with perimeter p and apothem a.

To prove   that the area of ABC . . . equals $\frac{1}{2}ap$.

The *plan* is to draw the radii AO, OB, etc., thus forming n triangles, prove the triangles congruent, find the area of each, and add the areas.

Outline of proof.

$\triangle AOB$, BOC, etc., are $\cong$.   Prove it.

The $\triangle$ have equal altitudes, a. $\triangle AOB = \frac{1}{2}a \cdot AB$. $\triangle BOC = \frac{1}{2}a \cdot BC$.

The proof is left for you.

COROLLARY   **The areas of two regular polygons of the same number of sides have the same ratio as the squares of their radii or as the squares of their apothems.**

Outline of proof.   Let the areas be denoted by A and A', the radii by r and r', the apothems by a and a', and the perimeters by p and p'.

Then $A = \frac{1}{2}ap$ and $A' = \frac{1}{2}a'p'$.

Hence $\dfrac{A}{A'} = \dfrac{\frac{1}{2}ap}{\frac{1}{2}a'p'} = \dfrac{ap}{a'p'} = \dfrac{a}{a'} \times \dfrac{p}{p'}.$

But $\dfrac{p}{p'} = \dfrac{a}{a'} = \dfrac{r}{r'}.$ Hence $\dfrac{A}{A'} = \dfrac{a^2}{a'^2}$ or $\dfrac{r^2}{r'^2}.$

The formal proof is left for you.

If two squares are inscribed in circles of 1-inch and 2-inch diameters, respectively, is the ratio of their areas 1 : 2 or 1 : 4?

EXERCISES

1. If the radii of two circles are 5 inches and 10 inches respectively, what is the ratio of the perimeters of the two inscribed regular decagons? What is the ratio of their areas?

2. If the radii of two circles are 3 inches and 9 inches respectively, what is the ratio of the areas of the two inscribed regular hexagons?

3. If the perimeter of a regular polygon inscribed in a circle whose radius is 2 inches is a inches, what is the perimeter of a regular polygon of the same number of sides inscribed in a circle whose radius is 3 inches?

4. If the area of a regular pentagon inscribed in a circle whose radius is 4 inches is a square inches, what is the area of a regular pentagon inscribed in a circle whose radius is 16 inches? whose radius is 8 inches?

EXTRA

5. In order to double the perimeter of a regular polygon, in what ratio must the radius of the circumscribed circle be increased?

6. If the radius of a circle is doubled, what is the effect upon the area of an inscribed regular polygon?

7. If it is desired to double the area of an inscribed regular hexagon, in what ratio must the radius of the circle be increased?

8. Find the ratio of the areas of two equilateral triangles whose altitudes are 6 and 12.

9. The area of one equilateral triangle is 9 times that of another. What is the ratio of their perimeters?

10. The areas of two equilateral triangles are $2k$ and k respectively. What is the ratio of their sides? their altitudes? their perimeters?

11. Find the area of a regular pentagon, one of whose sides is 31.5 ft. long. (Use trigonometry.)

12. Find the area of a regular pentagon inscribed in a circle whose radius is 8.4 in.

■ Regular Polygons in Design — *Optional*

The only regular polygons that can fill a plane surface by repeating one polygon many times are triangles, quadrilaterals, and hexagons. A regular triangle is, of course, an equilateral triangle and a regular quadrilateral is a square. The reason for this is that each angle of any one of these figures is an integral part of 360°. Six 60° angles will fit exactly about a point; four 90° angles and three 120° angles will also fit about a point.

How many degrees are there in each angle of an equilateral triangle? a square? a regular hexagon?

Figures 1, 2, and 3 show the use of such regular polygons in filling the space about a point.

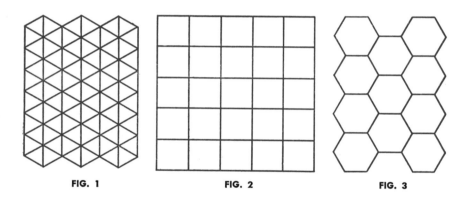

FIG. 1   FIG. 2   FIG. 3

If more than one kind of regular polygon is used, then a plane space can be filled in several other ways. In Figure 4 congruent regular hexagons and equilateral triangles are used; in Figure 5, you have congruent equilateral triangles and squares, and in Figure 6 congruent regular octagons and squares.

In each case the sum of the angles about a point is 360°.

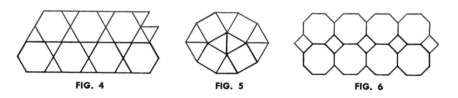

FIG. 4   FIG. 5   FIG. 6

Copy all these six drawings using larger regular polygons.

■ Measurement of the Circle

It can be shown that the ratio of the circumference to the diameter of a circle is the same for all circles; that is, $\frac{c}{d} = k$, where c is the circumference, d is the diameter, and k is a constant.

The word *circumference* (page 206) used in connection with *circle* has the same meaning as *perimeter* with *polygon*. We speak of the *perimeter* of a *polygon* but the *circumference* of a *circle*.

One of the great problems in the history of mathematics has been to find the value of the *constant*, which is the ratio of the circumference to the diameter of a circle. It has been found that there is no number in our decimal system that is *exactly* equal to this ratio. It can be approximated.

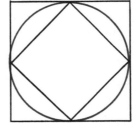

Look at this figure, in which a square is inscribed in a circle and another square is circumscribed about it. The circumference of the circle is obviously greater than the perimeter of the inscribed square but less than the perimeter of the circumscribed square. If the diameter of the circle is known, the two perimeters can be computed.

The perimeter of the circumscribed square divided by the diameter will be one number. The perimeter of the inscribed square divided by the diameter will be another number. Since the circumference is between the two perimeters, the circumference divided by the diameter will be a number lying between the other two numbers. This ratio is called π (pronounced pī).

■ The Value of π

Now if you will double the number of sides of the inscribed and circumscribed polygons shown above, you will have polygons whose perimeters are nearer to the circumference; yet the circumference will still lie between the two perimeters. If you continue this process indefinitely, the two perimeters will get closer and closer to the circumference. The ratio of the circumference divided by the diameter is still between the ratios made by the perimeters divided by the diameter.

The following table shows you what these ratios are as the number of sides of the polygons is increased.

NUMBER OF SIDES	PERIMETER OF INSCRIBED POLYGON DIVIDED BY DIAMETER OF CIRCLE	PERIMETER OF CIRCUMSCRIBED POLYGON DIVIDED BY DIAMETER OF CIRCLE
16	3.121445	3.182597
32	3.136548	3.151724
64	3.140331	3.144118
128	3.141277	3.142223
256	3.141513	3.141750
512	3.141572	3.141632
1024	3.141587	3.141602
2048	3.141591	3.141595
4096	3.141592	3.141593

Explain what the table tells you. Do you see that the two ratios become more nearly equal as the number of sides increases?

When the number of sides is 4096, both these ratios are 3.14159 to the nearest hundred thousandth. So if $\frac{c}{d}$ lies between these two, it must be 3.14159 correct to six figures.

There are other ways of finding the value of π. The method shown here is easy to understand. The first record of an attempt to evaluate π is credited to an Egyptian named Ahmes, about 1600 B.C. His value was 3.1605. Archimedes (287–212 B.C.), one of the greatest of mathematicians, proved that π lies between $3\frac{1}{7}$ and $3\frac{10}{71}$; that is, between 3.1429 and 3.1408. Later (150 A.D.) Ptolemy gave π the value of $3\frac{17}{120}$, or 3.14166. Since the invention of the calculus by Sir Isaac Newton (1642–1727), much simpler methods have been devised for evaluating π. In 1873 Shanks obtained the value of π to 707 decimal places. In 1949 π was completed to 2035 decimal places on an electronic computing machine in 70 hours. Calculated to 50 figures —

$\pi = 3.141,592,653,589,793,238,462,643,383,279,502,884,197,169,399,375,1$

The number of places which should be used for the value of π in any calculation depends on the number of significant figures in the original data. For exercises in this book you will use **3.14** as the value of π.

Since $\frac{c}{d} = \pi$, $c = \pi d$. Since $d = 2r$, $c = 2\pi r$.

COROLLARY **The circumference of a circle equals π times the diameter or 2π times the radius.**

1. Find the circumference of a circle whose diameter is 10 in. Express the result to the nearest tenth.

2. Find the circumferences of circles whose diameters in inches are as follows: 5   8   14   2   30

3. Find the circumference of a circle whose radius is 3 inches. Express the result to the nearest tenth.

4. Find to three figures the circumferences of circles whose radii in inches are as follows: 2.65   3.29   42.6   17.4

■ Ratio of Circumferences

Just as the perimeters of two regular polygons of the same number of sides have the same ratio as their radii, so the circumferences of two circles have the same ratio as their radii.

THEOREM
79

The circumferences of two circles have the same ratio as their radii.

Outline of proof.   Let c_1 and c_2, and r_1 and r_2 represent the circumferences and radii of the circles.   (c_1 is read "c sub 1.")

Then $c_1 = 2\pi r_1$ and $c_2 = 2\pi r_2$.   Hence $\dfrac{c_1}{c_2} = \dfrac{r_1}{r_2}$ (Why?)

EXERCISES

1. If $r_1 = 1$ in. and $r_2 = 4$ in., find the ratio of c_1 to c_2.

2. If you double the radius of a circle, you _?_ its circumference.

3. The radius of a circle is a in. and the circumference is b in. What would be the radius if the circumference is $2b$ in.?

4. Find the diameter, correct to hundredths, of a circle whose circumference is 24.6 in.   If $c = \pi d$, $d = $ _?_.

5. What is the length of the arc intercepted by a central angle of 60° in a circle whose radius is 8 inches?

6. What is the length of the arc intercepted by a central angle of 85° in a circle of radius 5 inches?

7. What is the length of the arc intercepted by a central angle of 120° in a circle of radius 30 inches?

■ The Area of a Circle

An elementary solution of the problem of finding the area of a circle may be obtained by a study of inscribed polygons. You see that the area of an inscribed regular polygon increases as the number of its sides increases, and approaches more and more closely the area of the circle. In Theorem 78, the area of a regular polygon was proved to be $\frac{1}{2}ap$, where a is the apothem and p is the perimeter. As the number of sides of the polygon increases, its apothem approaches the radius of the circle and its perimeter approaches the circumference of the circle.

Postulate   The area of a circle is $\frac{1}{2}rc$.

COROLLARY   The area of a circle is πr^2.

Outline of proof. In $A = \frac{1}{2}rc$, substitute $2\pi r$ for c. Hence $A = \frac{1}{2}r \cdot 2\pi r$, or $A = \pi r^2$.

Just as the areas of two regular polygons of the same number of sides are to each other as the squares of their radii, so the areas of two circles are to each other as the squares of their radii.

THEOREM **80**	*The areas of two circles have the same ratio as the squares of their radii.*

Outline of proof.   Let A_1, A_2, r_1, and r_2 be the areas and radii respectively of the two circles.

Then $A_1 = \pi r_1^2$ and $A_2 = \pi r_2^2$. Hence $\dfrac{A_1}{A_2} = \dfrac{r_1^2}{r_2^2}$.   Why?

EXERCISES

1. Find the areas of circles whose radii in inches are as follows:

a 6	b 8	c 13	d 9	e 30	f 2.6
g 3.3	h 4.3	i 100	j 17	k 26	l 43

2. If the radii of two circles are 3 and 5 inches respectively, what is the ratio of their areas?

3. If the radius of one circle is twice the radius of another, what is the ratio of their circumferences and of their areas?

4. What must be done to the radius of a circle to make the area of the circle four times as great?

5. If the area of a circle is 4π square inches, what is the radius of a circle of twice the area?

■ Sector and Segment of a Circle

△ *A sector of a circle is the figure formed by two radii and their intercepted arc.* The colored portion of the figure is a sector of a circle.

1. If central angle AOB is $\frac{1}{8}$ of 360°, then the area of the sector is __?__ of the area of the circle.

2. Find the area of sector AOB when the radius is 6 in. and $\angle AOB$ is 30°.

COROLLARY   The area of a sector whose radius is r and whose arc contains n degrees is $\dfrac{n}{360}\,\pi r^2$.

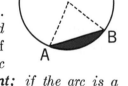

3. Complete: The areas of two sectors of the same circle or of equal circles have the same . . .

△ *A segment of a circle is the figure formed by a chord and its arc.* The colored portion of the figure is a segment of the circle. *If the arc is a minor arc, the segment is a* **minor segment;** *if the arc is a major arc, the segment is a* **major segment.**

The area of a segment can be found by subtracting the area of a triangle from the area of a sector. The area of segment AB equals the area of sector AOB minus the area of $\triangle AOB$.

EXAMPLE: In a circle of radius 2 inches find the area of a segment whose arc has a central angle of 60°.

Area of circle $= \pi r^2 = 4\pi$

Area of sector $= \frac{1}{6}$ of circle $= \frac{1}{6} \cdot 4\pi = \dfrac{2\pi}{3}$

Area of triangle $= \frac{1}{2}h \cdot AB = \frac{1}{2}\sqrt{3} \cdot 2 = \sqrt{3}$

Area of segment $= \dfrac{2\pi}{3} - \sqrt{3} = .36$ *Ans.* **.36** square inch.

SECTORS AND SEGMENTS   **457**

1. Find the area of the three segments formed by inscribing an equilateral triangle in a circle of radius 5 inches.

2. Find the area of the six segments formed by inscribing a regular hexagon in a circle of radius 4 inches.

■ Three Famous Historical Problems — *Optional*

Using only the compass and straightedge, the Greek mathematicians struggled in vain (1) to trisect any angle, (2) to construct a square equal in area to a given circle, and (3) to construct a cube equal in volume to twice a given cube.

The first of these problems has been a challenge to many persons, some of them high school pupils, and often we find in newspapers alleged solutions of it. It has been proved that the problem cannot be solved without the use of some instrument other than the compass and straightedge. We now know that it is futile to attempt to solve the problem.

You may enjoy looking for the fallacy in this method of trisecting an angle, attributed to Archimedes (225 B.C.):

1. Extend any chord AB to C so that BC equals the radius.

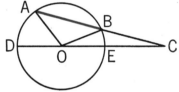

2. Draw line $CEOD$ through the center O of the circle.

3. Then $\angle EOB = \frac{1}{3}\angle AOD$.

Mathematicians for centuries were challenged by the second problem, which is commonly referred to as "squaring the circle." They could have done it if they had been able to find a line equal in length to the circumference of a circle when the radius was known. Of course, this could easily be done by rolling a circle along a straight line, but this is not allowable under the rules laid down by the Greeks. In 1882 a mathematician named Lindermann proved that the problem could not be solved.

The third problem, called "the duplication of the cube," would require the construction of a segment x, such that $x^3 = 2y^3$, where y is the edge of the given cube and x is the edge of the required cube of double volume. It has been proved that this problem also cannot be solved, using only compass and straightedge.

■ Squaring the Circle — *Optional*

Although, using straightedge and compass only, a square cannot be constructed exactly equal to a given circle, an approximate construction can be accomplished. One method is illustrated here.

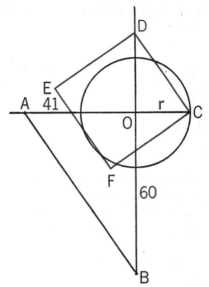

1. In any circle construct two perpendicular diameters and extend them as shown.

2. From the center, O, of the circle, make $AO = 41$ units and $BO = 60$ units. (The unit can be chosen so that A and B fall outside the circle.) Draw AB.

3. Through C construct CD parallel to AB.

4. A square with side CD will be *very nearly* equal in area to the circle.

Outline of proof.

$\triangle AOB \sim \triangle COD$. Why?

$$\frac{OB}{OD} = \frac{OA}{OC}, \quad \text{or} \quad \frac{60}{OD} = \frac{41}{r}$$

$$OD = \frac{60r}{41}, \quad \text{or} \quad \frac{60}{41}r$$

$$\overline{DC}^2 = r^2 + (\tfrac{60}{41}r)^2 \text{ (Pythagorean Theorem)}$$

$$\overline{DC}^2 = 3.14158239r^2 \text{ by actual computation. This is the}$$
area of the square.

The area of the circle is πr^2 or $3.14159265r^2$.

To five places $(3.1416r^2)$ the areas of the square and of the circle are equal.

SUPPLEMENTARY EXERCISES

1. Find the radius of a circle whose circumference is 14π feet.

2. Find the radii of circles whose areas are respectively 100π, 12π, 40π, 100, 48, and 32 square feet.

3. Find the areas of circles whose circumferences are respectively 8π, 10π, 12π, 24, 36, and 125 inches.

4. Find the circumferences of circles whose areas are respectively 9π, 24π, 16, 25, and 32 square inches.

5. Find the area of a ring made by two concentric circles of radii 8 and 10 inches respectively.

Let factoring aid you in computation. $S = \pi r^2$; $S' = \pi r'^2$; $S - S' = \pi r^2 - \pi r'^2 = \pi(r^2 - r'^2) = \pi(r + r')(r - r')$.

6. What is the radius of a circle the circumference of which is equal to the sum of the circumferences of circles with radii: **a** 6 and 8 inches; **b** 5 and 12 inches; **c** 2 and 4 inches; **d** 3 and 5 inches?

7. If two circles have radii of 3 and 4 inches respectively, what will be the radius of a circle whose area is equal to the sum of the areas of these two circles?

$S = \pi r^2$; $S' = \pi r'^2$; $S + S' = \pi(r^2 + r'^2)$. πR^2 must equal $\pi(r^2 + r'^2)$. Find the radius R so that $R^2 = r^2 + r'^2$.

8. Construct a circle whose area will be equal to the sum of the areas of two given circles.

9. Construct a circle whose circumference will be twice the circumference of a given circle.

10. The radius of a circle is 12 inches. What is the radius of a circle with a circumference three fourths as long?

11. Construct a circle whose circumference is three fourths that of a given circle.

12. The radius of a circle is 8 inches. What is the radius of a circle which has twice the area?

13. The radius of a circle is 5 inches. What is the radius of a circle which has three times the area?

14. If the diameter of a circle is 32 feet, what is the length of an arc of 75°?

15. A circular pond 200 feet in diameter is surrounded by a walk 4 feet wide. What is the area of the walk?

16. Two circles of radii 2 and $2\sqrt{3}$ inches respectively have their centers 4 inches apart. Compute the area common to both circles. (This surface is the sum of two segments, one on each side of the common chord.)

17. The dimensions of a rectangle are 6 and 8 inches. A circle of radius 2 inches rolls around this rectangle. What is the length of the locus of the center of this circle? What is the area within the locus?

18. The side of an equilateral triangle is 12 inches. Find the area of the circumscribed circle.

19. Two pipes of radii 4 inches and 12 inches lie side by side. What is the length of the shortest piece of wire which will just go around both of them? (What is the length of OO'? of CO'? How many degrees are there in $\angle O'$?)

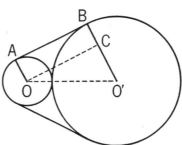

EX. 19

20. Semicircles are drawn on the three sides of a right triangle whose arms are 3 and 4 inches respectively. Prove that crescent ADC + crescent $CEB = \triangle ABC$.

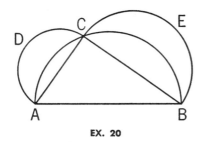

EX. 20

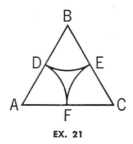

EX. 21

21. ABC is an equilateral triangle with side 2 inches. D, E, and F are the middle points of the sides. If an arc is drawn with each vertex as center and half the side as radius as shown in the diagram, find the area of the surface bounded by the arcs DE, EF, and FD.

22. The radius of a wheel is 10 inches. How many complete turns will the wheel make in rolling 1 mile? (Use $\pi = \frac{22}{7}$.)

1. The area of a regular hexagon inscribed in a circle is the mean proportional between the areas of the inscribed and circumscribed equilateral triangles.

2. Semicircles are described on the sides of a square each of whose sides is 10 inches. Find the area of the shaded portion. See figure.

3. AC is a diameter of a circle, and semicircles are described on AB and BC, as shown in the figure. Prove that the ratio of the shaded area to the area of the circle is equal to the ratio of BC to AC.

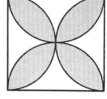

4. Prove that the circle inscribed in a square is one half the area of the circle circumscribed about the square.

5. If the chord of a segment of a circle is 8 inches long and the height of the segment is 2 inches, what is the radius of the circle?

6. The length of the arc subtended by the sides of a regular inscribed decagon is $\frac{3}{5}\pi$. What is the area of the circle?

7. Show that the length of a side of a regular polygon of 12 sides is $R\sqrt{2 - \sqrt{3}}$ if R is the radius of the circle.

8. Prove that the area of the hexagon formed by joining all possible pairs of alternate vertices of a regular hexagon is one third the area of the given hexagon.

9. The areas of two sectors having equal angles in unequal circles are to each other as the squares of the radii.

10. In a circle whose radius is 10 inches an equilateral triangle ABC is inscribed. On AB as diameter a semicircle is described which goes outside the circle. Find the area of the crescent-shaped figure that is formed.

11. What is the area of a circle where a chord 10 inches long cuts off a major arc of 270 degrees?

12. A, B, and C are points in a straight line in that order. Semicircles are described on AB, BC, and AC as diameters on the same side of AC. BD is perpendicular to AC and intersects the largest semicircle at D. Prove that the area bounded by the three semicircles is equal to the area of the circle whose diameter is BD.

■ Mensuration of Solids — *Optional*

From your previous study of mathematics you should be able to complete the following statements:

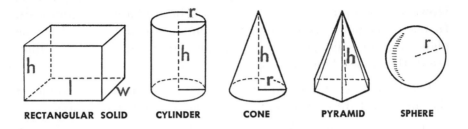

RECTANGULAR SOLID   CYLINDER   CONE   PYRAMID   SPHERE

EXERCISES

1. $V = lwh$ is the formula for finding . . .

2. $V = \pi r^2 h$ is the formula for finding . . .

3. $V = \frac{1}{3}\pi r^2 h$ is the formula for finding . . .

4. $V = \frac{4}{3}\pi r^3$ is the formula for finding . . .

5. $V = \frac{1}{3}Bh$ (where B is the area of the base) is the formula for finding . . .

6. $S = 2lw + 2hl + 2hw$ is the formula for finding . . .

7. $S = 2\pi rh$ is the formula for finding . . .

8. $A = 2\pi r^2 + 2\pi rh$ (A meaning total area) is the formula for finding . . .

9. Compute the volume V of a rectangular solid in which $l = 3$ ft., $w = 2$ ft., and $h = 1\frac{1}{2}$ ft.

10. Compute the area S of the solid in Ex. 9.

11. Compute the volume V of a cylinder in which $r = 2$ ft. and $h = 1\frac{1}{2}$ ft.

12. Compute the total area A of the cylinder in Ex. 11.

13. Compute the volume V of a pyramid whose base is a regular hexagon 6 in. on a side and whose altitude h is 12 in.

14. Compute the volume of a sphere whose radius is 3 in.

■ Comparing Plane and Solid Geometry — *Optional*

As you might expect, the definitions of plane geometry are used in solid geometry without change wherever they are applicable. However, in solid geometry there may be a change in emphasis. In plane geometry you know that points and lines are all in one plane, but in solid geometry you must determine whether lines are in the same plane or in different planes.

The following statements will help you to recognize some of the important differences between plane and solid geometry.

1. a Two points determine a straight line.
   b Three points determine a plane.

2. a Three points do not necessarily lie in the same straight line.
   b Four points do not necessarily lie in the same plane.

3. a In a plane only one line can be drawn perpendicular to a given line at a given point.
   b In space an infinite number of lines can be drawn perpendicular to a given line at a given point.

4. a Two lines perpendicular to the same line are not parallel unless all three lines are in the same plane.
   b Two lines perpendicular to the same plane are parallel.

5. a In a plane two nonparallel lines intersect at a point.
   b In space two nonparallel lines do not necessarily intersect.
   c Two nonparallel planes intersect in a straight line.

6. a One and only one line can be drawn parallel to a given line in a plane through a point outside the line.
   b Through a point outside a plane an infinite number of lines can be drawn parallel to the plane.
   c Through a point outside a plane one and only one plane can be parallel to the given plane.

7. a The shortest distance between two points in a plane is a straight line joining the two points.
   b The shortest distance between two points on a sphere is the arc of a great circle passing through the two points.

I. Vocabulary

1. Illustrate the use of each of the following terms:

Regular polygon

Inscribed polygon

Circumscribed polygon

Center of regular polygon

Radius of regular polygon

Apothem of regular polygon

Central angle of regular polygon

Circumference

π (Pi)

Sector of circle

Segment of circle

II. Theorems

2. Complete the following statements:

a A circle can be inscribed in . . .

b A circle can be circumscribed about . . .

c The central angle of a regular polygon of n sides equals . . .

d The apothem of a regular polygon is perpendicular . . .

e The radius of a regular polygon bisects . . .

f If a circle is divided into three or more equal arcs, the chords . . .

g If a circle is divided into three or more equal arcs, the tangents . . .

h Regular polygons of the same number of sides are . . .

i The perimeters of similar polygons have the same ratio as . . .

j The perimeters of two regular polygons of the same number of sides have the same ratio as . . .

k The area of a regular polygon is half . . .

l The areas of two regular polygons of the same number of sides have the same ratio as . . .

III. Construction Problems

3. Explain how to

a inscribe a square in a circle.

b inscribe a regular hexagon in a circle.

IV. Formulas

4. Identify the following formulas:

$$c = \pi d \text{ or } 2\pi r \qquad A = \pi r^2 \qquad A = \frac{n°}{360°}\pi r^2$$

TEST 1

Which of these statements are True *and which are* False?

1. *ABCDE* is a regular pentagon. *O* is the center of the circumscribed circle. Then $\angle AOB = 72°$.

2. The area of a regular hexagon with radius 2 in. is $12\sqrt{3}$ sq. in.

3. The area of a square inscribed in a circle whose radius is 3 in. is 36 sq. in.

4. A circle has a radius 2″. To draw a circle with three times the area, I would use a radius 6″.

5. The side of an equilateral triangle inscribed in a circle of radius 8 is $8\sqrt{3}$.

6. The side of an equilateral triangle circumscribed about a circle of radius r is $2r\sqrt{3}$.

7. The side of a square inscribed in a circle of radius 5 is $5\sqrt{2}$.

8. The side of a square circumscribed about a circle of radius r is $2r\sqrt{2}$.

9. The side of a regular hexagon inscribed in a circle of radius r is r.

10. The side of a regular hexagon circumscribed about a circle of radius r is $\frac{2}{5}r\sqrt{5}$.

11. Two regular polygons inscribed in a given circle are similar.

12. Two similar polygons inscribed in a given circle are regular.

13. *ABCDEF* is a regular polygon in a circle with center *O*. If *AE* equals 4 units, the area of *ABCDEF* is $8\sqrt{3}$ sq. units.

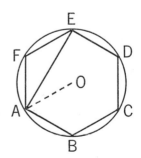

TEST 2

Leave answers in terms of radicals and π.

1. O is the center of a regular octagon. One central angle is _?_°. One exterior angle is _?_°.

2. $ABCDE$ is a regular polygon with side 6″. The radius is 5″. Then the apothem is _?_ in.

3. If the side of a regular hexagon is 12 cm., its apothem is _?_ in. The area of the hexagon is _?_ sq. in.

4. ABC is an equilateral triangle inscribed in a circle whose center is O. $OA = 6$ in., $OD \perp AB$. $OD = $ _?_ in. $COD = $ _?_ in. $\angle OAB = $ _?_°. $\angle AOD = $ _?_°. Area of $\triangle ABC = $ _?_ sq. in.

5. If one central angle of a regular polygon is 15°, one angle of the polygon is _?_°.

6. The side of one regular pentagon is 5 in. and the side of another is 7 in. The ratio of their perimeters is _?_ : _?_ and the ratio of their areas is _?_ : _?_.

7. ABC is an equilateral triangle circumscribed about a circle whose center is O. $OD = 6$ in., $\angle ODB = $ _?_°, $\angle DBO = $ _?_°, $OB = $ _?_ in., $AB = $ _?_ in., $COD = $ _?_ in. Area of $\triangle ABC = $ _?_ sq. in.

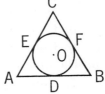

8. D, E, and F are the middle points of the sides of equilateral triangle ABC. $AB = 8$ in. The area of the colored part is _?_ sq. in. The area of the triangle ABC is _?_ sq. in. The area of the triangle DEF is _?_ sq. in.

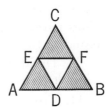

9. $ABCDEF$ is a regular hexagon with an area of 6 sq. in. RST is a triangle formed by extending alternate sides of the hexagon $ABCDEF$. ACE is a triangle formed by connecting alternate vertices of the hexagon. The area of $\triangle RST$ is _?_ sq. in. and the area of $\triangle ACE$ is _?_ sq. in.

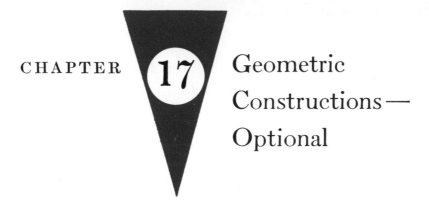

CHAPTER **17** Geometric Constructions — Optional

In previous chapters you have become familiar with the following constructions. Review them now.

1. Constructing a line segment equal to a given line segment.

2. Constructing an isosceles or equilateral triangle.

3. Bisecting a given line segment or constructing the perpendicular bisector of a line.

4. Bisecting a given angle.

5. Constructing an angle equal to a given angle.

6. Constructing a line perpendicular to a given line at a point on the line or from a point outside the line.

7. Constructing a line parallel to a given line **a** at a given distance from it, **b** through a given point.

8. Constructing a parallelogram by making **a** the opposite sides parallel, **b** the opposite sides equal, **c** two sides parallel and equal, **d** the diagonals bisect each other.

9. Dividing a line into any number of equal parts.

10. Constructing a tangent to a circle at a point on the circle.

11. Circumscribing a circle about a triangle.

12. Inscribing a circle in a triangle.

13. Constructing the fourth proportional to three given lines.

14. Dividing a line segment into parts that have the same ratio as two given segments.

15. Constructing the mean proportional between two given lines.

16. Transforming a polygon of n sides into a triangle.

17. Transforming a rectangle into an equal square.

18. Inscribing a square in a circle.

19. Inscribing a regular hexagon in a circle.

■ Construction of Triangles with Given Parts

The six parts of a triangle are the three sides and the three angles. The following are the six possible combinations of these parts in groups of three:

1. Three sides (*s.s.s.*).
2. Two sides and the included angle (*s.a.s.*).
3. Two angles and the included side (*a.s.a.*).
4. Two angles and a side opposite one of them (*a.a.s.*).
5. Two sides and an angle opposite one of them (*s.s.a.*).
6. Three angles (*a.a.a.*).

To construct a definite triangle, three parts are always *necessary*. Three parts, however, are not always *sufficient* to determine such a triangle. Given lines and angles in any one of the first four combinations above, only one triangle (if any) can be constructed using the given parts. By this we mean that a triangle of definite size and shape is determined. The fifth combination determines not more than two triangles. The sixth combination cannot determine a triangle, for there are triangles of an infinite number of sizes with the same three angles.

Constructions for combinations 1, 2, and 3 are suggested below.

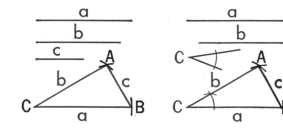 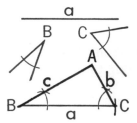

Note that in lettering the figures the small letters represent sides opposite angles denoted by the capital of the same letter; side *a* is opposite $\angle A$, side *b* is opposite $\angle B$, and side *c* is opposite $\angle C$. You must abide by this system of labeling when given certain parts and deciding their positions.

In the first figure, line segments *a*, *b*, and *c* were given and $\triangle ABC$ has these parts. In the second figure the triangle was constructed so that $BC = a$, $\angle C$ equals the given $\angle C$, and $CA = b$. What was done in the third figure?

■ Triangle Construction (a.a.s.)

Construction **Constructing a triangle, given two angles and a**
Problem **side opposite one of them.**

Here you are given, for example, $\angle A$, $\angle C$,
and c. First draw a triangle that represents
the triangle you wish and mark the given
parts, like the colored parts in the figure at
the right. Study the figure to see how you
can make the construction.

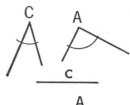

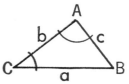

If you construct $\angle C$ first, you do not know
where to place side c. (Try it.) If you construct side c first and then $\angle A$, you do not
know where to place $\angle C$. (Try it.) You
will be at a loss as to how to begin until you
remember that the sum of the angles of a triangle is 180°. With
what is given you can easily find $\angle B$, and then the construction is simple.

To find $\angle B$, first draw straight angle DEF.
Then construct $\angle GEF = \angle C$ and $\angle HEG = \angle A$.
The remaining $\angle DEH$ will be the desired $\angle B$,
since the sum of the three angles is 180°. You

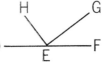

can now construct $\triangle ABC$, since you know $\angle A$, $\angle B$, and c, two
angles and the included side.

**To construct a triangle given two angles and a side opposite one
of them, first find the third angle. Then construct the triangle
using the method for two angles and the included side.**

EXERCISES

1. Is it possible to construct a triangle with any combination
of lengths of the three sides — for example, 10 in., 4 in., and
3 in.?

2. Construct an isosceles triangle that will have its perimeter
and its base equal to two given lines.

3. Construct an isosceles triangle, given the base and the
vertex angle.

■ Triangle Construction (s.s.a.)

Construction Problem **Constructing a triangle, given two sides and an angle opposite one of them.**

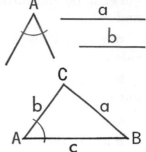

This is the fifth combination of parts. Suppose you have given $\angle A$, b, and a shown at the right.

First draw an analysis figure, a figure representing the one you are to make. From a study of this you will see that you can construct $\angle A$ equal to the given $\angle A$ and one side AC of the angle equal

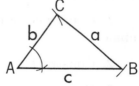

to b. Then with C as center and a as radius draw an arc meeting the second side of $\angle A$ at B. If a is not long enough to intersect the side, then the construction is impossible; no triangle results. When a is of sufficient length to intersect, you have the required triangle. There are several possibilities as you will see in the following exercises and in the analysis on the next page.

To construct a triangle, given two sides and an angle opposite one of them, first construct the angle, then the side given adjacent to the angle, and finally the side opposite the angle.

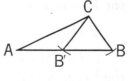

1. Construct $\triangle ABC$ so that $AC = 3$ cm., $BC = 1$ cm., and $\angle A = 30°$. (Make the 30° angle with a protractor.) What difficulty do you encounter?

2. Construct $\triangle ABC$ so that $AC = 3$ cm., $BC = 1.5$ cm., and $\angle A = 30°$. Note that the arc just touches AB and so $CB \perp AB$. In this case $\triangle ABC$ is a right triangle.

3. Construct $\triangle ABC$ so that $AC = 3$ cm., $BC = 2$ cm., and $\angle A = 30°$. How many times will the arc intersect the side of $\angle A$? In this case there are two triangles that satisfy the conditions, $\triangle ABC$ and $\triangle AB'C$.

4. Construct $\triangle ABC$ with $AC = 3$ cm., $BC = 3$ cm., and $\angle A = 30°$. How many triangles satisfy these conditions? What kind of triangle is it?

5. Construct $\triangle ABC$ with $AC = 3$ cm., $BC = 4$ cm., and $\angle A = 30°$. How many triangles satisfy these conditions?

The several possibilities in connection with the construction of a triangle, given two sides and the angle opposite one of them, are summarized below.

Let h be the distance from C to AB. Then if $\angle A$ is acute and —

a $a < h$, there is no triangle (a is not a side).

b $a = h$, there is one triangle, a right triangle.

c $a > h$ but $< b$, there are two triangles.

d $a = b$, there is one triangle, an isosceles triangle.

e $a > b$, there is one triangle.

If $\angle A$ is a right angle or an obtuse angle, a must be greater than b or there is no triangle. (Why?) When $a > b$, there is one triangle.

EXERCISES

1. Construct an isosceles triangle, given an arm and the vertex angle.

2. Construct a right triangle, given its two arms.

3. Can you construct a triangle if $a = 3$ in., $b = 2.5$ in., and $c = 6$ in.? Give a reason for your answer.

4. Construct an isosceles triangle that will have its perimeter and one arm equal to two given lines.

5. Construct an isosceles triangle, given an arm and one of the base angles.

6. Construct an equilateral triangle, given an altitude.

7. Construct an isosceles right triangle, given the altitude upon the hypotenuse.

8. Construct an isosceles triangle, given the altitude upon the base and the exterior angle at the vertex.

9. Construct a quadrilateral, given four sides and one angle.

10. Construct a triangle, given b, c, and $\angle C$.

■ Angle Construction

Construction Problems   Constructing angles of a certain number of degrees.

You know that a right angle contains 90°. If, therefore, you construct a right angle by making one line perpendicular to another, you will have an angle of 90°. By bisecting this angle, you will have an angle of 45°. If you construct $AB \perp CD$ and bisect $\angle ABD$, then $\angle CBE = 135°$.

Each angle of an equilateral triangle is 60°. To construct an angle of 60°, construct any equilateral triangle.

1. How would you construct an angle of 30°? 15°?

By constructing an angle of 60° and 15° adjacent to each other, you will obtain an angle of 75°.

2. How would you construct an angle of 120°? 150°?

3. How would you construct an angle of 105°? 165°?

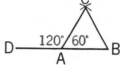

Summary. Starting with a 90° angle, these angles can be constructed by successive bisections: 45°, $22\frac{1}{2}°$, $11\frac{1}{4}°$, . . .

Starting with a 60° angle, these angles can be constructed by successive bisections: 30°, 15°, $7\frac{1}{2}°$, . . .

Any angle that is some combination of two or more of these angles (by either addition or subtraction) can be constructed.

EXERCISES

1. Construct angles of the following number of degrees: 90°, 45°, 22° 30′, 60°, 30°, 15°, 75°, 120°, 135°, 150°, 105°, and 165°.

2. Construct $\triangle ABC$ so that $\angle A = 60°$, $AB = 4$ cm., and $AC = 3$ cm. (Use a scale but do not use a protractor.)

3. Construct $\triangle ABC$ so that $\angle A = 30°$, $\angle B = 45°$, and $AB = 3.5$ cm.

4. Construct $\triangle ABC$ so that $\angle A = 60°$, $\angle C = 45°$, and $AB = 2.7$ cm.

5. Construct $\square ABCD$ so that $AB = 3$ cm., $\angle A = 60°$, and $AD = 2$ cm.

6. Why could you not construct $\square ABCD$ with $\angle A = 60°$, $AB = 4$ cm., and $\angle B = 100°$?

■ Using Methods of Constructing Triangles

The preceding five methods of constructing triangles (having given s.s.s., s.a.s., a.s.a., a.a.s., or s.s.a.) should be thoroughly mastered. They make possible the solution of many construction problems.

The following notation is standard and will be used: $\angle A$, $\angle B$, and $\angle C$ are the angles of $\triangle ABC$. a, b, and c are the sides opposite these angles, respectively. The altitude upon c is denoted by h_c (h sub c). Other altitudes are h_a and h_b. The median drawn to the middle point of c is m_c. The length of the bisector of $\angle A$ terminated by the opposite side is t_A.

EXAMPLE 1: Construct a triangle, given a, h_b, and b.

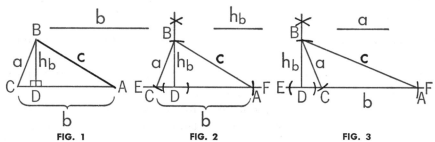

FIG. 1   FIG. 2   FIG. 3

First draw a freehand figure (Fig. 1) for the purpose of analysis. Draw given lines heavy and indicate given angles by arcs or right angles as shown. Study the figure to see if there is enough given to enable you to construct any of the three triangles ABC, ABD, or BCD by one of the five fundamental methods.

In this case you can construct $\triangle BCD$, knowing s.s.a. ($BC = a$; $BD = h_b$, and $\angle BDC$ a right angle). Begin with any point D on line EF of indefinite length and construct $\triangle BCD$. Note that side a may cut the base either to the left or the right of D (Fig. 2 or Fig. 3). Hence there are two possible constructions. You can now finish either of these figures by constructing $CA = b$ and drawing BA.

Example 2, which is on the next page, is a little more complex but follows the same kind of analysis.

Construct a triangle, given a, h_a, and m_a.

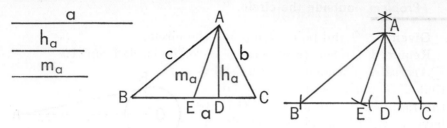

Given a, h_a, and m_a.
Required to construct $\triangle ABC$.
Analysis. The analysis figure shows that $\triangle DAE$ may be constructed by the method of *s.s.a.* E is the middle point of BC.

Construction

1. Construct $\triangle DAE$, given *s.s.a.*
2. Extend ED in both directions.
3. Bisect a and mark off EC and EB each equal to $\tfrac{1}{2}a$.
4. Draw AB and AC. Then $\triangle ABC$ is the required triangle.
Note that the construction is impossible if $h_a > m_a$.

Summary of Method

1. Put the given parts on paper. Label them.
2. Make a freehand sketch. Label it. Indicate the given parts.
3. Analyze your sketch to see which triangle you can construct first and how you will complete the figure.
4. Make the construction. Label your completed figure.
5. Discuss special conditions, if any exist, which will affect the construction.

EXERCISES

1. Construct $\triangle ABC$, given the following parts:

a a, h_b, b **b** c, h_a, $\angle A$ **c** b, h_c, a
d h_b, $\angle A$, b **e** h_b, $\angle A$, $\angle B$ **f** b, c, m_b
g c, m_c, $\angle B$ **h** c, t_B, $\angle B$ **i** t_C, $\angle B$, $\angle C$
j t_A, $\angle B$, c **k** h_b, m_b, b **l** h_a, m_a, c
m h_a, m_a, $\angle B$ **n** h_c, t_c, $\angle C$ **o** h_b, t_B, $\angle A$

2. Construct a parallelogram, given its sides and the altitude upon the longer side.

3. Construct a rhombus, given its diagonals.

Construction   **Constructing a tangent to a circle from a point**
    Problem   **outside the circle.**

    Given   ⊙O and point A outside the circle.

    Required   to construct a tangent to the circle from A.

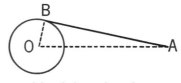

    Analysis. The analysis figure shows
that AB must be perpendicular to
the radius OB. If we draw OA, we
have a right triangle in which the
hypotenuse OA and one arm OB is
known. The problem is how to construct this right triangle.

    Construction.

    1. Draw OA, and upon it as diameter construct a semicircle
intersecting the given circle at B.

    2. Draw AB, which is the required
tangent.

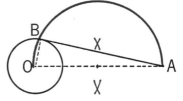

    Outline of proof.   Draw OB.

    1. ∠OBA is a right angle. Why?

    2. AB is tangent to circle O.
Why?

EXERCISES

    1. How many tangents may be drawn to a circle from an outside point?

    2. Draw a circle whose radius is 1 in. Place a point 2 in. from
the center and from it construct two tangents to the circle.

    3. Draw a circle and place a point A outside of it. Construct
an isosceles triangle with vertex angle at A so that all sides of the
triangle will be tangent to the circle. Draw an analysis figure.

    4. Construct a quadrilateral, given the sides and one diagonal.

    5. Construct a rhombus, given its perimeter and one angle.

EXTRA

    6. Construct a triangle when the base, the difference between
the other two sides, and the difference between the base angles
are given.

    7. Construct a right triangle so that the radii of the inscribed
and circumscribed circles are equal to two given line segments.

■ Analyzing a Construction Problem

In attacking a construction problem, first draw the given figure or the given parts of the figure, as the case may be. Then draw a freehand sketch of the figure as it will appear when the construction is finished. Examine this figure carefully to determine all parts that are known. If necessary, draw auxiliary lines until by analysis you discover lines that can be drawn in the given figure. The analysis of a sample problem is given below.

EXAMPLE: Construct a triangle, having given two of its angles and the radius of the circumscribed circle.

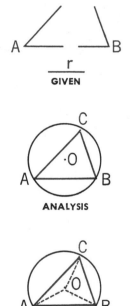

GIVEN

ANALYSIS

ANALYSIS

Given ∠A, ∠B, and line segment r, the radius of the circumscribed circle, as shown.

Required to construct △ABC.

For an analysis figure draw an inscribed triangle as if the construction were completed. A study of this figure shows you how to begin. Taking any point O as center and a radius equal to r, draw a circle. You can place any one of the vertices A, B, or C on the circle. The problem now is to place the other two vertices so that ∠A and ∠B are equal to the given angles. A study of the analysis figure at the right does not help you. If, however, you draw the radii AO, BO, and CO, you see a relationship that you can use. How does ∠COB compare with ∠A? How does ∠COA compare with ∠B?

Now you see how to proceed. If you have already placed point A on the circle, you can make ∠AOC equal to twice ∠B. This will locate C. Then make ∠COB equal to twice ∠A; point B will thus be located.

The construction and proof are left for you.

In a construction problem, draw an analysis figure and search for relationships which you can use in the construction figure.

1. Inscribe a regular hexagon in a circle whose radius is 2 inches. From the center of the circle construct a line perpendicular to one of the sides of a hexagon. Inscribe a circle in the hexagon.

2. Inscribe an equilateral triangle in a circle whose radius is 3 inches. Then inscribe a circle in the triangle.

3. Trisect a right angle.

4. Construct a parallelogram, given two sides and a diagonal.

5. Construct an isosceles triangle, given the vertex angle and the altitude upon the base.

6. Construct a right triangle, given an acute angle and the altitude upon the hypotenuse.

7. Construct a line through a point within an angle so that it will cut off equal distances from the vertex on the sides of the angle.

8. Through a given point outside a line construct a line that will make a given angle with the given line.

9. Construct a line tangent to a given circle and parallel to a given line.

10. Given a circle and a point within it. Construct a chord that will have the point as its middle point.

11. Given the positions of the middle points of the three sides of a triangle, construct the triangle.

12. Construct a triangle, given c, h_a, $\angle B + \angle C$.

13. Construct a triangle, given t_A, c, $\angle A + \angle C$.

14. Given two externally tangent circles and a line segment r. With r as radius construct a circle tangent to the given circles.

15. Construct a common external tangent to two nonintersecting circles. (SUGGESTION: Using the center of the larger circle as center and the difference between the radii of the two circles as radius, draw a circle.)

16. Construct a parallelogram so that a side and two diagonals are equal to three line segments.

■ Constructions Depending upon Loci

Construct a right triangle, given the hypotenuse and the altitude upon the hypotenuse.

Given c, h_c, and $\angle C$ a right angle.

Required   to construct $\triangle ABC$.

Analysis.   The analysis figure shows that you can draw $AB = c$. C must be at a distance of h_c from AB.   What is the locus of points at a distance h_c from AB? C is also the vertex of the right angle of a right triangle with AB as fixed hypotenuse.   What is the locus of C fulfilling this condition?

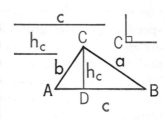

Construction

1. Draw $AB = c$.

2. Construct a line parallel to AB at the distance h_c from it.

3. Construct a semicircle with AB as diameter.

Either intersection of the parallel with the semicircle will be the vertex C of the required triangle.

Proof.   The proof is left for you.

Discussion.   If $h_c > \frac{1}{2}AB$, there will be no solution.   If $h_c = \frac{1}{2}AB$, the parallel will have one point in common with the semicircle.   If $h_c < \frac{1}{2}AB$, the parallel will intersect the circle twice.

EXERCISES

1. Given the hypotenuse of a right triangle and the median upon the hypotenuse.   Can the triangle be constructed?   Explain.

2. Construct a triangle, given one side, the median upon it, and the altitude upon another side.

3. Construct a triangle given a side, the altitude upon it, and the altitude upon another side.

4. Construct a triangle given one side and the altitude and the median on another.

5. Construct a triangle that shall have the base, the altitude upon the base, and the radius of the circumscribed circle equal to three given lines.

■ A Simple Construction in Aviation

In a perfectly calm atmosphere, an aviator can *head* his plane in the direction in which he wishes to go. His direction above the ground will be the same direction as his heading and his speed above the ground (*ground speed*) will be the same as his *air speed*. When the wind is blowing, the heading of the airplane and the direction it will go above the ground are not the same. The air speed and the ground speed are not the same. The diagram shows an airplane heading due north, *AB*, and a wind blowing from the west toward the east, *BC*. The line *AC* shows the actual course of the airplane over the ground.

Obviously, an aviator cannot always plan to head directly north or directly south, nor does the wind always oblige by blowing due east or due west. However, the plan and procedure in every case are basically the same.

Under any conditions the combined effect of travel of the airplane through the air and the travel of the air (wind) itself may be found by adding two *vectors*.

△ *A **vector** is a line that has both magnitude and direction.*

When used in airplane problems, a vector shows graphically both the speed and the direction of travel. In the vector diagram above, the line *AB* is the vector representing the heading and line *BC* is the vector representing the wind. Line *AC* is the resultant vector which shows the actual course and ground speed of the airplane. Vector *AC* connects the extremities of the vectors *AB* and *BC*.

On the next page we shall show you a simple construction an aviator has to make when he wishes to learn in what direction he should head his plane, knowing his air speed and the direction and speed of the wind. It is an application of the *s.s.a.* construction of triangles.

EXAMPLE: A pilot wishes to fly over the ground in a direction 90° in a clockwise direction from the north. His air speed is 120 miles an hour. The wind is reported as blowing from 40° at 25 miles an hour. In what direction must the pilot head in order to allow for wind drift and maintain the desired course? What is his ground speed?

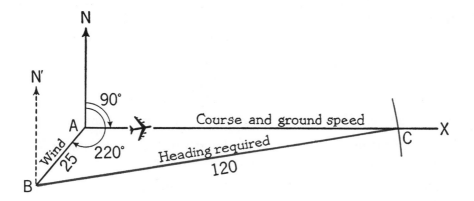

The plan is to construct a triangle from the given information in order to show the effect of the wind on the direction of flight. We have given two sides and an angle opposite one given side (s.s.a.).

1. AN is the north-south line. Draw a line AX of indefinite length, in a direction 90° from AN. This line shows the direction in which the pilot wishes to go.

2. From A, draw a line AB showing the direction of the wind. It should be 25 units long. (Choose a convenient scale.) It should be in the direction 220° from NA. The wind was blowing *from* 40° and hence *toward* 220° (40° + 180° = 220°). Draw the north-south line BN'.

3. With a radius of 120 units and with B as center, draw an arc cutting AX. Call the point C.
   The angle N'BC will show the required heading. The length of AC (number of units in AC) will show the ground speed.
   Note that you drew △ABC, knowing ∠A, AB, and BC.

■ A Changing Triangle

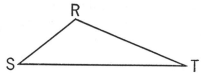

Can you visualize what the situation is for each of the following exercises and draw a figure for it?

In Exs. 1-9 suppose ST is fixed in length and that $\angle S$ remains constant. The other two sides can change in length and the other two angles will change in size.

1. As shown, $\angle R$ is an obtuse angle. As SR increases $\angle T$ will grow larger and $\angle R$ will grow smaller. (Why will $\angle R$ grow smaller?) Construct the figure which results when $\angle R$ becomes a right angle. Remember that ST and $\angle S$ remain constant.

2. As SR increases beyond its length in the right triangle you have constructed will $\angle R$ be acute or obtuse?

3. $\angle T$ is increasing. Construct the figure which results when $\angle T$ becomes a right angle.

4. Let SR continue to increase beyond its length in the second right triangle you have constructed. $\angle T$ becomes obtuse. Does it continue to be obtuse as SR increases? Does it have a largest possible value?

5. $\angle S$, of course, remains constant. As $\angle T$ increases what is happening to $\angle R$?

6. Under what circumstances is RT smallest?

7. ST remains constant. How does the altitude from R vary? How does the area of the triangle vary?

8. Construct the figure formed when $\angle T$ becomes equal to the original $\angle R$. Is this triangle similar to the original triangle? Explain.

9. Are the two right triangles mentioned in Exs. 1 and 3 similar? Explain.

10. Construct $\triangle RST$ so that SR is one half of ST and $SR \perp RT$. How many degrees are there in $\angle S$ and in $\angle T$?

11. If SR is one half of ST and $\angle R$ is greater than 90°, is $\angle S$ more or less than 30°? Can you tell without measuring?

Testing Your Understanding

TEST 1

Complete these sentences:

1. If ∠C is an obtuse angle of a triangle, then side c will be the _?_ side.

2. O is the center of a circle and OCB is a semicircle. The angle OCB is a _?_ angle and chord BC is _?_ to the smaller circle.

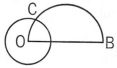

EX. 2

3. When constructing a triangle, given two angles and a side opposite one of them, I first find the _?_.

4. To construct an angle of 60°, or 30°, or 120°, I would first construct a (an) _?_ triangle.

5. AB and BD are tangents and O is the center of the circle. If ∠B = 40°, arc AF = _?_ °.

6. A circle is divided into five equal parts. The chords of the five arcs will be _?_ and each angle of the polygon formed will be _?_ °.

7. To inscribe a regular octagon in a circle, I would first construct two _?_ diameters and then _?_ the four central angles.

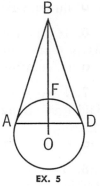

EX. 5

8. In any scalene triangle the altitude upon any side must be _?_ than either of the other two sides.

9. If a regular hexagon ABCDEF is inscribed in a circle whose radius is 5 in. and whose center is O, then AB = _?_ in. and ∠AOB = _?_ °.

TEST 2

Copy the right answer:

1. ABD is a straight line. If ∠ABC is equal to the vertex angle of an isosceles triangle, then each base angle equals _?_.

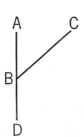

EX. 1

  a ½∠CBD   **b** 90° − ∠ABC   **c** ∠ABC

2. If the altitude CD of a triangle ABC bisects the base AB, the triangle is _?_.

a a right triangle   **b** an isosceles triangle   **c** an equilateral triangle

3. A definite triangle is determined by _?_.

a all three angles   **b** any two angles and a side   **c** any two sides and an angle

4. When you are required to construct a triangle, given two sides and an angle opposite one of them, the final step is to draw _?_.

a the angle   **b** the side opposite the angle   **c** the side adjacent to the angle

5. If you are given $\angle A = 30°$, $AC = 6$ cm., and $BC = 2$ cm., you can construct _?_.

a no triangle   **b** one triangle   **c** two triangles

6. If you are asked to construct a triangle in which $\angle A = 60°$, $AC = 6$ cm., and $BC = 8$ cm., there will be _?_.

a no solution   **b** one solution   **c** two solutions

7. I wish to construct a triangle ABC, given c, m_c, and $\angle B$. The first triangle I would construct would have the given parts _?_.

a *s.s.a.*   **b** *s.s.s.*   **c** *s.a.s.*

8. To inscribe an equilateral triangle in a circle, I would first divide the circle into _?_.

a 3 equal parts   **b** 6 equal parts   **c** 2 equal parts

CHAPTER **18** An Introduction to Analytic Geometry — Optional

GEOMETRY IS an old subject of learning, but in the course of centuries its scope has been broadened and deepened. It has influenced the thought and the practical affairs of men in varied ways. One of the interesting facts concerning geometry is the way new uses for it have been found.

In the fifteenth and sixteenth centuries new applications of geometry in navigation made possible the great period of oceanic exploration. Later geometry bore its part in the development of the age of steam, gasoline, and electric power. In the present century it has been employed in mapping molecules, in investigating the atom, in measuring the universe, and in determining safe air transportation. It will continue to be employed in new ways.

Closely connected with the elementary course in demonstrative geometry are several more advanced fields of geometry. One of these is *analytic geometry*, which combines algebra with geometry. It has as its basis a system of co-ordinates such as are used in drawing graphs in algebra. The idea of co-ordinates in geometry was used in ancient times in laying out towns and farm lands with respect to two perpendicular axes; points on the earth's surface and in the heavens were located by means of latitude and longitude. However, it remained for René Descartes in the early part of the seventeenth century to see that the co-ordinate system offered a means of combining algebra and geometry.

Analytic geometry can be used to prove exercises of demonstrative geometry, and its proofs are almost entirely by arithmetic and algebra. In this brief chapter you will be shown how this is done in order that you may see something of the interesting and useful methods of analytic geometry.

CO-ORDINATE SYSTEM **485**

■ Distance between Two Points

Before you can carry through proofs in analytic geometry, you must understand a few things that are basic to its method. The first of these is the way to find the length of a line segment between two points whose co-ordinates are known.

1. The points A, B, C, and D have co-ordinates as shown in Figure 1. What is the length of the line AB? (You can find it by counting, or by subtracting 3 from 7.) What is the length of the line CD? (Subtract -6 from 3. $3 - (-6) = 9$.)

These two distances are very easy to find because the two points in each case lie on the same horizontal or vertical line.

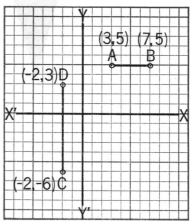

FIG. 1

2. What is the length of the line from $(0, 3)$ to $(0, 10)$? from $(0, -10)$ to $(0, -3)$? from $(5, -4)$ to $(5, 6)$? from $(3, -2)$ to $(7, -2)$?

3. To find the distance AB not on a horizontal or vertical line (Fig. 2), draw a vertical line through B and a horizontal line through A, making the right triangle ABC. C is the point $(7, 2)$. (Why?) If you now find the lengths of AC and CB, you can compute the length of AB by means of the Pythagorean Theorem. $AC = 7 - 1$, or 6, and $CB = 10 - 2$, or 8. Hence $AB = \sqrt{6^2 + 8^2} = \sqrt{100} = 10$.

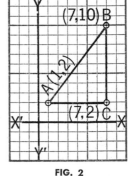

4. In the same way find the distance from $(4, 3)$ to $(-3, 4)$; from $(4, -3)$ to $(-3, 4)$; from $(0, 0)$ to $(7, -5)$; from $(-2, 0)$ to $(4, 8)$; from $(5, -2)$ to $(-1, -3)$.

FIG. 2

This suggests a general method for finding the distance between two points without drawing a figure:

a *Find the difference between the x's and square the difference.*
b *Find the difference between the y's and square the difference.*
c *Add the two squares and take the square root of the sum.*

5. Find the distance from $(7, -2)$ to $(-3, 5)$. (The difference between the x's is 10. The difference between the y's is 7. $\sqrt{10^2 + 7^2} = \sqrt{149}$.)

6. Find the distance from $(9, 2)$ to $(5, 7)$; from $(8, -3)$ to $(4, 6)$; from $(-7, -3)$ to $(-4, 5)$; from $(-2, -3)$ to $(-5, -2)$.

EXERCISES

1. Find the lengths of the sides of the triangles determined by each of the following groups of three points. (It may help you to understand the problem to plot the points and draw the sides of the triangles.)

a $(7, 2), (5, 8), (2, 3)$ b $(6, 4), (4, -2), (0, 5)$

c $(-3, 5), (0, 0), (7, 2)$ d $(-4, 0), (4, -4), (7, 5)$

2. Show by finding the lengths of the sides that the points $(-3, 2), (6, 5)$, and $(3, -1)$ are the vertices of an isosceles triangle.

3. The points $(0, 0), (5, 0), (0, 4)$, and $(5, 4)$ are the vertices of a rectangle. Show that the diagonals are equal. What is the area of this rectangle?

4. The points $(3, -1), (5, 7), (2, 8)$, and $(-3, 3)$ are the vertices of a quadrilateral. Find its perimeter.

5. Show that the points $(0, 2), (7, 1), (12, 4)$, and $(5, 5)$ are the vertices of a parallelogram.

6. Show that the points $(-3, -1), (3, 3)$, and $(5, 0)$ are the vertices of a right triangle. (Is the square of the longest side equal to the sum of the squares of the other sides?)

■ The Distance Formula

The method you have used in the above exercises to find the length of a line segment between two given points may be expressed by the formula —

$$d = \sqrt{(x_2 - x_1)^2 + (y_2 - y_1)^2}$$

where (x_1, y_1) and (x_2, y_2) represent any two points. Note that this formula expresses algebraically what the rule on page 486 expresses in words. It is used exactly as the rule is used.

It makes no difference which of the two points is taken as (x_1, y_1) and which as (x_2, y_2), because the differences are squared and you will get the same result whichever choice you make.

1. Using the formula, find the distance from (3, 1) to (7, 5); from (5, − 3) to (2, 2); from (7, 2) to (− 1, − 4); and from (− 6, 1) to (2, − 3).

2. If $(a, 2b)$ represents one point and $(b, 2a)$ represents another, what, in terms of a and b, is the distance between the two points?

3. What is the distance in terms of a and b between the points (0, 0) and (a, b)? between (a, b) and $(0, 2b)$? between $(2a, 0)$ and (a, b)?

4. A certain fixed point is represented by (5, 3). A variable point is represented by (x, y), where x and y may take any values you please. What is the distance in terms of x and y from (5, 3) to (x, y)? State algebraically that this distance must always be 5 units. What is the locus of points at a distance of 5 units from the point (5, 3)? If you graph the equation which states that (x, y) must always be 5 units from (5, 3), what will be the nature of the graph? If the co-ordinates of the point (x, y) can change but must always satisfy this equation, may x and y take any values you please or are they restricted?

■ Midpoint of a Line Segment

You can find a number halfway between two numbers by taking their average. Similarly, *to find the co-ordinates of the midpoint of the line segment between two given points, take the average of the x's and the average of the y's.*

1. What number is halfway between 6 and 18? halfway between 7 and 14? halfway between − 3 and 5?

2. Test the statement in the first paragraph by drawing a line from (2, 3) to (8, 7). Bisect the line and determine the co-ordinates of the midpoint, first by counting and then by the rule given above. (The average of the x's is 5. The average of the y's is _?_.)

1. Find the midpoint of the lines between each of the following pairs of points:

a (3, − 2), (7, 8)   b (6, 1), (4, 2)
c (− 2, 5), (4, 0)   d (4, − 1), (− 3, 7)

2. What is the midpoint of the line between (a, b) and (c, d)? between $(a, 0)$ and $(0, b)$?

3. The points $(1, 1)$, $(6, 3)$, and $(4, 7)$ are the vertices A, B, and C respectively of $\triangle ABC$. Find the length of the median from A. (First find the co-ordinates of the midpoint of BC.)

4. Show that the points $(1, 2)$, $(8, 1)$, $(13, 4)$, and $(6, 5)$ are the vertices of a parallelogram. What is the length of each diagonal? Show by the methods of this chapter that the diagonals bisect each other. (This can be done by showing that the co-ordinates of the midpoint of one diagonal are the same as the co-ordinates of the midpoint of the other.)

5. The points $(2, 2)$, $(4, -6)$, and $(8, 4)$ are the vertices A, B, and C respectively of $\triangle ABC$. Show that the line joining the midpoints of AC and BC is equal to one half AB.

■ Slope of a Straight Line

If a road rises 2 ft. in a horizontal distance of 20 ft., we say that it rises 1 ft. for every 10 ft., or that its *slope* is $\frac{1}{10}$. Similarly, if a straight line rises 12 units in a horizontal distance of 4 units, we say that it rises 3 units for every horizontal unit, or that its slope is 3. A slope may be negative as well as positive. If y *increases as x increases*, the slope is positive. If y *decreases as x increases*, the slope is negative.

In the figure, the slope of the line AB which passes through the points $(-4, -6)$ and $(8, 4)$ is $+\frac{10}{12}$ or $+\frac{5}{6}$, for y increases 10 units as x increases 12 units. The slope of the line CD is $-\frac{5}{10}$ or $-\frac{1}{2}$, for y decreases 5 units as x increases 10 units.

The slope of a line between two points may be found by dividing the difference between the y's by the difference between the x's. Care must be taken of the algebraic signs.

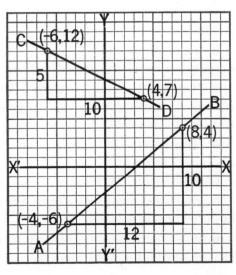

EXAMPLE 1: What is the slope of the line through $(-1, 3)$ and $(5, -2)$?

The difference between the y's is -5; the difference between the x's is 6. Hence the slope of the line is $-\frac{5}{6}$.

EXAMPLE 2: What is the slope of the line through $(-2a, b)$ and $(2a, -b)$?

The difference between the x's is $4a$. The difference between the y's is $-2b$. Hence the slope is $\dfrac{-b}{2a}$.

Lines that have the same slope are *parallel*. Conversely, parallel lines have the same slope.

If the slope of one line is $\dfrac{a}{b}$ and the slope of another line is $-\dfrac{b}{a}$ (the negative reciprocal), the two lines are **perpendicular** to each other. (The proof of this statement requires trigonometry beyond the scope of this book.) For example, if the slope of one line is $\frac{2}{3}$ and that of another is $-\frac{3}{2}$, the lines are perpendicular to each other. The converse of this statement is also true.

EXERCISES

1. Find the slope of the line passing through the following pairs of points:

   a $(2, 1)$, $(7, 8)$ b $(4, -2)$, $(5, 5)$
   c $(-2, 5)$, $(7, -3)$ d (a, b), (c, d)

2. Show that the points $(3, -1)$, $(10, -2)$, $(15, 1)$, and $(8, 2)$ are the vertices of a parallelogram.

3. The points $(-3, -4)$, $(5, -2)$, and $(2, 6)$ are the vertices A, B, and C respectively of a triangle. Show that the line joining the middle points of any two sides is parallel to the third side.

4. The points $(-3, 2)$, $(6, 5)$, and $(3, -1)$ are the vertices A, B, and C respectively of $\triangle ABC$. Show that the median from C is perpendicular to AB.

5. Show by means of slopes that $(-1, -1)$, $(5, 2)$, and $(7, 3)$ lie in the same straight line.

6. Are $(-2, 4)$, $(8, 6)$, and $(3, 0)$ the vertices of a right triangle? Give a reason for your answer.

7. The points $(-2, -5)$, $(6, -3)$, $(8, 5)$, and $(0, 3)$ are the vertices A, B, C, and D respectively of a quadrilateral. Show that AC and BD bisect each other at right angles. Show that $ABCD$ is a rhombus.

■ The Equation of a Mathematical Graph

A mathematical graph is a locus of points satisfying certain conditions. To find the equation of a graph is to find the relationship between the co-ordinates x and y of any point on the graph. This equation must be satisfied by the co-ordinates of any point on the graph and by no others.

EXAMPLE 1: What is the equation of a straight line which passes through the *origin* — that is, the point $(0, 0)$ — and has a slope $\frac{3}{2}$?

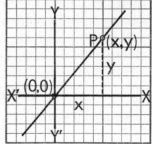

Take any point P on the line and designate it by (x, y). Then, by the conditions of the problem $\frac{y}{x}$, the slope of the line in terms of x and y, must equal $\frac{3}{2}$. The equation of the line is therefore $\frac{y}{x} = \frac{3}{2}$ or $y = \frac{3}{2}x$.

EXAMPLE 2: What is the equation of a line that passes through the point $(-3, -5)$ and has a slope $\frac{1}{2}$?

Take any point P on the line and designate it by (x, y). The difference between the y's is $y - (-5)$ or $y + 5$. The difference between the x's is $x - (-3)$ or $x + 3$. Hence the slope of the line in terms of x and y is $\frac{y + 5}{x + 3}$. By the conditions of the problem this must equal $\frac{1}{2}$. The equation is $\frac{y + 5}{x + 3} = \frac{1}{2}$ or, simplified, $x - 2y = 7$.

EXERCISES

1. What is the equation of a line through the origin with a slope 2? with a slope $-\frac{2}{3}$? with a slope $\frac{4}{5}$?

2. What is the equation of a line through the point $(-4, 3)$ with a slope 1? with a slope $\frac{3}{2}$? with a slope $-\frac{5}{2}$?

Equation of Circle with Given Center and Radius

A circle is the locus of points at a given distance from a given point. With this statement as a basis, you can easily write the equation of a circle when its center and radius are given.

EXAMPLE 1: What is the equation of a circle with center A at (2, 3) and radius 5?

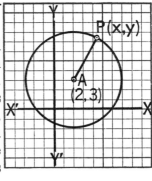

Take any point P on the circle and designate it by (x, y). This point, to be on the circle, must be at a distance 5 from A. The distance from (2, 3) to (x, y) in terms of x and y is $\sqrt{(x-2)^2 + (y-3)^2}$. If, therefore, you say that this expression equals 5, what you have said is that the point (x, y) may vary its position but its distance from (2, 3) must always be 5.

The equation of the required circle is

$$\sqrt{(x-2)^2 + (y-3)^2} = 5$$

Squaring both sides, you get

$$(x-2)^2 + (y-3)^2 = 25$$

Simplifying, you have

$$x^2 + y^2 - 4x - 6y - 12 = 0$$

EXAMPLE 2: What is the equation of a circle with center A at (− 3, 4) and radius 7?

$$\sqrt{(x+3)^2 + (y-4)^2} = \underline{\ ?\ }$$

EXERCISES

1. What is the distance from (a, b) to (3, 4)?

2. What is the distance from (c, d) to (− 2, 5)?

3. Write and simplify the equations of circles with centers and radii as follows:

a (3, 2); 4

b (3, 5); 2

c (− 4, 6); 3

d (3, − 2); 1

e (− 4, − 5); 5

f (7, − 3); 6

■ Proving Theorems by Analytic Geometry

EXAMPLE 1: Prove that the midpoint of the hypotenuse of a right triangle is equally distant from the vertices.

The first point to consider is the placement of a right triangle, representing all right triangles, on the co-ordinate system. It must be a right triangle, but must not have any other particular limitations. It is most convenient to place the vertex of the right angle at the origin and the sides CA and CB along the axes (Fig. 1). Thus we make sure that one angle is a right angle. If we take CA as $2a$ units long and CB as $2b$ units, where a and b may be any length, we have a general right triangle. The co-efficient 2 is taken to avoid fractions when finding the co-ordinates of the midpoint of AB.

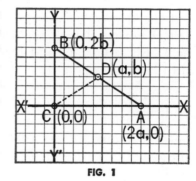

FIG. 1

We then proceed to find the co-ordinates of D, which is the midpoint of AB, and the lengths of DB, DA, and DC.

D is the point (a, b) (page 488).
$DC = \sqrt{(a - 0)^2 + (b - 0)^2} = \sqrt{a^2 + b^2}.$
$DB = \sqrt{(a - 0)^2 + (b - 2b)^2} = \sqrt{a^2 + b^2}.$
$DA = \sqrt{(2a - a)^2 + (0 - b)^2} = \sqrt{a^2 + b^2}.$
Hence $DC = DB = DA$.

EXAMPLE 2: Prove that the lines joining the mid-points of the sides of any quadrilateral, taken in order, form a parallelogram.

You are given any quadrilateral ABCD and wish to prove that EFGH, made by joining the mid-points of the sides, is a parallelogram. (See Fig. 2, page 494.)

You may place the vertex A at the origin and the vertex B on the X-axis. If you designate the points B, C, and D as $(2a, 0)$, $(2d, 2e)$, and $(2b, 2c)$, the quadrilateral will represent *any* quadrilateral.

PROOF BY ANALYTIC GEOMETRY   **493**

The mid-points *E, F, G,* and *H* are $(a, 0)$, $(a + d, e)$, $(b + d, c + e)$, and (b, c).

Now show that *EF* and *GH* have the same slope and are therefore parallel. Likewise *EH* and *FG*. To get the slope of *EF*, note that the difference between the *y*'s is *e* and the difference between the *x*'s is *d*.

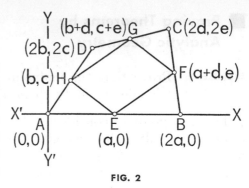

FIG. 2

1. Prove analytically (that is, by the methods of this chapter) that the diagonals of any rectangle are equal. Place the rectangle *ABCD* so that *A* is at the origin, *B* is on the *X*-axis, and *D* is on the *Y*-axis. *A, B, C,* and *D* will be the points $(0, 0)$, $(a, 0)$, (a, b), and $(0, b)$. Explain.

2. Prove analytically that the diagonals of a square are perpendicular to each other.

3. Prove analytically that in any triangle the line joining the mid-points of two sides is parallel to the third side and equal to one half of it.

Analytic geometry unifies algebra and geometry. Any point in a plane corresponds to a pair of numbers, and any pair of numbers corresponds to a point in a plane. Also, just as points can be represented by numbers, so lines and curves can be represented by equations. Geometry and algebra are so closely associated that a mathematician often speaks of the "point (a, b)" or the "straight line $y = 2x - 3$," without realizing that he is talking about a pair of numbers or an equation.

The proofs just given illustrate the great power of analytic geometry. By using algebraic methods in connection with the co-ordinate system, many geometric propositions may be demonstrated simply and easily. Many new propositions, which might otherwise have never been known, have been discovered through analytic geometry. If you continue the study of mathematics, you will find this method of geometry to be increasingly useful.

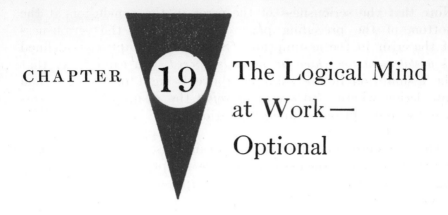

CHAPTER **19** The Logical Mind
at Work —
Optional

IN THIS chapter you will look further into the implications of a course in demonstrative geometry for critical thinking about non-geometric problems. The chapter helps you to build a bridge between geometric and non-geometric thinking.

■ Deductive Reasoning in Non-Geometric Situations

When a person talks or writes about a controversial or debatable topic, you will notice that his final statements are generally conclusions. These conclusions are reached by the use of *assumptions, facts,* and *reasoning processes.* All three components must be beyond reproach in order to make his conclusions acceptable. It is often possible for a gifted orator to convince a large part of his audience that his conclusions are correct even though he may make unsuitable assumptions, misrepresent facts, or employ questionable reasoning tactics.

One questionable assumption can cause a conclusion to be doubtful even when facts and reasoning processes are without error. The following example shows how this can happen:

Questionable assumption: Real estate values will rise throughout the next ten years.

Fact: Mr. Jackson bought a house this year and intends to sell it in six years.

Questionable conclusion: Mr. Jackson will sell his house at a price greater than his purchase price.

Note that the seriousness of the error in the conclusion at the bottom of the preceding page corresponds to the seriousness of the error in the assumption. Since an assumption is defined as *a statement for which no proof is offered*, you cannot say that the assumption in the example above is right or wrong. You can decide whether to *accept* or *reject* the assumption. In this case the assumption is called "questionable."

One misrepresented fact or claim can cause a conclusion to be faulty even though the assumptions are acceptable and the reasoning processes valid. A simplified example of such a situation is given below:

> *Assumption:* A dentifrice that could stop tooth decay would be one of the greatest benefits to public health.
>
> *Claim:* Emerald Ribbon toothpaste stops tooth decay.
>
> *Faulty conclusion:* Emerald Ribbon toothpaste is one of the greatest benefits to public health.

In these two examples it was quite easy to pick out the doubtful or misleading statements that led to faulty conclusions. Errors are not always so obvious. Assumptions can be presented in such a subtle way that they *appear* to be facts. Sometimes assumptions bearing on a conclusion are not even stated in the argument. Unstated assumptions are called *tacit*, or *implied*, *assumptions*. Implied assumptions must be detected if an accurate evaluation is to be made of the conclusions. Just as assumptions may be difficult to isolate and identify, so may facts be disguised in various ways.

The third element leading to valid conclusions, namely, correct reasoning, is essential to one who wants to think clearly at all times. In order to reason in a valid or sound manner, it is necessary to know some of the ways mistakes in reasoning can be made. As you learned earlier (see page 251), a misleading argument is called a *fallacy*.

You will have opportunity on succeeding pages to learn more about implied assumptions, some facts, and typical fallacies of reasoning.

■ Stated Assumptions

It may surprise you to learn that many of the beliefs you have held all your life are based on assumptions. There is nothing wrong with this; assumptions are a necessity. To understand fully the meaning of a conclusion, it is essential to consider the assumptions upon which the conclusion is based. Once the assumptions are known and are found to be acceptable, then the conclusions drawn from them can be accepted — provided valid reasoning has been used.

One of the world's most celebrated arguments is embodied in the Declaration of Independence, signed July 4, 1776. A selection from it follows. Read it carefully.

> "We hold these truths to be self-evident: That all men are created equal; that they are endowed by their Creator with certain unalienable rights; that among these are life, liberty, and the pursuit of happiness. That to secure these rights, governments are instituted among men, deriving their just powers from the consent of the governed; that, whenever any form of government becomes destructive of these ends, it is the right of the people to alter or abolish it, and to institute a new government, laying its foundation on such principles, and organizing its powers in such form, as to them shall seem most likely to effect their safety and happiness...."

Would you say that most of these statements are facts, or are they assumptions? Perhaps a class discussion of these statements would prove interesting.

■ Implied Assumptions

Implied assumptions, as you know, are those not explicitly stated in an argument. They may be perfectly acceptable when known, but often skill is required to detect and identify them. For the purpose of discussion the statements on the following page may be considered as some of the assumptions in the minds of the men who drafted the Constitution of the United States. Notice how many phases of our lives are influenced by implied assumptions. If you will discuss items 1 to 5 in class, one at a time, you will discover much more about them than is mentioned here.

1. *Men are intelligent.*

   a Is there a connection between this assumption and the fact that the United States Constitution grants its citizens the right and power to elect their own public officials?

   b Does the Constitution rely upon its citizens to *use* the privilege of voting?

   c What will this mean to you when you are of voting age?

   d United States citizens are granted a high degree of freedom. What relation is there between freedom and the intelligence of those who have it?

2. *Men are willing to abide by those measures which are good for the majority of people.*

   a When an issue is being voted upon in the Houses of Congress, what per cent of the votes cast must be in favor if the issue is to be decided favorably?

   b Do you know when a two-thirds majority is necessary to pass a bill?

   c Why do you suppose certain bills require a two-thirds majority?

   d When a man is sent to jail is he being affected by this assumption?

3. *If a dispute arises between two parties, each will abide by the decision of a recognized third party.*

   a Has our system of law, as it pertains to the functions of courts and judges, anything to do with this?

   b When two nations "quarrel" has there always been a third party to which they could turn for a *fair* hearing?

4. *Men desire power, but often tend to abuse it once they have it.*
   If you are not familiar with the basic structure of the administrative, legislative, and judicial branches of our government, ask an authority to explain to you the connection between this assumption and the "checks and balances" provided by our Constitution.

5. *Men are willing to compromise.*

   a What does a political party of the United States do when it suffers defeat in an election?

   b Have you ever read of the actions of defeated parties of other nations?

   c Is "good sportsmanship" involved in this assumption?

The comments made about each of the preceding assumptions are concerned, for the most part, with the ways in which these assumptions may have affected the contents of the Constitution, but it is easy to realize that these assumptions play a great part in the conduct of your daily activities. As you learn more about the Constitution, you will realize that it is a masterpiece of human thought. Its elegance reflects the intelligence of the clear and logical minds of those men who created it.

For the purpose of promoting sales, advertisements frequently use implied assumptions followed by claims which may or may not be factual. In any case, the conclusion that an advertisement strives for is, "You should buy our product."

For example, if an advertisement reads, "Ace typewriters are truly noiseless," the reader is encouraged to reason in this manner:

If a make of typewriter is truly noiseless, then I should buy that kind.

Ace typewriters are truly noiseless.

I should buy an Ace typewriter.

Once the second and third statements are known the assumption from which they are derived can be found. It is important that you recognize the implied assumption for what it is, then you can decide if you agree with it. Would you agree with the assumption in the example just given? Is noise necessarily the most important factor to consider when purchasing a typewriter?

The following statements (claims) are illustrations of advertisements. In each case:

a *Write the implied assumption.*
b *Write the claim.*
c *For your conclusion, answer the question, "If I needed such a product, would I buy this brand for the reason stated?"*

1. Smooth Grass Seed is the first choice of gardeners.
2. Whistle Shampoo leaves your hair soft as silk.
3. Bee Shoes have the longest wearing soles.
4. Thousands of dentists and physicians recommend Kap Capsules.
5. Zip Motor Oil means longer life for your car.
6. Dooper Paint makes decorating a pleasure.
7. Hi Tires are the safest on the highway.
8. Purr Gasoline gives you better engine performance.

■ Is It a Fact?

An acceptable assumption, followed by a fact that is treated with valid reasoning, will lead to a valid conclusion. The question is, "What is a fact?" The answer, surprisingly enough, is not as clear cut as one might expect.

On page 499 you saw that advertisements make claims for their products that may or may not agree with the truth even though readers are encouraged to look upon these claims as facts. It is often necessary to resort to laboratory tests to ascertain the truth. Watch out for claims that are not facts.

Recorded statements of history, when fully substantiated, are accepted as facts. We believe, for example, that Pearl Harbor was attacked on December 7, 1941. We take as a fact that a certain Lisa Mendon of our acquaintance was graduated from high school on June 12 of last year. Unsubstantiated historical statements, however, are not surely in the realm of facts. Did George Washington cut down the cherry tree?

Do our senses give us facts? Not necessarily; they are not always accurate; they can be mistaken. When an automobile accident occurs, a definite sequence of events takes place. Yet if two or more witnesses to the accident relate their observations, it is likely that no two of the reports will be in complete agreement. People see, hear, smell, feel, and taste with varying degrees of precision. You must beware of calling an *observation* a *fact*. Test several persons' observations of the contents of a room.

Facts rely on knowledge. What is accepted as factual by one person may seem absurd to another person with greater or less knowledge. Early people believed that the world was flat. They changed their belief when explorers and mariners sailed continuously in one direction and eventually came back to the starting point. Similarly, before the sixteenth century, people believed that the earth stood still and the sun rotated about it. After Copernicus, a Polish astronomer (1473–1543), published his findings that the earth rotated on its axis and revolved about the sun, people began gradually to accept his statements as the true ones.

When you are searching for the truth (a fact) make sure you go to a reliable source or to a person with the proper knowledge.

Be sure you have all the facts in a case. Being aware of some of the facts and not all of them does not generally lead to a valid conclusion. Facts can be misleading when one or more are not known. Consider the illustration below, that involved a candidate for mayor of his city. The candidate stated:

"After a careful examination of the treasurer's records and a study to make sure that there are no other means for providing the needed funds, then and only then I will see that the taxes on the property in this city are increased."

Two days later, an unscrupulous opponent quoted him as saying:

"After a careful examination of the treasurer's records, I will see that the taxes on property in this city are increased."

It is a fact that the first man said this, but his opponent was unfair when he quoted a part of the original statement and not the whole of it. When attempts are made to correct this kind of dishonesty, the corrections seldom repair the damage already done.

It is even possible for all the facts to be clear and yet have the end result distorted through a particular interpretation of these facts. If the members of the West High School basketball team have heights of 6' 4", 6' 2", 5' 8", 5' 7", and 5' 7", the average height is 5' 10". This is truthful and is mathematically correct, yet it is misleading because it does not give an accurate description of the situation. The fact that two players are 6' 4" and 6' 2" gives a different aspect to the complete picture of the team.

It is the function of newspapers to report facts to their readers. Then, in editorials, the facts are interpreted. These interpretations should not prevent readers from clear and independent thinking.

In general, while it may seem that facts are indisputable, they can often be a source of error if not handled with the utmost care. It is wise to ask the following questions when in doubt:

a   Is this merely the recording of an event?
b   Could individual differences in powers of observation change the result?
c   Is the whole story being told?
d   Does the observer possess the necessary technical knowledge?
e   Could the circumstances under which the observations were made influence the result?

EXERCISES

Read each statement and then indicate by letters which of the following five questions you would want to ask to insure that the given statement is a fact:

a *Is this merely the recording of an event?*

b *Could individual differences in powers of observation change the result?*

c *Is the whole story being told?*

d *Does the observer possess the necessary technical knowledge?*

e *Could the circumstances under which the observations were made influence the result?*

1. The bank closed at 3:00 P.M. last Tuesday.

2. A witness to the accident reported that the car door flew open before the car overturned.

3. The mountain peaks are white because of the snow and ice present.

4. This material is 100% wool.

5. Malaria is transmitted to man by the bite of the Anopheles mosquito.

6. The secretary said she lost her job because of illness.

7. The stars are self-luminous celestial bodies similar to our sun.

8. Jane went to the movies last night.

9. It is the shadow of the moon which darkens the earth when the moon is between the sun and the earth and all three are in a straight line.

10. Many spectators believed the foul was committed before the ball bounced out of bounds.

11. The candidate was defeated because of a lack of campaign funds.

12. The reporter was told that the front wall of the burning building collapsed before the roof fell.

13. Discuss the implications of Statement 5 if it had been made sixty years ago.

14. Discuss the implications of Statements 7 and 9 if they had been made many centuries ago.

■ Inductive Reasoning

In Chapter 1 you learned what was meant by inductive reasoning. Later, on page 170, you came to the conclusion that the sum of the angles of a polygon is the product of 2 less than the number of sides and 180°. This conclusion was reached after examining several polygons and observing that the same formula would work for each one. You know that your conclusion was reached by inductive reasoning — reasoning that proceeded from the specific to the general.

In Chapter 4 you learned that deductive reasoning proceeds from the general to the specific.

The method of inductive reasoning was largely overlooked by the Greeks and by scholars of the Middle Ages. It was not until the time of Copernicus that men began to seek new truth by the scientific method which has at its heart the method of induction.

The following examples illustrate some of the ways induction is used. You will note that observation is an essential part of this reasoning process.

1. Medical researchers experiment with a new treatment under many different conditions, carefully observe the results of their experiments, then form conclusions concerning the effectiveness of the new treatment.

2. The grade you receive in this course is a general conclusion resulting from dozens of observations by your teacher of your knowledge of geometry. Your written and oral work are the specific instances which are observed.

3. A factory which manufactures home appliances earns a good reputation for the production of quality merchandise after it has sold thousands of products that have proved durable, efficient, and free from frequent repair. The reputation gained is the general conclusion resulting from the specific satisfactions of thousands of customers.

4. A large firm, which conducts its business by mail, sends out several thousand letters every month. It receives orders from only four per cent of those receiving letters. Each letter sent provides a specific case to be observed. The conclusion is that four per cent placed an order, and future mailings will reflect this return.

The four situations described above should help you understand more fully the nature of inductive reasoning. It is all about us and is a very necessary part of our lives. This kind of reasoning, however, has many aspects. As you might expect, it also has some disadvantages.

Induction may be one of two types: *perfect* or *imperfect.* When the induction is *perfect* all cases have been observed and the conclusion is based upon the results thus found. For example, if the sophomore class of your high school plans a picnic and every member of the class is asked whether he will come, then the conclusion can be reached as to how many lunches to order. Here the induction is perfect because the conclusion affects a number of persons equal to the number observed. When induction is perfect you will note that the conclusion is merely a statement of fact concerning the results obtained from the observed cases.

Imperfect induction is much more common, however. Imperfect induction was used on page 170 in concluding that the sum of the angles of any polygon is the product of 2 less than the number of sides and 180°. Several polygons were examined and the results which held for those polygons were said to hold for *all* polygons. A generalization of this kind involves what is called the **inductive leap** because the conclusion affects many more cases than those actually observed. In mathematics, a generalization made from imperfect induction can be disproved if one exception can be found. (Note that the inductive leap on page 170 is validated in Theorem 18, on page 171, by using the letter n which takes in all cases.)

At first glance you might agree to this generalization: "All exterior angles of a hexagon are acute angles." But if one hexagon can be found which provides a contradiction to the statement, then the generalization must be discarded. Since it is possible to have a hexagon with at least one obtuse exterior angle, the stated generalization is not correct.

You might think that $x^2 + x + 17$ gives a prime number for all values of x. It does give a prime number for many values of x. For $x = 1, 2, 3, \ldots 15$ it gives values of 19, 23, 29, $\ldots$ 257, all of which are prime numbers. However, when $x = 17$, the value of $x^2 + x + 17$ is $17^2 + 17 + 17$, which is obviously divisible by 17. Here again one exception disproves the general rule.

EXERCISES

In the following exercises a decide if the given generalization involves an inductive leap, and b if it does, see if you can find one exception that will destroy the validity of the generalization:

1. A student constructed the bisector of ∠B in three different isosceles triangles somewhat like the one shown. After observing his constructions, he concluded: The bisector of a base angle of an isosceles triangle, when extended, bisects the side opposite that angle.

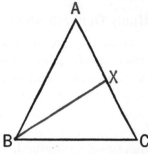

2. A questionnaire was given to all 35 employees of a small factory. The results showed that 29 were in favor of joining a group insurance plan covering accident and health emergencies. Hence, the employer arranged to start such a program for the 29 who were interested.

3. Life insurance records of the life spans of thousands of U.S. citizens show that women outlive men.

4. An algebra student was studying the subtraction of signed numbers. After working these problems —

$$(+ 8) - (+ 6) = + 2, \qquad (+ 8) - (- 6) = + 14,$$
$$(- 8) - (- 6) = - 2, \qquad (- 8) - (+ 6) = - 14,$$

he concluded: when two signed numbers are to be subtracted, the sign of the difference agrees with the sign of the number having the larger absolute value.

5. A geometry pupil constructed two pairs of triangles as shown. The parts marked with color were constructed equal. He realized he had made two pairs of congruent triangles and concluded: If two sides and the angle opposite one of them in one triangle are equal to the corresponding parts of another triangle, then the triangles are congruent.

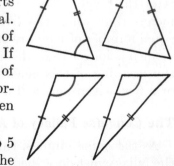

6. A student wrote the numbers 1 to 5 in a column, then made a column of the squares of the numbers, and finally a column of the differences of the consecutive squares. He concluded: The differences of the squares of consecutive integers are consecutive odd numbers.

■ Fallacies of Reasoning

Frequently a fallacy (see page 251) is not easy to detect. This is especially true in non-mathematical situations. There is space here to discuss only a few of the more common fallacies.

Hasty Generalization

Inductive reasoning leads to a conclusion which approaches the truth (perfect induction) only to the extent that a large number of cases are examined. The certainty of an inductive conclusion is, as a rule, a matter of degree — the larger the number of cases examined, the more probable is the generalization. When too few cases are observed and a generalization is made concerning the results obtained, that generalization is likely to be in error. This misuse of the inductive method is called *hasty generalization*. It is one of the common fallacies of inductive reasoning. The generalizations made in Exercises 1, 4, and 5 on page 505 are examples of hasty generalization. For example, in Exercise 1, if the student had constructed several isosceles triangles, some with long legs and relatively short bases, he would not have been tempted to generalize so quickly. A hasty generalization may prove to be a correct one, but a conclusion reached hastily is not a sign of careful thinking.

The Fallacy of Accident

A second fallacy that stems from the inductive method is the *fallacy of accident*. This fallacy results from a misinterpretation of the real meaning of a general statement. Exercise 3 on page 505 is of this type. The statement "women outlive men" actually means that when the lives of several thousand women and an equal number of men are studied, the average length of life for the women is longer than the average length of life for the men. Once the meaning of this generalization is clear, you can see that one, or a few, exceptions will not disprove it.

The Converse Fallacy of Accident

As the name implies, this fallacy has a converse relationship to the fallacy just described. The converse fallacy of accident occurs when a specific case that is obviously an exception is noted, and, based on this exceptional case, a generalization is made. For example, a certain college student who was blind had a seeing-eye dog with him at all times. Another student noting this, argued that since the blind student had a pet on the campus other students should be allowed to have pets while in college.

Note the difference between the two fallacies: In the fallacy of accident a generalization is applied to a special case that it is not meant to cover. In the converse fallacy a special case is observed, then it is argued that, since the special case is allowed, all other cases should be allowed.

EXERCISES

Tell which fallacy of induction is illustrated by each situation:

1. Fire engines do not have to stop for stop signals, therefore any car whose driver is in a hurry should not have to stop for stop signals.

2. When a student has been absent from school, he must turn in all make-up assignments within three days after his return. John has missed 18 school days because of a serious illness, so he must turn in all of his make-up work within three days after his return.

3. On two occasions Nancy was late in keeping an appointment with her friend Margaret. The next day Margaret told her mother that Nancy was always late for appointments.

4. In the state where Bill lives a person cannot obtain a driver's license until he is sixteen years old. However, state law provides that a license may be issued *under special conditions* to a person at the age of fourteen. John is fourteen, lives on a farm, and has a driver's license. Bill feels that, since John has a license, anyone should be permitted a license when he is fourteen.

5. Jean was told that college graduates earn more money than persons not graduated from college. She does not believe this since she knows a man who is very wealthy and this man did not graduate from high school.

6. All cars must stop for stop signals, therefore police cars should stop for stop signals.

7. High school students should be in bed by 10:30 P.M., therefore Henry cannot attend the New Year's party as he would not get home until after midnight.

8. Cheerleaders do not have to pay for their tickets to the game, so other students should not be required to pay either.

Reasoning from the Converse

Perhaps you have heard a conversation like this:

"It is too bad that you dislike athletics, John."

"Never mind, it proves I am a great man. All great men dislike athletics, you know."

This is an example of *arguing from the converse* of a statement. Study these two syllogisms:

All great men dislike athletics.	All men who dislike athletics are great men.
I dislike athletics.	I dislike athletics.
I am a great man.	I am a great man.

Which syllogism is valid? If you decided that the syllogism on the right is valid, you are correct. Its major premise (assumption) is the converse of the remark made by John. Do you believe either of these major premises to be true?

Even when a statement is true, you cannot assume its converse to be true.

Reasoning from the Inverse

You already know that the inverse of a true statement may or may not be true. It is true only after it is proved to be so. When you arrive at a conclusion after assuming the inverse of a statement to be true, you are committing the fallacy of *reasoning from the inverse.*

Mary Lou said, "Everyone knows that cocker spaniels make excellent pets. Betty's dog is not a good pet because it is not a cocker spaniel." When these comments are analyzed in syllogisms they are:

Cocker spaniels make excellent pets.	Dogs that are not cocker spaniels are not excellent pets.
Betty's dog is not a cocker spaniel.	Betty's dog is not a cocker spaniel.
Betty's dog is not an excellent pet.	Betty's dog is not an excellent pet.

Which syllogism is valid? Is the valid syllogism composed of the remarks made by Mary Lou?

Reasoning by Analogy

The statement "If two things are alike in some respects, then they are alike in all respects," illustrates *reasoning by analogy*. It should be quite clear that reasoning in this way will not always lead to correct conclusions. In order to be correct, the foregoing statement must be revised to read "If two things are alike in some respects, then they may be alike in all respects." Of course, a conclusion reached in this manner may be correct, but not merely because it is derived from an analogy. Although reasoning by analogy is not a method of proof, it is very useful for suggesting theories which may be proved in other ways.

For example, two metals, X and Y, have three properties in common. Metal X is also capable of withstanding very high temperatures, so it may be assumed that metal Y is capable of withstanding very high temperatures. This is not proof that metal Y has the fourth property. Further experiment with metal Y is needed to reveal the true answer.

Another example: John was an excellent football player in high school. His brother Tom is just as husky and can run as fast as John. To conclude that Tom will be an excellent football player ignores the possibility that his mental attitude toward the game may not be anything like John's mental attitude.

Connecting the Wrong "Ifs" and "Thens"

An example illustrating this fallacy in its simplest form is: The movement of the tree leaves causes the wind to blow. In general, the error lies in supposing that because two things happen together or one happens after the other, one must be the cause of the other. In this example the movement of tree leaves is cited as the "cause" and the blowing of the wind as the "effect." You know it to be a fact that the opposite is true.

In the example above there are two things that are related to each other. Many times one condition is credited as the cause of another, when in reality there may be no relation between the two, an opposite relation, or an undetermined relation. Such situations pose problems which are very difficult to solve. Scientists are continually searching for causal relationships. They realize they can make little progress unless they understand the true relationships between cause and effect; and they experiment untiringly to see if their theories are correct.

Reasoning in a Circle

On page 183 you saw an example of how circular reasoning can occur in geometry. This fallacy in thinking is called *begging the question*. It occurs when a person attempts to prove something, and in his "proof" he actually assumes as true that which he is proving. In non-mathematical situations this error is often very subtle.

Suppose Mary is trying to convince her friends that Teenstore is the best place to buy clothes. She tells them Teenstore is best because its prices are moderate and it carries the best of everything. Has she really proved anything? Note that her "proof" merely restates, in slightly different terms, her original claim. This fallacy often goes undetected because words are not carefully defined or are not used with exactness.

Non sequitur Reasoning

Your study of the syllogism shows you how given premises can lead to a valid conclusion, but when a conclusion simply does not follow from the stated premises, the *non sequitur* (it does not follow) fallacy is committed. If errors of this type were always as obvious as the following, little trouble would be presented by the non sequitur fallacy.

All girls have curly hair.

Mary Bennet is a girl.

Therefore, Mary Bennet is a good ice skater.

Here it is easy to notice that the conclusion has no bearing on the premises, but in most errors of this type the conclusion is *believable* even though it is not reached by valid reasoning. Consider this example:

If one eats large amounts of candy then he will have poor teeth.

Bill Benson eats large amounts of candy.

Bill Benson has frequent toothaches.

To have a valid conclusion in a syllogism, the conclusion must follow the *then* part of the general statement. Here the valid conclusion is "Bill Benson will have poor teeth."

■ Miscellaneous Pitfalls to Sound Reasoning

Lack of Careful Definitions

Before you studied geometry, you may have thought, as many people do, that to define a word you must merely supply a synonym for it. This is one way to define a term, but such definitions are entirely inadequate for use in geometry and often are inadequate for general use. Many words in our language already have several meanings and the meanings themselves change from year to year as a result of usage. When a term is used more than once in the same argument, be certain that its meaning remains the same throughout the argument.

In discussions of general matters, the reasoning often goes astray because words and terms are not used with exactitude as they are in geometry. It has been said that if debaters would define their terms, there would be few debates. If each word had an exact meaning and everyone understood this meaning, the communication of knowledge would be a simple matter indeed. One reason you have been able to draw valid conclusions in geometry is because you used terms with exactness. To draw valid conclusions in other fields of thought this same exactness in the use of terms is required.

When you are reading or when you are listening to a discussion, note how a recognized authority in any field of learning uses terms with the utmost precision and care.

Prejudiced Conclusions

Since people differ so greatly in background, in interest, and in outlook on life, it is almost impossible for them to be without prejudice in some matters. Prejudices are objectionable when they are allowed to replace reason. One of the biggest advantages you have had in your study of geometry is that you could learn about the processes of reasoning while dealing with geometric figures. Would your conclusions have been as unemotional if you had discussed topics related to lowering the voting age to eighteen, United States foreign policy, a comparison of this year's basketball team to the team of three years ago, or the effect of TV programs on the conduct of teen-agers?

It is easier to discover prejudices of others than it is to recognize your own. This is natural and should cause you to be alert for prejudices that will slant your own thinking. An excellent example of unprejudiced thinking is given in this story:

A teacher asked her pupils to write down what they would think if they went into a room and found cobwebs there.

With one exception, the children gave the following type of answer:

"The room had not been dusted lately," or "The owner was careless," or "The tenants were dirty and lazy."

The answer of one child showed that, in her thinking, she was less prejudiced toward other people's shortcomings and was looking for a positive reason. She wrote:

"A spider had been there."

Reasoning by authority

When a famous person announces how he feels about a specific issue and others then repeat his words as proof, the reasoning is *by authority*. The words of the famous person should be accepted as proof, however, only if he is an authority in the field to which his decision pertains, if he has evidence to support his decision, and if other authorities in his field are in general agreement. In other words, you believe another person because you assume he has used sound reasoning to reach a conclusion about a matter you do not have the opportunity to investigate. Obviously, reasoning by authority can be hazardous.

EXERCISES

Study these exercises and tell which fallacy or pitfall occurs in each:

1. Students who are hard workers get good grades.
   Bill must be a hard worker because he gets good grades.
2. All rattlesnakes are dangerous.
   This is not a rattlesnake so it is not dangerous.
3. My blood circulation is poor because my feet are cold.
4. Pretty girls have a pleasant smile.
   Grace is a pretty girl, so Grace has white teeth.
5. These two lines are parallel because whenever two lines are cut by a transversal making corresponding angles equal, then the lines will never meet.

6. A dope is a silly person.

A drug is a dope.

A drug is a silly person.

7. John's father, a staunch Republican (or Democrat), believes that the Democratic (or Republican) senator said the wrong thing again in his speech last night.

8. I use this brand of face powder because my favorite TV actress says it is the best.

9. Nothing is better than good health.

To be penniless is to have nothing.

To be penniless is better than good health.

10. Mike bought some cheap razor blades so he will probably cut his face while shaving.

Cheap razor blades always give poor shaves.

11. Terry's dad does not belong to a union because factory workers belong to unions and Terry's dad works in a store.

12. Tom's car has tubeless tires so it is a Super-X model. All Super-X models come equipped with tubeless tires.

13. Research scientists studied as much mathematics as they could while in high school.

Tom will be a research scientist because he studied mathematics all four years of high school.

14. If a person owns a car which no one under twenty-five drives then he will not have to pay extra for his car insurance.

Mr. Pearson owns a car and lets his nineteen-year-old son drive it, so he must pay extra for his car insurance.

15. There are few fresh strawberries available in New York in January because they are expensive.

16. Expensive clothes are made of the best quality materials.

Caroline's clothes ought to last longer because she pays a lot for them.

17. X-brand rugs are the best because only the finest materials are used in their construction.

18. Eighteen-year-olds should not vote because they are minors.

19. Robert believes that trucks do not pay enough in fees for use of the highways because his older brother told him so.

20. A builder of long experience says that prefabricated methods of building homes are inferior to traditional methods.

■ Caution.   Induction and Deduction at Work!

As you look back over the ways in which induction and deduction have been used in geometry, it may appear to you that inductive conclusions are not as certain as valid deductive conclusions. It is true that inductive conclusions must be made cautiously but this does not discredit their value. In practice, induction occurs so frequently and works so harmoniously with deduction that the important question is not "Which is better?" but rather, "How do they work together?"

To explain this, a look at an illustration will help.

When John started high school he was not sure how much time to spend studying each night. He decided one hour was enough. (This would be the assumed generalization used at the start.)

For the first four weeks he spent one hour each night on his homework. (A deductive application to specific instances.)

He found at the end of this period that his grades were not as high as he wanted them to be. (This is the observation of specific cases — his daily performances in school.)

He decided to spend more time each night doing his homework. (An inductive generalization reached after the observation of the specific cases.)

He then spent more time in daily study at home. (Deductive application to specific instances.)

This example helps to emphasize the presence of the inductive and deductive processes. A scientist working on a problem in his laboratory will adhere to a similar pattern. He will begin work with an assumption in mind, experiment with several cases and observe the results, form a generalization inductively, apply this generalization deductively in new experiments as he again observes results, very likely revising his first inductive conclusion. This pattern may be repeated several times before he considers his conclusions final.

To show that there is a relationship between an inscribed angle and its arc you draw ten random cases and measure. You find that, in every case, the angle has half as many degrees as the arc. You make the inductive leap. Then you prove the relationship by algebra as in Theorem 34. Induction and deduction are working together.

Can you give other illustrations of ways in which these two processes assist each other?

A Final Message

In your study of geometry you have learned many useful mathematical facts about the world in which you live. As you learned these facts, you were also finding out how people think about their problems and how they use sound reasoning to arrive at valid conclusions. Geometry is a logical system; as such, it began with some undefined terms, postulates, and accurate definitions. Then the geometrical information at hand led you to new conclusions as you proved theorems. To establish these theorems you made use mostly of deductive methods of proof. Very often there was an inductive approach to the deductive proofs. These are the basic elements of every logical system; you merely used geometry as a vehicle to carry you through one of these systems so you could see it in operation. Certain dangers and fallacies have been pointed out so that you can be on your guard against them when they appear in the future.

You should be forewarned that there will be problems in life much harder to solve than those you meet in geometry. The problems of life rarely appear as neat little syllogisms which can be easily analyzed and solved. You must develop your ability to analyze complex problems and to establish your own valid conclusions. This is a difficult task, but it is not impossible.

A university president once said: "All the problems of the world could easily be solved if men were only willing to think." By thinking he meant reasoning, the process by which we combine two statements into a third and so reach new truth. This is certainly the most important process carried on by man, and you will note that it is not man's inability to think, but his unwillingness to do so, that gives so much concern.

It is within the power of the average person to become a sound thinker if he will only use the mental power that has been given him. To do this he must make a habit of suppressing his wishes and emotions and of getting down to a calm, cold analysis of his postulates and of the processes by which he draws conclusions from them. If you get out of this course a stimulus to thought and some guidance in the correct processes of thinking, your study of geometry will have been very profitable.

MAINTAINING BASIC MEANINGS AND SKILLS

These pages of exercises are designed to maintain the basic arithmetic and algebraic meanings and skills. They should be used from time to time during the year. Many of the exercises in the earlier groups can be done mentally. Teachers of geometry recognize that the maintenance of these basic meanings and skills is an important objective. Students should not record their answers in the book.

GROUP 1

Fractions

Complete each of the following. Tell what principle is illustrated by each exercise.

a   b

1. $\dfrac{3}{8} + \dfrac{2}{8} =$ $\dfrac{a}{b} + \dfrac{c}{b} =$ $\dfrac{7}{12} - \dfrac{2}{12} =$ $\dfrac{a}{b} - \dfrac{c}{b} =$

2. $\dfrac{6}{8} = \dfrac{6 \div 2}{8 \div 2} =$ $\dfrac{ab}{ac} = \dfrac{ab \div a}{ac \div a} =$

3. $\dfrac{3}{4} = \dfrac{3 \times 5}{4 \times 5} =$ $\dfrac{a}{b} = \dfrac{a \times c}{b \times c} =$

4. $\dfrac{7}{4} = \dfrac{4}{4} + \dfrac{?}{4}$ $\dfrac{a+b}{c} = \dfrac{a}{c} + \dfrac{?}{c}$

5. $\dfrac{1}{3} + \dfrac{1}{2} = \dfrac{2}{6} + \dfrac{3}{6} =$ $\dfrac{1}{a} + \dfrac{1}{b} = \dfrac{b}{ab} + \dfrac{?}{ab} =$

6. $\dfrac{1}{3} - \dfrac{1}{4} = \dfrac{4}{12} - \dfrac{3}{12} =$ $\dfrac{1}{a} - \dfrac{1}{b} = \dfrac{?}{ab} - \dfrac{a}{ab} =$

7. $\dfrac{2}{3} + \dfrac{4}{5} = \dfrac{?}{15} + \dfrac{?}{15} =$ $\dfrac{a}{b} + \dfrac{c}{d} = \dfrac{?}{bd} + \dfrac{?}{bd} =$

8. $\dfrac{1}{2}$ of $\dfrac{1}{3} = \dfrac{1}{?}$ $\dfrac{1}{a} \times \dfrac{1}{b} =$ $\dfrac{1}{3}$ of $\dfrac{4}{5} = \dfrac{4}{?}$ $\dfrac{1}{a} \times \dfrac{b}{c} =$

9. $\tfrac{2}{3}$ of $\tfrac{4}{5} = 2(\tfrac{1}{3}$ of $\tfrac{4}{5}) = 2 \times \tfrac{4}{15} =$ $\dfrac{a}{b} \times \dfrac{c}{d} =$

GROUP II

Division of Fractions

1. How many half dollars are there in 4 dollars? $4 \div \frac{1}{2} = \underline{\ ?\ }$. Note that $4 \div \frac{1}{2}$ is the same as 4×2.

2. How many quarters are there in 3 dollars? $3 \div \frac{1}{4} = \underline{\ ?\ }$. Note that $3 \div \frac{1}{4}$ is the same as 3×4.

3. How many eighths of an inch are there in $1\frac{1}{2}$ inches? $1\frac{1}{2} \div \frac{1}{8} = \underline{\ ?\ }$. Note that $\frac{3}{2} \div \frac{1}{8}$ is the same as $\frac{3}{2} \times \frac{8}{1}$.

4. How many lengths each $\frac{3}{4}$ inch are there in three inches? Answer by referring to a ruler. $3 \div \frac{3}{4} = \underline{\ ?\ }$. Note that $3 \div \frac{3}{4}$ is the same as $3 \times \frac{4}{3}$.

5. Complete: To divide by a fraction, $\underline{\ ?\ }$ the fraction and multiply.

Do these divisions:

6. $\frac{5}{8} \div \frac{1}{8}$ **7.** $\frac{3}{8} \div \frac{1}{4}$ **8.** $\frac{2}{3} \div \frac{3}{4}$

9. $1\frac{5}{8} \div \frac{1}{4}$ **10.** $2\frac{1}{4} \div \frac{1}{8}$ **11.** $2\frac{1}{4} \div \frac{3}{4}$

12. $1\frac{1}{2} \div \frac{1}{8}$ **13.** $5\frac{1}{2} \div 7\frac{1}{3}$ **14.** $8\frac{1}{2} \div 5\frac{2}{3}$

15. $3\frac{1}{5} \div 10\frac{2}{3}$ **16.** $6\frac{2}{3} \div 4\frac{1}{6}$ **17.** $7\frac{1}{6} \div \frac{5}{6}$

18. $3\frac{1}{2} \div \frac{7}{8}$ **19.** $9\frac{1}{5} \div \frac{4}{5}$ **20.** $\frac{3}{4} \div \frac{2}{3}$

21. $\dfrac{a}{b} \div \dfrac{c}{b}$ **22.** $\dfrac{a}{b} \div \dfrac{c}{d}$ **23.** $1 \div \dfrac{a}{b}$

24. $\dfrac{9a}{b} \div \dfrac{12a}{c}$ **25.** $\dfrac{1}{c} \div \dfrac{a}{c}$ **26.** $d \div \dfrac{5d}{p}$

27. $\dfrac{8b}{c} \div \dfrac{3b}{a}$ **28.** $\dfrac{xy}{c} \div \dfrac{xy}{d}$ **29.** $\dfrac{3a}{4} \div \dfrac{3}{2b}$

30. $\dfrac{d}{w} \div \dfrac{w}{d}$ **31.** $\dfrac{a}{x} \div \dfrac{x}{e}$ **32.** $\dfrac{ad}{bc} \div \dfrac{a}{b}$

33. $\dfrac{8}{3a} \div 16$ **34.** $\dfrac{x}{y} \div \dfrac{3}{y}$ **35.** $\dfrac{5x}{8y} \div 15x$

36. $\dfrac{3y}{a} \div \dfrac{1}{a}$ **37.** $\dfrac{1}{a} \div \dfrac{a}{b}$ **38.** $\dfrac{a}{s} \div \dfrac{3a}{4s}$

GROUP III

Fractions, Decimals, Per Cents

1. You recognize that the following four expressions are equivalent: $\frac{1}{4}$, $\frac{25}{100}$, .25, and 25%. They differ in form (algorism) but not in value. Tell the other three equivalent forms of:

a $\frac{1}{2}$ b $\frac{1}{4}$ c 10%

d .20   e $\frac{12\frac{1}{2}}{100}$ f 37.5%

g .625   h 150%   i $\frac{4}{5}$

j $\frac{5}{4}$ k 4%   l .01

m 1.1   n 1.01

2. Which of the following expressions should be omitted?

3 out of 4 equals:

a $\frac{3}{4}$ b $3 \div 4$ c 75%   d $3\overline{)4}$ e .75

1.1 equals:

a $\frac{11}{10}$ b $1\frac{1}{10}$ c 111%   d $1 + .1$

1 out of 100 equals:

a 1%   b .01   c 1.01   d $\frac{1}{100}$ e $1\overline{)100}$

$\frac{1}{3}$ equals:

a $33\frac{1}{3}$%   b $1 \div 3$ c .3   d $\frac{3\frac{1}{3}}{10}$ e $\frac{33\frac{1}{3}}{100}$

1% equals:

a 1 out of 100   b $\frac{1}{100}$ c .01   d 1.01   e $100\overline{)1}$

3. Arrange these in order of size, from largest to smallest:

a 10%   b .11   c $\frac{1}{8}$ d $8\overline{)4}$ e .375   f 1 ft. $\div$ 3 ft.

4. Convert to per cents:

a 1 out of 100   b 1 out of 50   c 1 out of 200

d 7 out of 8   e 1.5   f 1.01

5. Perform the indicated operations:

a $1 + .01$ b $.10 + .01$ c $3 \times .2$

d $1 \div \frac{1}{10}$ e $2 \div .1$ f $3 \div .01$

g $1.2 \div .1$ h $.01\overline{).1}$ i $.1\overline{)1.1}$

j $.01\overline{)1.0}$ k $.3 \times 6$ l $1.4 \div .7$

GROUP IV

Signed Numbers

1. State the principle illustrated by:

a $(+4)(+3) = +12$

b $(+4)(-3) = -12$

c $(-4)(+3) = -12$

d $(-4)(-3) = +12$

2. The product of an odd number of negative factors is a _?_ number.

3. State the principle illustrated by:

a $\dfrac{+12}{+3} = +4$

b $\dfrac{+12}{-3} = -4$

c $\dfrac{-12}{+3} = -4$

d $\dfrac{-12}{-3} = +4$

4. The quotient of two signed numbers having unlike signs is _?_; the quotient of two signed numbers having like signs is _?_. If the dividend is positive and the divisor is negative, the quotient is _?_.

5. What are these products and quotients?

$(+8)(+9)$ $(+8)(-9)$ $(-8)(+9)$ $(-8)(-9)$
$(+20) \div (+4)$ $(+2.5)(-4)$ $(+\frac{1}{2}) \div (+\frac{1}{4})$
$(+20) \div (-4)$ $(-3.1)(-10)$ $(+\frac{1}{2}) \div (-\frac{1}{8})$
$(-20) \div (+4)$ $(+2.4)(-100)$ $(-\frac{1}{4}) \div (-\frac{1}{8})$
$(-20) \div (-4)$ $(-1.5)(+10)$ $(+2) \div (-.2)$

6. What are these sums?

$(+6) + (+6)$ $(+2x) + (+3x)$ $(-3ab) + (ab)$
$(+6) + (-6)$ $(-2x) + (+3x)$ $(+2xy) + (-3xy)$
$(-6) + (+6)$ $(+2x) + (-3x)$ $(-xy) + (+xy)$
$(-6) + (-6)$ $(-2x) + (-3x)$ $(-5ab) + (+4ab)$

7. What are the following differences?

$(+8) - (+8)$ $(-6) - (-4)$ $(+3x) - (-2x)$
$(+8) - (+6)$ $(-6) - (-6)$ $(-2x) - (+3x)$
$(+8) - (0)$ $(-6) - (-8)$ $(-2x) - (-3x)$
$(+8) - (+10)$ $(-6) - (+6)$ $(+2x) - (+3x)$

GROUP V

Exponents

a^3 *means* $a \times a \times a$. $3n^2$ *means* $3 \times n \times n$. $(a^2)(a^3)$ *means* $(a \cdot a)(a \cdot a \cdot a)$.

1. State the meaning of **a** $3ab^2$ **b** $(2x^2)(x^3)$ **c** $2a^2b$ **d** $(x^2y)(xy^3)$

2. If a is 2, what is a^2? $3a^2$? $a \times a^2$? a^3? $(2)(a)(2a)$?

3. If $a = -2$, what is a^2? $2a^2$? $(a)(a^2)$? a^3? $3a^3$? $(a^2)(a^3)$?

4. If $a = 2$ and $b = 3$, what is $a^2 + 3b$? $3a^2 + 2b$? $2a + b^2$? $a^3 + b^2$?

5. If $a = 2$ and $b = -3$, what is $(a - b)$? $(a + b)$? $(a)(b)$? $2ab$? $a^2 - b^2$? $a^2 + b^2$?

6. If $a = 1$, $b = -2$, and $c = 3$, then

$2a + 3b - c =$	$(a + b) - c =$	$b - 2a =$
$2a - 3b + c =$	$a + (b - c) =$	$2c + 3b =$
$a^2 + b^2 + c^2 =$	$b + (a - c) =$	$ab^2c^3 =$
$3a^2 - b^2 - c =$	$-c + (a + b) =$	$(a + c) \div b =$

7. If $a = \frac{1}{8}$, $b = \frac{1}{4}$, and $c = -\frac{1}{2}$, then

$2a + b + c =$	$a - c =$	$\dfrac{1}{b} =$	$a^2 =$
$a + b + c =$	$b - c =$		$b^3 =$
$(a + b + c)^2 =$	$bc =$	$\dfrac{1}{c} =$	$c^4 =$
$a \div b =$	$abc =$		$c^2 - b =$
$b \div a =$	$\dfrac{1}{a} =$	$\dfrac{1}{a} + \dfrac{1}{b} - \dfrac{1}{c} =$	$2a + b - c =$
$c \div a =$			

8. If $x = 4$, $y = -8$, and $z = -12$, then

$x + y + z =$	$2y + 4x =$	$y^2 - z =$	$z \div x =$
$x + y - z =$	$z + 3x =$	$z^2 - 10y =$	$z \div y =$
$x - y - z =$	$2z + 3y =$	$x^2 - y^2 =$	$y \div z =$

9. $\dfrac{x^5}{x^2} = \dfrac{\cancel{x} \cdot \cancel{x} \cdot x \cdot x \cdot x}{\cancel{x} \cdot \cancel{x}} = x^3$, and $\dfrac{x^2}{x^5} = \dfrac{\cancel{x} \cdot \cancel{x}}{\cancel{x} \cdot \cancel{x} \cdot x \cdot x \cdot x} = \dfrac{1}{?}$

10. $\dfrac{a^3x^2}{ax^3} = \dfrac{\cancel{a} \cdot a \cdot a \cdot \cancel{x} \cdot \cancel{x}}{\cancel{a} \cdot x \cdot \cancel{x} \cdot \cancel{x}} = \qquad \dfrac{ax^3}{a^3x} =$

11. In $\dfrac{x^b}{x^q}$ the exponent of x in the quotient is __?__.

GROUP VI

Equations

Solve these equations for x:

1. $x + 3 = 2$
2. $x - 3 = 3$
3. $x - 4 = 5$
4. $x - 4 = -5$
5. $x + 5 = 5$
6. $2x + 1 = 11$
7. $2x - 1 = 11$
8. $2x + 5 = 7$
9. $2x - 5 = -7$
10. $\frac{1}{2}x + 2 = 6$
11. $\frac{1}{2}x - 2 = 6$
12. $x + a = b$
13. $x - a = b$
14. $x + 1 = b$
15. $x - b = 1$
16. $ax = b$
17. $ax + b = 0$
18. $ax + b = c$
19. $ax - b = c$
20. $x + \frac{1}{2} = \frac{1}{4}$
21. $x - \frac{1}{2} = \frac{1}{8}$
22. $.5x = 5$
23. $.1x = 10$
24. $.2x + 2 = 4$
25. $.1x + 1 = .2$
26. $2 - x = 1$
27. $3 - x = -6$
28. $4 + \frac{1}{2}x = -1$
29. $\frac{x}{2} = -10$
30. $\frac{2x}{3} = 10$
31. $\frac{3x}{5} = 6$
32. $\frac{2x}{3} = -8$
33. $\frac{1}{x} = 4$
34. $\frac{1}{x} = \frac{2}{3}$
35. $\frac{2}{x} = \frac{3}{4}$
36. $1 - \frac{1}{2}x = 2\frac{1}{2}$
37. $.1x = \frac{1}{2}$
38. $.4x = 20$
39. $3x - x = 12\frac{1}{2}$
40. $5x - 2x = 37.5$
41. $2x - \frac{1}{2}x = 16$
42. $\frac{x}{a} = b$
43. $\frac{x}{b} = \frac{1}{a}$
44. $\frac{x}{a} = \frac{1}{b}$
45. $x - \frac{1}{4}x = 12$
46. $\frac{2}{3}x + \frac{1}{2}x = 42$
47. $\frac{3}{4}x - \frac{2}{3}x = 2.5$
48. 25% of $x = 16\frac{1}{4}$
49. 16% of $x = 32$
50. $.25x = 3\frac{1}{4}$
51. $.75x = 1$
52. $x + 2a = b$
53. $x - 2a = b$
54. $2x + a = b$
55. $2x - a = b$
56. $\frac{x}{2a} = 2b$
57. $3x = 2b$
58. $ax + bx = c$
59. $ax - bx = c$
60. $ax - bx = a - b$

GROUP VII

Variables

1. In $y = 3x$, if x increases from 2 to 5, then y _?_ from _?_ to _?_.

2. In $y = x - 4$, if x increases from 4 to 10, then y _?_ from _?_ to _?_.

3. In $y = \dfrac{1}{x}$, if x increases from 2 to 5, then y _?_ from _?_ to _?_.

4. In $y = 6 - x$, if x increases from 2 to 8, then y _?_ from _?_ to _?_.

5. In $y = \dfrac{6}{x}$, if x decreases from 3 to 1, then y _?_ from _?_ to _?_.

6. In $y = \dfrac{10}{x - 4}$, if x increases from 5 to 8, then y _?_ from _?_ to _?_.

7. In $ab = c$, if a and b are doubled, then c is _?_.

8. In $A = \frac{1}{2}bh$, if b and h are doubled, then A is _?_.

9. In $V = lwh$, if l and w are doubled and h is halved, then V is _?_.

10. In $i = prt$, if p is doubled and rt remains constant, then i is _?_. If r and t are doubled and p remains constant, then i is _?_. If p, r, and t are each increased 100%, then i becomes _?_ times as large.

11. In $ab = 100$, if a is doubled, then b is _?_.

12. In $y = mx + b$, if x increases and m and b are constant, then y _?_. If m and b are doubled and x is unchanged, then y is _?_.

13. In $x = \dfrac{1}{a} + \dfrac{1}{b}$, if a and b decrease, then x _?_.

14. In $y = 10^x$, if x increases from 2 to 3, then y _?_ from _?_ to _?_.

15. In $y = 1 - x^2$, if x increases from $\frac{1}{10}$ to $\frac{1}{2}$, then y _?_ from _?_ to _?_.

522 VARIABLES

GROUP VIII

Parentheses and Fractions

1. Find the value of the following when $a = 2$, $b = -3$, $c = 5$, and $d = 0$:

a $5ab$	**b** a^2b	**c** b^2
d ab^2	**e** $4ab^2d$	**f** $-6bc$
g $a+b$	**h** $a-b$	**i** a^2+b^2
j a^2-b^2	**k** $a^2-2ab+b^2$	**l** a^3b^3
m $(a+b)^2$	**n** $(a-b)^2$	**o** $(b-a)^2$

2. Remove parentheses and combine terms if possible:

a $a-(b+c)$	**b** $a-(b-c)$	**c** $a+(-b+c)$
d $a-(-b+c)$	**e** $30-(a+2)$	**f** $30-(a-2)$
g $3x-(x-5)$	**h** $5a-(2b+7a)$	**i** $90-(2a+3b)$
j $90-(2a-3b)$	**k** $180-(180-a)$	**l** $180-(90+5a)$
m $3a-2(a-2b)$	**n** $90-5(2a-3)$	

3. Write as one fraction:

a $\dfrac{a}{2}+\dfrac{b}{3}$ **b** $\dfrac{2a}{3}-\dfrac{3b}{0}$ **c** $\dfrac{5a}{3}+\dfrac{3a}{4}$

d $5+\dfrac{a}{2}$ **e** $5-\dfrac{a}{3}$ **f** $7-\dfrac{2a}{5}$

g $12-\dfrac{a+b}{2}$ **h** $15-\dfrac{2a-b}{3}$ **i** $42-\dfrac{3x+4y}{5}$

j $90-\dfrac{90-a}{2}$ **k** $180-\dfrac{90+2a}{3}$ **l** $60-\dfrac{a}{2}+\dfrac{b}{3}$

m $4-\dfrac{2b}{3}-\dfrac{3a}{4}$ **n** $\dfrac{2a}{3}+\dfrac{3a}{4}+\dfrac{6b}{2}$ **o** $15-\left(\dfrac{2x}{3}+\dfrac{y}{2}\right)$

p $20-\left(\dfrac{m}{2}-\dfrac{n}{6}\right)$ **q** $45+\dfrac{5x+7y}{2}$ **r** $60+\left(\dfrac{a}{2}+\dfrac{b}{3}\right)$

s $60-\left(\dfrac{a}{2}-\dfrac{b}{3}\right)$ **t** $\dfrac{3a}{2}-\dfrac{5a}{3}-\dfrac{a}{4}$ **u** $\dfrac{6a-1}{3}-\dfrac{2a-1}{2}$

GROUP IX

Per Cents

1. Write these fractions as per cents:

$\frac{1}{8}$ $\qquad$ $\frac{1}{4}$ $\qquad$ $\frac{3}{8}$ $\qquad$ $\frac{1}{2}$ $\qquad$ $\frac{5}{8}$ $\qquad$ $\frac{3}{4}$ $\qquad$ $\frac{7}{8}$

2. Write each of these decimals as a per cent:

.1 $\qquad$ .01 $\qquad$ .015 $\qquad$ 1.01 $\qquad$ 1.1 $\qquad$ .001

3. Write these per cents as common fractions:

10% $\quad$ $12\frac{1}{2}\%$ $\quad$ $16\frac{2}{3}\%$ $\quad$ 20% $\quad$ 25% $\quad$ $33\frac{1}{3}\%$ $\quad$ $67\frac{1}{2}\%$

4. Express each of these quotients as a per cent, correct to the nearest tenth of a per cent:

$\frac{1}{7}$ $\qquad$ $\frac{7}{12}$ $\qquad$ $\frac{5}{16}$ $\qquad$ $\frac{7}{8}$ $\qquad$ $\frac{15}{32}$

5. 2% of $50 =$ $\qquad$ **6.** 2.5% of $50 =$ $\qquad$ **7.** 4.5% of $180 =$

8. 5.25% of $200 =$ $\qquad$ **9.** $\frac{1}{2}\%$ of $600 =$ $\qquad$ **10.** $1\frac{1}{2}\%$ of $90 =$

11. $3\frac{3}{4}\%$ of $600 =$ $\qquad$ **12.** 2.1% of $150 =$ $\qquad$ **13.** 150% of $10 =$

14. 250% of $6 =$ $\qquad$ **15.** 175% of $8 =$ $\qquad$ **16.** 225% of $10 =$

17. Refer to the line segments shown here and complete:

a is _?_% of b
a is _?_% of c
a is _?_% of d
b is _?_% of a
c is _?_% of a
d is _?_% of a

a |———| $\qquad$ $a = 4$
b |—————| $\qquad$ $b = 6$
c |———————| $\qquad$ $c = 8$
d |—————————| $\qquad$ $d = 10$

18. Find a number such that —

a $\frac{3}{4}$ of it is 12 $\qquad$ **b** $\frac{2}{3}$ of it is 16

c $\frac{7}{8}$ of it is 56 $\qquad$ **d** $\frac{4}{5}$ of it is 30

e 75% of it is 18 $\qquad$ **f** 80% of it is 60

g 150% of it is 75 $\qquad$ **h** 120% of it is 42

19. In which of the preceding exercises were you finding **a** what per cent one number is of another? **b** a certain per cent of a number? **c** a number when a per cent of it is known?

GROUP X

Interest

Use the simple interest formula, $i = prt$, to solve the following:

1. At 6% per annum, what is the interest on —

a $500 for 1 yr.? b $500 for 3 mo.?

c $500 for 4 mo.? d $1000 for 90 da.?

e $200 for 30 da.? f $150 for 120 da.?

g $800 for 1 yr. 6 mo.? h $450 for 1 yr. 3 mo.?

2. At 5% per annum, what principal will yield —

a $10 in 1 yr.? b $12.50 in 6 mo.?

c $5 in 4 mo.? d $2.50 in 1 mo.?

e $1.50 in 6 mo.? f $.06 in 1 yr.?

g $1 in 30 da.? h $2.50 in 120 da.?

3. Find the time required for $200 to yield $6 at 6%.

4. If $p = \$4000$, $r = .05$, and $t = 2$, $i = \underline{\ ?\ }$

5. If $p = \$150$, $r = \frac{4}{100}$, and $i = \$3$, then $t = \underline{\ ?\ }$

6. If $p = \$3000$, $r = \frac{5}{100}$, and $i = \$50$, then $t = \underline{\ ?\ }$

7. If $p = \$4000$, $i = \$300$, and $t = 3$, $r = \underline{\ ?\ }$

8. Check: At 6% the interest on any principal for 60 days is $\frac{1}{100}$ of the principal.

9. Is it true that if p, r, and t are doubled, then i is doubled?

10. Is it true that if p is doubled, r is halved, and t remains unchanged, then i remains unchanged?

11. On January 1 a man borrowed $250 with interest at 5% per annum. On the following July 1 he paid off the loan. How much did he owe? $(t = \underline{\ ?\ } \text{ mo.})$

12. Find the interest on a promissory note for $120 at 6%, made March 20 and repaid the following August 28. $\left(t = \dfrac{\text{no. days}}{360}\right)$

13. Compute the annual interest or carrying charge on a debt of $300,000,000,000, bearing interest at 3%.

GROUP XI

Some Equations in Geometry

1. A, B, and C are the angles of a triangle. What is the number of degrees in each?

	A	B	C
a	$20°$	$50°$	$x°$
b	$30°$	$x°$	$2x°$
c	$60°$	$x° + 10°$	$x°$
d	$70°$	$x° - 15°$	$x°$
e	$2x° + 3°$	$4x° - 20°$	$\dfrac{x°}{2}$
f	$\dfrac{x° - 4°}{2}$	$\dfrac{x° + 5°}{3}$	$2x° - 1°$

2. ABC is a triangle with AB extended to D. Fill in the blanks with the correct values.

	$\angle CBD$	$\angle A$	$\angle C$
a	$a°$	$b°$	?
b	$a° + b°$	$b°$	?
c	$a° - b°$	?	$b°$
d	$2a° + 3°$	$a° - 2°$	?
e	$\dfrac{a°}{3}$	$\dfrac{a°}{4}$	?
f	$\dfrac{a°}{2} - 3°$	?	$\dfrac{a°}{5} + 6°$

3. One acute angle of a right triangle is three times the other. Find each in degrees and minutes.

4. Two angles are supplementary. Two thirds of the larger is less than three halves of the smaller by 10°. Find the number of degrees in each angle.

SUGGESTION: Smaller angle | x
Larger angle | $180 - x$
Then $\frac{2}{3}(180 - x) = \frac{3}{2}x - 10$

5. Two angles are supplementary. One half of the larger exceeds one fourth of the smaller by 30°. Find the number of degrees in each angle.

GROUP XII

Writing and Solving Formulas

1. If a articles of the same kind cost b cents, what should c articles cost?

2. If an automobile travels a miles in t hours, at the same rate how long should it take to travel b miles?

3. An agent sold n dollars' worth of goods, for which he received a commission of 5%. How much money should he return to the company?

4. A man can do a piece of work in a days. His son can do it in b days. How much of the work would both together do in one day?

5. If n represents the units' digit and t the tens' digit in a two-digit number, what expression will represent the number?

6. An aviator can travel a miles an hour when there is no wind. How far can he travel in t hours against a wind that is blowing b miles an hour?

7. A pupil solved a problems correctly in a test containing b problems. What per cent of the problems did he solve correctly?

8. Solve the following formulas for the letter indicated:

a $A = lw$; $l =$

b $A = \frac{1}{2}bh$; $b =$

c $V = lwh$; $l =$

d $p = a + b + c$; $b =$

e $p = 2l + 2w$; $l =$

f $i = prt$; $t =$

g $d = rt$; $r =$

h $a + b = c$; $a =$

i $A = \pi r^2$; $\pi =$

j $V = \pi r^2 h$; $h =$

k $\frac{a}{b} = c$; $b =$

l $\frac{a + b}{c} = d$; $b =$

m $\frac{pq}{p + q} = 1$; $p =$

n $F = \frac{9}{5}C + 32$; $C =$

o $A = \frac{1}{2}h(b + b')$; $h =$

p $S = 2\pi r^2 + 2\pi rh$; $h =$

q $A = 4\pi r^2$; $r^2 =$

r $S = x^2 + 4xh$; $h =$

s $V = \frac{4}{3}\pi r^3$; $r =$

t $C = \frac{5}{9}(F - 32)$; $F =$

GROUP XIII

Graphs of Linear Equations

1. Figure 1 represents a sheet of graph paper on which the horizontal line XX' is the X-axis and the vertical line YY' is the Y-axis. On a sheet of graph paper draw the X-axis and the Y-axis.

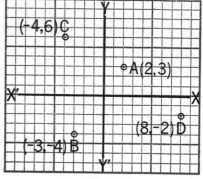

a Plot the point $x = 2$, $y = 3$. This is the point A in Figure 1, indicated as $(2, 3)$.

b Plot the point $x = -3$, $y = -4$. Which point is this in Figure 1? How is this point indicated?

c Plot the point $x = -4$, $y = 6$; the point $x = 8$, $y = -2$.

FIG. 1

2. On another sheet of graph paper draw the X- and Y-axes and plot the following points:

a $(3, 5)$	**b** $(-4, 7)$	**c** $(-2, -3)$	**d** $(5, -1)$
e $(0, 0)$	**f** $(4, 0)$	**g** $(-7, 0)$	**h** $(0, -3)$

3. Draw the graph of the equation $7x - 4y = -1$.

SOLUTION. First solve for y. $y = \dfrac{7x + 1}{4}$. (You could solve for x, instead.) By trial choose, if possible, three integral values of x that will result in integral values of y. Make a table of these values, as shown at the right. Then plot the three points for each of these pairs of values of x and y. Draw a line through the points (see Fig. 2).

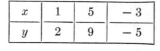

x	1	5	-3
y	2	9	-5

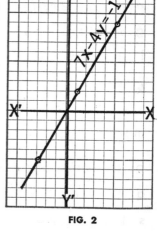

4. Draw the graphs of the following equations:

a $y = 4x$	**b** $y = -4x$
c $2x = 3y$	**d** $2x = -3y$
e $y = 3x + 5$	**f** $4x - y = 5$
g $2x + 7y = 3$	**h** $3x + y = 6$
i $3x - 2y = -8$	**j** $3x - 2y = -1$
k $5x - 3y = 0$	**l** $2x + 3y = 4$

FIG. 2

Simultaneous Equations

1. Draw the graph of the equation $2x + y = 7$. On the same axes draw the graph of $x + 2y = 5$. What are the co-ordinates of the point of intersection of the two graphs? Do these values of x and y satisfy both equations?

2. Draw the graphs and find the co-ordinates of the points that satisfy the following pairs of equations:

a $3x + y = 7$
   $x - y = 1$

b $2x + y = 5$
   $8x - y = 45$

c $2x + 3y = 3$
   $3x - 2y = 11$

d $2x - 5y = -11$
   $4y + 3x = -5$

e $3x + 2y = -12$
   $2x - 4y = 8$

f $5x + 2y = 10$
   $2x + 3y = 15$

g $2x + 3y = 9$
   $x + 2y = 8$

h $\frac{1}{2}x + \frac{2}{3}y = 8$
   $3x - 2y = -6$

3. Solve the following pairs of equations algebraically. (SUG-GESTION: Multiply both sides of each equation by a number such that the coefficients of x (or y) are the same with opposite sign. Add the members of the two equations to eliminate one of the unknowns.)

a $2x + y = 5$
   $3x - y = 0$

b $2x - y = 4$
   $x + 3y = 9$

c $2x - 3y = -6$
   $5x - 2y = 7$

d $3x + 2y = 4$
   $2x - y = 5$

e $7x + 3y = 35$
   $5y - 2x = -10$

f $2x - 3y = 9$
   $3x + 2y = -6$

g $6x - y = -2$
   $2x + 3y = 16$

h $4x + 9y = 5$
   $2x - 3y = 0$

i $6x + 3y = 7$
   $4x - 9y = 12$

j $2x + y = 1$
   $3y = 4x - 12$

k $0.5x - 0.9 = 4y$
   $2x + 0.5y = 10.2$

l $\frac{1}{2}(x - 2) + y = 3$
   $x + \frac{3}{4}(y + 3) = 9$

m $ax + by = c$
   $2ax + 2by = d$

n $ax + by = c$
   $ax - by = d$

Tables for Reference

Linear Measure

12 inches (in.) = 1 foot (ft.)
3 feet = 1 yard (yd.)
5.5 yards = 1 rod (rd.)
320 rods = 1 mile (mi.)
A mile = 320 rd. = 1760 yd. = 5280 ft.

Square Measure

144 square inches (sq. in.) = 1 square foot (sq. ft.)
9 square feet = 1 square yard (sq. yd.)
30.25 square yards = 1 square rod (sq. rd.)
160 square rods = 1 acre (A.)
640 acres = 1 square mile (sq. mi.)
640 acres = 1 section (U. S. public lands)

Metric and English Equivalents

2.54 centimeters (cm.) = 1 inch
1 meter (m.) = 39.37 inches
1 kilometer (km.) = about .62 mile
1 liter (l.) = 1.1 quarts
1 kilogram (kg.) = 2.2 pounds

Symbols

=	is equal to, equals	$\cong$	is congruent to
$\neq$	is not equal to	$\sim$	is similar to
<	is less than	$\odot$	circle
>	is greater than	‖	is parallel to, parallel
$\triangle$	triangle	$\square$	parallelogram
$\angle$	angle	$\sqrt[n]{}$	nth root of

$\perp$ is perpendicular to, perpendicular

The plural of any symbol representing a noun may be formed by adding s; for example, $\angle\!\!\!\angle$ means angles.

Table of Tangents, Cosines, and Sines

∠	TANGENT $\left(\dfrac{opp.}{adj.}\right)$	COSINE $\left(\dfrac{adj.}{hyp.}\right)$	SINE $\left(\dfrac{opp.}{hyp.}\right)$	∠	TANGENT $\left(\dfrac{opp.}{adj.}\right)$	COSINE $\left(\dfrac{adj.}{hyp.}\right)$	SINE $\left(\dfrac{opp.}{hyp.}\right)$
0°	.0000	1.0000	.0000	45°	1.0000	.7071	.7071
1	.0175	.9998	.0175	46	1.0355	.6947	.7193
2	.0349	.9994	.0349	47	1.0724	.6820	.7314
3	.0524	.9986	.0523	48	1.1106	.6691	.7431
4	.0699	.9976	.0698	49	1.1504	.6561	.7547
5	.0875	.9962	.0872	50	1.1918	.6428	.7660
6	.1051	.9945	.1045	51	1.2349	.6293	.7771
7	.1228	.9925	.1219	52	1.2799	.6157	.7880
8	.1405	.9903	.1392	53	1.3270	.6018	.7986
9	.1584	.9877	.1564	54	1.3764	.5878	.8090
10	.1763	.9848	.1736	55	1.4281	.5736	.8192
11	.1944	.9816	.1908	56	1.4826	.5592	.8290
12	.2126	.9781	.2079	57	1.5399	.5446	.8387
13	.2309	.9744	.2250	58	1.6003	.5299	.8480
14	.2493	.9703	.2419	59	1.6643	.5150	.8572
15	.2679	.9659	.2588	60	1.7321	.5000	.8660
16	.2867	.9613	.2756	61	1.8040	.4848	.8746
17	.3057	.9563	.2924	62	1.8807	.4695	.8829
18	.3249	.9511	.3090	63	1.9626	.4540	.8910
19	.3443	.9455	.3256	64	2.0503	.4384	.8988
20	.3640	.9397	.3420	65	2.1445	.4226	.9063
21	.3839	.9336	.3584	66	2.2460	.4067	.9135
22	.4040	.9272	.3746	67	2.3559	.3907	.9205
23	.4245	.9205	.3907	68	2.4751	.3746	.9272
24	.4452	.9135	.4067	69	2.6051	.3584	.9336
25	.4663	.9063	.4226	70	2.7475	.3420	.9397
26	.4877	.8988	.4384	71	2.9042	.3256	.9455
27	.5095	.8910	.4540	72	3.0777	.3090	.9511
28	.5317	.8829	.4695	73	3.2709	.2924	.9563
29	.5543	.8746	.4848	74	3.4874	.2756	.9613
30	.5774	.8660	.5000	75	3.7321	.2588	.9659
31	.6009	.8572	.5150	76	4.0108	.2419	.9703
32	.6249	.8480	.5299	77	4.3315	.2250	.9744
33	.6494	.8387	.5446	78	4.7046	.2079	.9781
34	.6745	.8290	.5592	79	5.1446	.1908	.9816
35	.7002	.8192	.5736	80	5.6713	.1736	.9848
36	.7265	.8090	.5878	81	6.3138	.1564	.9877
37	.7536	.7986	.6018	82	7.1154	.1392	.9903
38	.7813	.7880	.6157	83	8.1443	.1219	.9925
39	.8098	.7771	.6293	84	9.5144	.1045	.9945
40	.8391	.7660	.6428	85	11.4301	.0872	.9962
41	.8693	.7547	.6561	86	14.3007	.0698	.9976
42	.9004	.7431	.6691	87	19.0811	.0523	.9986
43	.9325	.7314	.6820	88	28.6363	.0349	.9994
44	.9657	.7193	.6947	89	57.2900	.0175	.9998
45	1.0000	.7071	.7071	90		.0000	1.0000

Table of Square Roots

NO.	SQUARE ROOT	NO.	SQUARE ROOT	NO.	SQUARE ROOT	NO.	SQUARE ROOT	NO.	SQUARE ROOT
1	1.000	51	7.141	101	10.050	151	12.288	201	14.177
2	1.414	52	7.211	102	10.100	152	12.329	202	14.213
3	1.732	53	7.280	103	10.149	153	12.369	203	14.248
4	2.000	54	7.348	104	10.198	154	12.410	204	14.283
5	2.236	55	7.416	105	10.247	155	12.450	205	14.318
6	2.449	56	7.483	106	10.296	156	12.490	206	14.353
7	2.646	57	7.550	107	10.344	157	12.530	207	14.387
8	2.828	58	7.616	108	10.392	158	12.570	208	14.422
9	3.000	59	7.681	109	10.440	159	12.610	209	14.457
10	3.162	60	7.746	110	10.488	160	12.649	210	14.491
11	3.317	61	7.810	111	10.536	161	12.689	211	14.526
12	3.464	62	7.874	112	10.583	162	12.728	212	14.560
13	3.606	63	7.937	113	10.630	163	12.767	213	14.595
14	3.742	64	8.000	114	10.677	164	12.806	214	14.629
15	3.873	65	8.062	115	10.724	165	12.845	215	14.663
16	4.000	66	8.124	116	10.770	166	12.884	216	14.697
17	4.123	67	8.185	117	10.817	167	12.923	217	14.731
18	4.243	68	8.246	118	10.863	168	12.961	218	14.765
19	4.359	69	8.307	119	10.909	169	13.000	219	14.799
20	4.472	70	8.367	120	10.954	170	13.038	220	14.832
21	4.583	71	8.426	121	11.000	171	13.077	221	14.866
22	4.690	72	8.485	122	11.045	172	13.115	222	14.900
23	4.796	73	8.544	123	11.091	173	13.153	223	14.933
24	4.899	74	8.602	124	11.136	174	13.191	224	14.967
25	5.000	75	8.660	125	11.180	175	13.229	225	15.000
26	5.099	76	8.718	126	11.225	176	13.267	226	15.033
27	5.196	77	8.775	127	11.269	177	13.304	227	15.067
28	5.292	78	8.832	128	11.314	178	13.342	228	15.100
29	5.385	79	8.888	129	11.358	179	13.379	229	15.133
30	5.477	80	8.944	130	11.402	180	13.416	230	15.166
31	5.568	81	9.000	131	11.446	181	13.454	231	15.199
32	5.657	82	9.055	132	11.489	182	13.491	232	15.232
33	5.745	83	9.110	133	11.533	183	13.528	233	15.264
34	5.831	84	9.165	134	11.576	184	13.565	234	15.297
35	5.916	85	9.220	135	11.619	185	13.601	235	15.330
36	6.000	86	9.274	136	11.662	186	13.638	236	15.362
37	6.083	87	9.327	137	11.705	187	13.675	237	15.395
38	6.164	88	9.381	138	11.747	188	13.711	238	15.427
39	6.245	89	9.434	139	11.790	189	13.748	239	15.460
40	6.325	90	9.487	140	11.832	190	13.784	240	15.492
41	6.403	91	9.539	141	11.874	191	13.820	241	15.524
42	6.481	92	9.592	142	11.916	192	13.856	242	15.556
43	6.557	93	9.644	143	11.958	193	13.892	243	15.588
44	6.633	94	9.695	144	12.000	194	13.928	244	15.621
45	6.708	95	9.747	145	12.042	195	13.964	245	15.652
46	6.782	96	9.798	146	12.083	196	14.000	246	15.684
47	6.856	97	9.849	147	12.124	197	14.036	247	15.716
48	6.928	98	9.899	148	12.166	198	14.071	248	15.748
49	7.000	99	9.950	149	12.207	199	14.107	249	15.780
50	7.071	100	10.000	150	12.247	200	14.142	250	15.811

Index

12
11
10
9
8
7
6